Cambridge International GCSE
Physics

There's a lot to learn for Cambridge International GCSE Physics.... luckily, we've squeezed it *all* into this CGP book — every fact, theory and practical skill!

What's more, there are plenty of exam-style questions for every section, plus a set of practice papers that'll really put your Physics knowledge to the test.

You can use it for both the Core and Extended courses — throughout the book, you can see the supplement content for the Extended course clearly marked.

How to access your free Online Edition

This book includes a free Online Edition to read on your PC, Mac or tablet.
You'll just need to go to **cgpbooks.co.uk/extras** and enter this code:

2185 2544 7978 7503

By the way, this code only works for one person. If somebody else has used this book before you, they might have already claimed the Online Edition.

Complete
Revision & Practice
Everything you need to pass the exams!

Contents

Some of the content in the specification is 'Supplemental'. This content will only be assessed if you're taking the Extended version of the Cambridge International GCSE. We've marked up all the content that's only for the Extended course with purple brackets, like the ones on this box, or the example below:

Information or questions with a bracket like this are for the Extended course only.

Supplement

Supplement

Published by CGP

Editors: Emily Garrett, Josie Gilbert, Sharon Keeley-Holden, Charlotte Sheridan and George Wright.

From original material by Paddy Gannon.

With thanks to Mark Edwards and Duncan Lindsay for the proofreading.

With thanks to Emily Smith for the copyright research.

ISBN: 978 1 78908 704 8

Printed by Elanders Ltd, Newcastle upon Tyne.

Clipart from Corel®
Illustrations by: Sandy Gardner Artist, email sandy@sandygardner.co.uk

Based on the classic CGP style created by Richard Parsons.

Speed and Velocity

Speed and velocity are similar, but in physics they're not quite the same...

Speed is Calculated from Distance and Time

 KEY TERM   Speed is the distance you travel per unit time.

For any object moving at a constant speed, the distance moved, speed, and time taken are related by this formula:

You'd use the same formula to calculate velocity (see below).

$$\text{speed} = \frac{\text{total distance}}{\text{time taken}}$$

distance

speed (or velocity)

$$\frac{s}{v \times t}$$

time

Speed is measured in m/s (metres per second). To calculate speed in m/s make sure the distance you use in the formula is in metres and the time is in seconds. Other common units of speed are km/h and mph (miles per hour).

Use this formula triangle to rearrange the equation. Just cover up the thing you're trying to find, and what's left visible is the formula you're after.

 **EXAMPLE:**

A cat walks 20 m in 40 s.
a) Calculate its speed.
b) How long will it take the cat to walk 75 m at this speed?

a)   Use the formula for speed.

$v = s \div t$
$= 20 \div 40 = 0.5$ m/s

b)   Rearrange $v = s \div t$ using the formula triangle to get $t = s \div v$.

$t = s \div v$
$= 75 \div 0.5 = 150$ s

The example above is calculating constant speed, but usually in real life speed varies over distance.

You can still use the same equation in these cases, but the speed you'll calculate will just be an average speed for that specific distance or length of time.

$$\text{average speed} = \frac{\text{total distance}}{\text{total time taken}}$$

Velocity is Speed in a Given Direction

Speed is a scalar and velocity is a vector — see p.9 for more on scalars and vectors. — Supplement

Velocity is very similar to speed, but it has a direction too. It has the same units as speed, and the formula for average speed can also be used to calculate average velocity.

 KEY TERM   Velocity is how fast you're going with the direction specified, e.g. 30 km/h north or 20 m/s at 60° above the horizontal.

This means you can have objects travelling at a constant speed with a changing velocity. This happens when the object is changing direction whilst staying at the same speed.

Velocity is speed in a certain direction...

Learn the formula for speed but watch out for the units. If you're given the time in minutes, multiply by 60 to convert it to seconds. And make sure you're happy converting between km, cm and m.

Acceleration

Things rarely travel at the same speed — this is where acceleration and deceleration come in.

Changing Speed Means Acceleration

1) Acceleration is related to changing speed.

2) The faster the speed is changing, the greater the acceleration.

3) Deceleration means the speed is decreasing — the object is slowing down.

4) The unit of acceleration is m/s². Not m/s, which is speed (or velocity), but m/s².

5) The force of gravity makes objects accelerate towards the Earth. The acceleration of free fall (g) is approximately constant and 9.8 m/s² near the Earth. So an object in free fall will accelerate towards the Earth at 9.8 m/s².

Changing Direction Means Acceleration Too

1) Acceleration is actually how quickly velocity is changing. The definition is:

 KEY TERM — Acceleration is the change in velocity per unit time.

2) This change in velocity can be a change in speed or a change in direction, or both. You only have to worry about the change in speed bit for calculations. The formula for it is:

$$\text{acceleration} = \frac{\text{change in velocity}}{\text{change in time}}$$

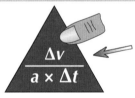

Here 'Δv' is the change in velocity and 'Δt' is the change in time. You can work these out by taking away the initial value from the final value.

EXAMPLE:

A cat accelerates from 2.0 m/s to 6.0 m/s in 5.6 s. Find its acceleration.

Substitute the values into the formula.

$a = \Delta v \div \Delta t = (6.0 - 2.0) \div 5.6$
$= 4.0 \div 5.6 = 0.714... = 0.71$ m/s² (to 2 s.f.)

This formula for acceleration only works when the acceleration is constant.

3) A negative value for acceleration means something is slowing down (decelerating).

EXAMPLE:

A ball initially moving at 10 m/s has an acceleration of –1.4 m/s². How long does it take to reach a speed of 4.0 m/s?

Substitute the values into the formula.

$\Delta t = \Delta v \div a = (4.0 - 10) \div (-1.4)$
$= (-6.0) \div (-1.4) = 4.28... = 4.3$ s (to 2 s.f.)

 EXAM TIP — ## Make sure you're comfortable with using this equation...

Don't get confused if a question says an object starts 'at rest' or 'is initially stationary'. This just means that the initial velocity is 0. And if the object finishes at rest, the final velocity is 0.

Supplement

Supplement

Distance-Time Graphs

Distance-time (D-T) graphs tell you how fast an object is moving and how far it's travelled.
Simple as that really. Make sure you get them straight in your head before turning over...

Distance-Time Graphs Tell You How Far Something has Travelled

The different parts of a distance-time graph describe the motion of an object:

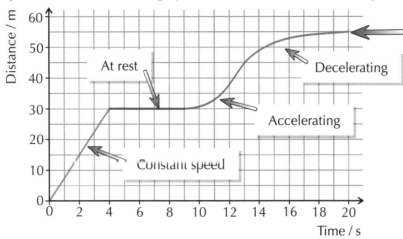

After 20 seconds, the object has travelled 55 m from its starting point.

1) The gradient (slope) at any point gives the speed of the object. For a constant speed, the distance travelled increases by the same amount for equal time intervals so the graph will be a straight slope.

2) Flat sections are where the object is at rest. When an object is at rest the distance travelled doesn't change.

3) A steeper graph means it's going faster.

4) Curves represent acceleration.

5) A curve getting steeper means it's speeding up (increasing gradient). This is acceleration.

6) A levelling off curve means it's slowing down (decreasing gradient). This is deceleration.

7) When an object is accelerating or decelerating the distance travelled does not increase by the same amount for equal time intervals.

Calculating Speed from a Distance-Time Graph

To calculate the speed from a distance-time graph, just work out the gradient:

Calculate the speed of the object from the graph above, between 0 and 4 s.

The vertical change between 0 and 4 s is 30 m.

$$\text{speed} = \text{gradient} = \frac{\text{change in vertical}}{\text{change in horizontal}} = \frac{30}{4} = 7.5 \text{ m/s}$$

Don't forget to use the scales of the axes to work out the gradient. Don't measure in cm!

Read the axes of any graph you get given carefully...

Make sure you don't get confused between distance-time graphs and speed-time graphs (which are coming up next). They do look quite similar, but they tell you different things...

Speed-Time Graphs

Even more graphs! Just like distance-time graphs, speed-time graphs are a way of representing journeys.

You Can Show **Journeys** on a **Speed-Time Graph**

How an object's speed changes as it travels can be plotted on a speed-time graph.

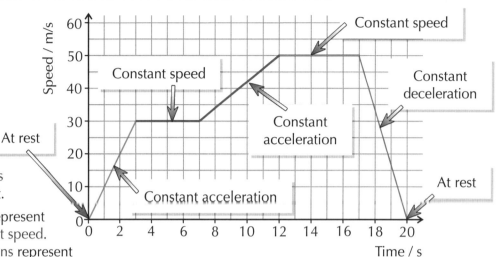

1) Points along the x-axis represent being at rest.

2) Horizontal sections represent travelling at a constant speed. Non-horizontal sections represent travelling at a changing speed.

3) Uphill sections (/) are acceleration. Downhill sections (\) are deceleration.

4) The steeper the graph, the greater the acceleration or deceleration.

5) The area under any section of the graph (or all of it) is equal to the distance travelled in that time interval.

You may also be given the data points and asked to work out what's happening based on those.

EXAMPLE: **The speed-time graph of a car's journey is plotted and shown below. How far does the car travel during the first 15 s of the journey?**

The distance travelled is equal to the area under the speed-time graph.
Split the area into a triangle and a rectangle, then add together their areas.

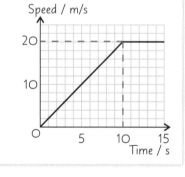

The area of a triangle is ½ × base × height.

$$\text{area of triangle} = \frac{1}{2} \times 10 \times 20$$
$$= 100 \text{ m}$$

The area of a rectangle is base × height.

$$\text{area of rectangle} = 5 \times 20$$
$$= 100 \text{ m}$$

$$\text{total area under the graph} = 100 + 100 = 200 \text{ m}$$

6) The gradient of a speed-time graph is equal to the acceleration, as acceleration is change in velocity ÷ time. If the gradient is constant (a straight line), then the acceleration is constant.

7) Changing acceleration on a speed-time graph is shown by a curve.

Constant acceleration means that the object's speed increases by the same amount in each equal time interval.

8) To find the instantaneous acceleration at a certain point along a curve you need to draw a tangent to the curve at that point and find its gradient.

EXAMPLE: **The speed-time graph of a toy's movement is plotted and shown to the right. What is the toy's acceleration at $t = 7.0$ s?**

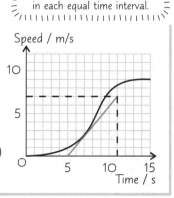

Draw a tangent at $t = 7.0$.
The acceleration will be the tangent's gradient.

$$\text{gradient} = \frac{\text{change in vertical}}{\text{change in horizontal}} = \frac{7.0 - 0}{11 - 5} = \frac{7.0}{6} = 1.16... = 1.2 \text{ m/s}^2 \text{ (to 2 s.f.)}$$

Supplement

Supplement

Mass, Weight and Gravity

It might seem a bit odd, but it's true — mass and weight are not the same thing.
The difference between them is all thanks to the force of gravity...

Weight and Mass are Different Things

To understand this you must learn all these facts about mass and weight:

 Mass is the amount of matter in an object which is at rest relative to the observer.

 Weight is a gravitational force that acts on an object with mass, measured in newtons.

1) For an object on or near Earth, the weight of the object is the gravitational force pulling it towards the centre of the Earth.

2) Mass is not a force. It is just the amount of 'stuff' in an object and it is measured in kilograms.

3) An object has the same mass whether it's on Earth or on the Moon — but its weight will be different. A 1 kg mass will weigh less on the Moon (about 1.6 N) than it does on Earth (about 9.8 N), simply because the force of gravity pulling on it is less.

Supplement

4) The weight that a mass experiences is due to it being in a gravitational field. So if the gravitational field strength (g) changes, the weight of the mass will change.

5) You can compare the weight of two objects using a balance (an old-fashioned pair of balancing scales). The object with the greater weight will also have the greater mass.

Weight can be measured using a newton meter or spring balance. Mass can be measured on a mass balance.

Mass, Weight and Gravitational Field Strength are Related

Gravitational field strength is the force exerted by gravity per unit mass, and is given by the formula:

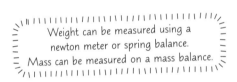 **gravitational field strength (N/kg) = weight (N) ÷ mass (kg)** $g = W/m$

The letter "g" represents the strength of the gravity and its value is different for different planets. On Earth $g = 9.8$ N/kg. This is equal to the acceleration of an object in free fall on Earth, 9.8 m/s². On the Moon, where the gravity is weaker, g is only about 1.6 N/kg.

 **EXAMPLE:**

Calculate the weight, in newtons, of a 5 kg mass, both on Earth and on the Moon.

1) On Earth, $g = 9.8$ N. $W = mg = 5 \times 9.8 = 49$ N

2) On the Moon, $g = 1.6$ N. $W = mg = 5 \times 1.6 = 8$ N

Weight is dependent on gravity — mass is not...

In everyday life, people tend to talk about their body "weight" in kg — but that's actually their body mass.

Density

Density tells you how much mass is packed into a given volume of space.

Density Relates the Mass of a Substance to its Volume

 KEY TERM — Density is a substance's mass per unit volume.

1) Density is a measure of the 'compactness' of a substance.

2) You can calculate density using the formula below. The units of density may be kg/m³ or g/cm³. It depends on the units of the mass and volume used in the formula. E.g. if the mass is in kg and the volume is in m³, the density calculated will be in kg/m³.

$1 \text{ g/cm}^3 = 1000 \text{ kg/m}^3$

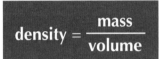 $$\text{density} = \frac{\text{mass}}{\text{volume}}$$

 $$\rho = \frac{m}{V}$$

3) The density of an object depends on what it's made of. Density doesn't vary with size or shape.

4) The average density of an object determines whether it floats or sinks. A solid object will float on a fluid if it has a lower density than the fluid. It will sink if its density is greater than that of the fluid.

You Need to be Able to Measure Density of Solids and Liquids

To Find the Density of a Solid Object

1) Use a balance to measure its mass (see p.163).

2) For some solid shapes, you can find the volume using a formula. E.g. the volume of a cuboid is just width × height × length.

Make sure you know the formulas for the volumes of basic shapes.

3) For an irregularly-shaped solid which sinks, you can find its volume by displacement. You do this by submerging the solid in a eureka can filled with water (see p.163). The water displaced by the object will be transferred to the measuring cylinder:

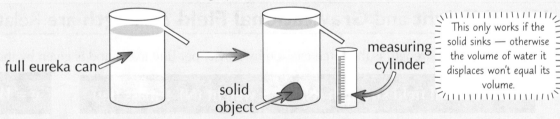

full eureka can   measuring cylinder   solid object

This only works if the solid sinks — otherwise the volume of water it displaces won't equal its volume.

4) Record the volume of water in the measuring cylinder. This is the volume of the object.

5) Put the object's mass and volume into the formula above to find its density.

To Find the Density of a Liquid

1) Place a measuring cylinder on a balance and zero the balance (see p.163).

2) Pour some of the liquid into the measuring cylinder. Record the mass and volume of the liquid.

3) Use the formula to find the density.

Use Densities to Decide if One Liquid will Float on Another Liquid

1) Some liquids float on top of other liquids. For example, vegetable oil floats on water.

2) Oil does this because it has a lower density than water (the same reason some solids float).

3) However, two liquids sometimes mix. Therefore, a less dense liquid will only float on a more dense liquid if they do not mix.

Supplement

Warm-Up & Exam Questions

It's time to take a break and check how much of the information on the previous few pages has gone in. These warm-up questions will help to get your brain working before you tackle the exam questions.

Warm-Up Questions

1) Samuel runs across a field. What information would you need to calculate his average speed?
2) How are speed and velocity different?
3) What are the units of acceleration?
4) What is represented by the gradient of a distance-time graph?
5) Describe the shape of the line on a speed-time graph for an object travelling at a steady speed.
6) What are the units of mass? What are the units of weight?
7) What is the formula for density?

Exam Questions

1 A cyclist travels 1500 m from his house to his local shops in 300 seconds.

What is the cyclist's average speed?

☐ **A** 3 m/s ☐ **B** 0.2 m/s ☐ **C** 5 m/s ☐ **D** 45 m/s

[Total 1 mark]

2 A student ran home from a bus stop. Below is a distance-time graph for her journey.

How long did it take the student to run home?

☐ **A** 60 s ☐ **B** 30 s

☐ **C** 0 s ☐ **D** 100 s

[Total 1 mark]

3 A student has an ice cube with a mass of 115 g. One side of the ice cube is 5 cm long.

(a) (i) Calculate the volume of the ice cube in cm^3.

[1]

(ii) Calculate the density of the ice cube in g/cm^3.

[1]

(iii) The density of water is 1 g/cm^3. Using your answer to 3 (a) part (ii), predict whether the ice cube will float or sink in water.

[1]

(b) The student wants to measure the density of a metal toy soldier which sinks in water. Describe the steps he could take to do this.

[4]

[Total 7 marks]

Exam Questions

4   **Figure 1** shows a speed-time graph for a car during a section of a journey.

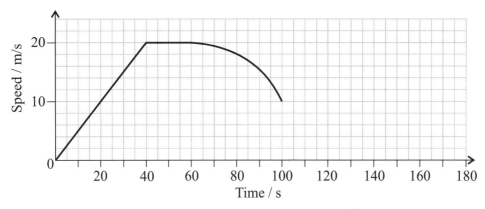

Figure 1

(a)   Describe the motion of the car between 0 and 40 seconds.

[1]

(b)   Calculate the distance travelled by the car in metres between 40 and 60 seconds.

[3]

(c)   After 100 seconds, the car moves with a constant speed of 10 m/s for the next 60 seconds.
Describe what the next part of the graph would look like.

[1]

(d)   Calculate the acceleration of the car in m/s² between 0 and 40 seconds.

[3]

[Total 8 marks]

5   A student is measuring gravitational field strength, *g*, in a classroom experiment. He takes an object
with a mass of 2.5 kg and suspends it from a newton meter held in his hand, getting a value of 24.5 N.

(a)   Calculate the gravitational field strength in the student's classroom.

[2]

(b)   The Moon's gravitational field is weaker than the Earth's.
    (i)   State how the mass of the object on the Moon compares to its mass on Earth.

[1]

    (ii) State how the weight of the object would differ if the student performed
        the same experiment on the Moon. Explain your answer.

[2]

[Total 5 marks]

6   A tractor ploughing a field accelerates at a constant −2 m/s² for 5 seconds, after which its speed is 1 m/s.

(a)   Calculate the tractor's speed in m/s before it started accelerating.

[2]

(b)   After its speed reaches 1 m/s, the tractor decelerates at a constant rate, taking 5 seconds
to come to a stop. Sketch a speed-time graph for the whole journey of the tractor.

[2]

[Total 4 marks]

Supplement

Resultant Forces

When multiple forces act on an object, you can replace them all with just one equivalent force acting in a single direction that has the same effect as all the forces combined. This is the resultant force.

A **Resultant Force** is the **Overall Force** on a Point or Object

1) In most real situations there are at least two forces acting on an object.

 KEY TERM The resultant force is a single force that has the same effect as all the forces acting at a single point.

If there are forces acting but they cancel to zero in one direction, there is no resultant force in that direction.

2) If the forces all act along the same line (they're all parallel), the overall effect is found by adding those going in the same direction and subtracting any going in the opposite direction.

 **EXAMPLE:** **For the diagram shown on the right, calculate the resultant force acting on the van.**

1) Consider the horizontal and vertical directions separately.

Vertical: 1500 − 1500 = 0 N
Horizontal: 1200 − 1000 N = 200 N

2) State the size and direction of the resultant force.

The resultant force is 200 N to the left.

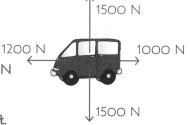

1500 N
1200 N   1000 N
1500 N

Forces are Vectors

Learn the difference between vector and scalar quantities.

 KEY TERM Vector quantities have a magnitude and a direction.

Some examples of vector quantities are: force, weight, velocity, acceleration, momentum, electric field strength, and gravitational field strength.

Other quantities are scalar quantities:

 KEY TERM Scalar quantities have only magnitude and no direction.

Some examples of scalar quantities are: speed, distance, mass, temperature, time, and energy.

Vectors are usually represented by an arrow — the length of the arrow shows the magnitude, and the direction of the arrow shows the direction of the quantity.

The lengths of the arrows on the skydiver show the sizes of the forces acting, and their directions show the directions that the forces are acting. As the length of the arrow for weight is greater, there is a downwards resultant force acting on the skydiver.

air resistance
weight

 EXAM TIP Resultant force — one force with the same result as many...

Forces that act along the same line can be added or subtracted, no matter how many are acting. Remember, if the forces add or subtract to zero, they are balanced — so there's no resultant force.

Calculating Resultant Vectors

Scale diagrams and trigonometry are useful for calculating resultant forces. Read on to find out how...

Learn **Two** Methods for Finding **Resultant Vectors**

You need to be able to find the resultant of two vectors which act at right angles to each other. Shown below is how to use both methods to solve a problem involving forces.

You can use these methods with any vectors, e.g. velocities. The only difference is you'll be working with different units, e.g. m/s instead of N.

The **Tip-To-Tail** Method

1) Draw all the forces acting on an object, to scale, 'tip-to-tail'. Then draw a straight line from the start of the first force to the end of the last force — this is the resultant force.

2) Measure the length of the resultant force on the diagram to find the magnitude, and measure the angle to find the direction of the force.

EXAMPLE:

A man is on an electric bicycle that has a driving force of 4.0 N north. However, the wind produces a force of 3.0 N east. Find the magnitude and direction of the resultant force.

1) Start by drawing a scale drawing of the forces acting.

2) Choose a sensible scale (e.g. 1 cm = 1 N).

3) Draw the resultant from the tail of the first arrow to the tip of the last arrow.

4) Measure the length of the resultant with a ruler and use the scale to find the force in N.

5) Use a protractor to measure the direction as an angle from one of the other forces.

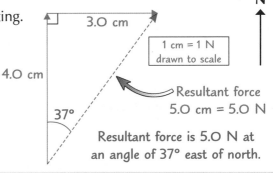

3.0 cm

N

1 cm = 1 N
drawn to scale

4.0 cm

Resultant force
5.0 cm = 5.0 N

37°

Resultant force is 5.0 N at an angle of 37° east of north.

The **Trigonometry** Method

1) You can also use Pythagoras' theorem and trigonometry. Start by drawing the forces 'tip-to-tail' as you did above, and drawing the resultant from the start of the first force to the end of the last force. This diagram doesn't need to be to scale.

2) The resulting triangle is right-angled, so you can use Pythagoras: $\longrightarrow$ $a^2 + b^2 = c^2$
c is the hypotenuse and a and b are the other two sides.
So the size of the resultant force can be found by finding c.

3) You can find the angle that the force acts at using trigonometry. Trigonometry lets you find an angle in a right-angled triangle if you know the length of two of its sides. You'll need to use the tan formula for the angle of the resultant.

$$\tan \theta = \frac{\text{opposite}}{\text{adjacent}}$$

hypotenuse

opposite

θ

adjacent

EXAMPLE:

A man is on an electric bicycle that has a driving force of 4.0 N north. However, the wind produces a force of 3.0 N east. Find the magnitude and direction of the resultant force.

1) Draw the vectors tip-to-tail and draw in the resultant. Use Pythagoras to find the magnitude of the resultant.

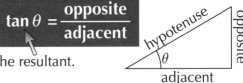

3.0 N

4.0 N

θ

$a = 4.0$ N, $b = 3.0$ N
$4.0^2 + 3.0^2 = c^2 = 16 + 9 = 25$
$c = \sqrt{25} = 5$ N

2) Then use trigonometry to find θ. In this example, the side opposite the angle is 3.0 N and the side adjacent to the angle is 4.0 N.

$\tan \theta = \frac{3}{4} = 0.75$
$\tan^{-1}(0.75) = 36.86...$
$= 37°$ (to 2 s.f.) east of north

Forces and Motion

There are some very important rules on this page, so it's really essential to understand them.

A **Force** Can **Change Motion**

1) There are five ways that forces can change the motion of objects. They can make them start moving, stop moving, speed up, slow down or change direction.

2) But if the forces cancel each other out, the motion won't change:

> A resultant force changes the velocity of an object by changing its speed or direction.
>
> If there is no resultant force on a stationary object, the object will remain at rest. If there is no resultant force on a moving object, it will continue moving at a constant speed in a straight line.

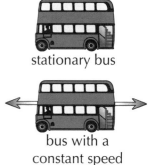

stationary bus

bus with a constant speed

3) So, when a train or car or bus or anything else is moving at a constant speed, the frictional and driving forces on it must all be balanced. The speed will only change if there's a non-zero resultant force acting on the object.

Acceleration is **Proportional** to the **Resultant Force**

1) A non-zero resultant force will always produce acceleration (or deceleration) in the direction of the force.

2) The larger the resultant force acting on an object, the more the object accelerates — the force and the acceleration are directly proportional. You can write this as $F \propto a$.

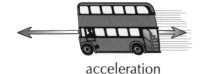

acceleration

3) Acceleration is also inversely proportional to the mass of the object (p.5) — so an object with a larger mass will accelerate less than one with a smaller mass (for a fixed resultant force).

4) This can be expressed as the formula:

mass (kg)

resultant force (N) — $$F = ma$$ — acceleration (m/s^2)

Circular Motion is due to a **Perpendicular Force**

1) Velocity is both the speed and direction of an object (p.1).

2) If an object is travelling in a circular orbit (at a constant speed) it is constantly changing direction, so it is constantly changing velocity. This means it's accelerating.

3) If the object is accelerating, this means there must be a resultant force acting on it (see above).

4) This force acts towards the centre of the circle, and is perpendicular to the direction of the velocity.

5) This force that keeps something moving in a circle is called a centripetal force.

6) Learn these three rules linking the centripetal force, the velocity, the mass of the object and the radius of the motion (the distance of the object from the centre of the circle).

> 1) If the centripetal force is increased, the object's speed increases (for a constant mass and radius).
>
> 2) If the centripetal force is increased, the radius of the object's motion decreases (for a constant mass and speed).
>
> 3) If the object's mass is increased, the centripetal force must increase for the speed and radius to remain constant.

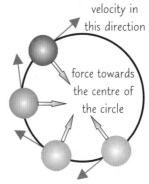

velocity in this direction

force towards the centre of the circle

Supplement

Supplement

Friction and Terminal Velocity

Friction slows stuff down. Most moving things encounter friction, including objects falling through the air.

Friction is Always There to Slow Things Down

> Solid friction is the force between two solid objects that are in contact, and are moving or trying to move relative to each other. Solid friction impedes motion and results in heating.

1) Friction always acts in the opposite direction to movement and prevents motion or makes it more difficult.
2) Solid friction results in heating because energy is transferred from the object's kinetic energy store to internal energy stores as the object slows down.

Friction in a Gas or Liquid is called Drag

The frictional forces that act on an object as it moves through a gas or liquid are known as drag. Air resistance is an example of drag.

Drag always increases with speed.

A car has much more air resistance to work against when travelling at 70 mph compared to 30 mph. So at 70 mph, the engine has to provide a much larger driving force to be able to balance the drag and maintain a steady speed.

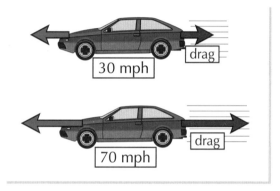

If an object has no force propelling it along, it will slow down and stop because of friction (unless you're in space where there's no friction).

Objects Falling Through Air or Liquid Reach a Terminal Velocity

1) Near the surface of the Earth, there is a uniform gravitational field. If there was no air resistance, objects falling towards the Earth would accelerate at a constant rate. So falling objects would get faster and faster until they collided with the Earth's surface.
2) Without resistance, all objects dropped from the same height would take the same time to fall, because they would all have the same acceleration.
3) The faster an object is moving, the greater the resistance (see above).
4) When falling objects first set off, the force of gravity is much greater than the resistance slowing them down, so they accelerate.
5) However, as their speed increases, so does the resistance. This gradually reduces the acceleration, until the force of resistance is equal to the accelerating force of gravity (so the resultant force is zero).
6) The object now falls at a steady speed. This maximum speed is known as the terminal velocity.
7) The same principle applies to objects falling through a liquid.

Motion is always opposed by friction (unless you're in a vacuum)

You can't move without counteracting friction. But it can be useful, e.g. for slowing something down.

Warm-Up & Exam Questions

It's time to put your knowledge to the test again. I won't force you to do these questions, but there's no better way for you to prepare for your exam, so give them a go.

Warm-Up Questions

1) If two forces are acting in the same direction, how do you find the resultant force?
2) State whether each of the following is a scalar or vector quantity:
   a) mass   b) velocity   c) force   d) time
3) What is the resultant force on an object moving at a constant velocity?
4) Write down the formula that links mass, force and acceleration.
5) An object moving in circular motion has a constant mass and speed. If the force acting on it increases, what happens to the radius of the orbit?
6) What is solid friction?
7) In which direction does drag act compared to the motion of an object?
8) What can you say about the forces on a falling object at its terminal velocity?

Exam Questions

1   **Figure 1** shows the forces acting on a lorry as it travels along a straight, level road.

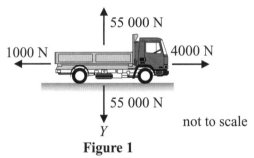

55 000 N

1000 N   4000 N

55 000 N

Y   not to scale

Figure 1

(a) (i)   What is the force labelled Y on the diagram?

[1]

(ii) Calculate the magnitude of the resultant force in the horizontal direction.

[1]

(iii) Calculate the magnitude of the resultant force in the vertical direction.

[1]

(b) What causes the frictional force acting in the opposite direction to the lorry's motion?

[1]

(c) The lorry stops accelerating and travels at a constant speed.
Tick the box below that describes the forces now experienced by the lorry.

□ **A**   The frictional force is greater than the driving force.

□ **B**   The driving force is greater than the frictional force.

□ **C**   The driving force and frictional force are equal.

□ **D**   There are no forces acting on the lorry.

[1]

[Total 5 marks]

Exam Questions

2 An aircraft is travelling through the air at a high speed.

    (a)   State what causes the outside of the aircraft to heat up as it travels through the air.

                                                                               [1]

A parachutist jumps out of the aircraft. After a period of time, she reaches terminal velocity.
The total weight of the parachutist and her equipment is 900 N.

    (b)   (i)   Determine the force of air resistance on the parachutist when she is at terminal velocity.
                  Explain your answer.

                                                                             [2]

          (ii) The parachutist falls directly downwards.
                In which direction does the air resistance act on the parachutist?

                                                                               [1]

    (c)   The parachutist deploys her parachute while at terminal velocity. This increases
          the air resistance she experiences. Predict what happens to her speed.

                                                                              [1]

    (d)   Explain how the parachutist's motion would differ if no air resistance acted on her as she fell.

                                                                                   [2]

                                                                         [Total 7 marks]

3 **Figure 2** shows two forces that are acting on a body. The body is represented by a dot in **Figure 2**.

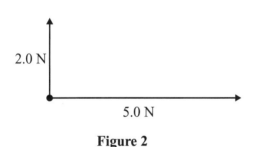

2.0 N

5.0 N

Figure 2

    (a)   Find the magnitude of the resultant of these two forces by drawing a scale diagram using the scale 1 cm = 1 N.

                                                              [2]

    (b)   Measure the angle the resultant force makes with the 5.0 N force.

                                                              [1]

                                                                [Total 3 marks]

4 **Figure 3** shows a camper van with a mass of 2500 kg.
It is being driven along a straight, level road at a constant speed.

constant speed

2500 kg

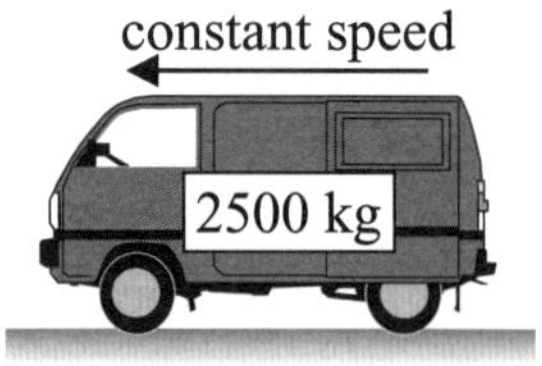

Figure 3

    (a)   A wind suddenly starts blowing straight at the front of the van with a force of 200 N, causing it to slow down. Calculate the van's acceleration in m/s^2.

                                                          [2]

    (b)   The van begins travelling at a constant speed before colliding with a stationary traffic cone that has a mass of 10 kg. The traffic cone accelerates at 29 m/s^2 in the direction of the van's motion. Calculate the force in N applied to the traffic cone by the van.

                                                                      [2]

    (c)   The van drives along a curved road at a constant speed.
          Explain whether the van is accelerating or not.

                                                                         [2]

                                                                     [Total 6 marks]

Supplement

Forces and Elasticity

Forces aren't just able to make objects change their motion, they can also make them change shape or size. Whether they change shape temporarily or permanently depends on the object and the forces applied.

Forces can Deform Objects

1) When you apply a force to an object you may cause it to change shape or size — it could stretch, compress, bend or twist.

2) To do this, you need more than one force acting on the object — otherwise the object would simply move in the direction of the applied force, instead of changing shape.

3) If an object such as a spring is supported at the top and a weight is attached to the bottom, it stretches. The amount it stretches by is the extension.

4) An object that has been elastically deformed goes back to its original shape and length after the force is removed. This type of object is called an elastic object.

5) An object that doesn't return to its original shape and length after the force is removed is permanently deformed.

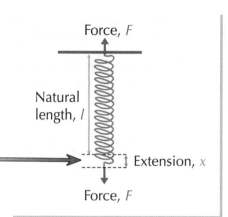

Load-Extension Graphs Show How Objects Stretch

1) The graph shows load against extension for an elastic solid. Load is how much force or weight is added to the end of the object.

2) The first part of the graph is a straight line. This shows that the extension and load are directly proportional to one another — if the load doubles, so does the extension, and if the load halves, the extension halves too.

3) When the load gets big enough, the graph starts to curve. This means load is no longer proportional to extension and a small increase in load leads to a large increase in extension.

4) The point where the graph starts to curve is the limit of proportionality (marked P on the graph).

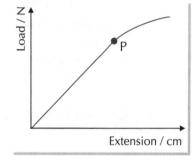

 The limit of proportionality is the point at which the load and extension stop being proportional.

Extension Varies with Force

1) The extension of a stretched spring (or certain other elastic solids) is directly proportional to the load or force applied — so $F \propto x$. Here it is written as an equation:

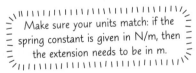

$$k = \frac{F}{x}$$

spring constant (N/cm)   force or load (N)   extension (cm)

Make sure your units match: if the spring constant is given in N/m, then the extension needs to be in m.

 The spring constant, k, is the force per unit extension.

2) The spring constant, k, depends on the material that you are stretching — a stiffer spring has a greater spring constant.

3) The equation also works for compression (where x is just the difference between the natural and compressed lengths — the compression).

4) This proportion no longer applies if the load gets too great. Past the limit of proportionality, extension is no longer proportional to force.

Investigating Springs

You can do an easy experiment to see how a spring stretches when masses are added.

You Can **Investigate** the Link Between **Force** and **Extension**

1) Before you start, set up the apparatus as shown in the diagram.
   Make sure you have plenty of extra masses.

2) It's a good idea to measure the mass of each of your masses (with a mass balance) and calculate its weight (the force applied) using $W = mg$ (p.5) at this point. This'll mean you don't have to do a load of calculations in the middle of the experiment.

Before you launch into the investigation, you could do a quick pilot experiment to check your masses are an appropriate size for your investigation:

- Using an identical spring to the one you'll be testing, load it with masses one at a time up to a total of five. Measure the extension each time you add another mass.

- Work out the increase in the extension of the spring for each of your masses. If any of them cause a bigger increase in extension than the previous masses, you've gone past the spring's limit of proportionality. If this happens, you'll need to use smaller masses, or else you won't get enough measurements for your graph.

clamp

spring

fixed ruler

tape (to mark end of spring)

hanging mass

extra masses

weighted stand

Method

1) Measure the natural length of the spring (when no load is applied) with a millimetre ruler clamped to the stand. Make sure you take the reading at eye level and add a marker (e.g. a thin strip of tape) to the bottom of the spring to make the reading more accurate.

2) Add a mass to the spring and allow the spring to come to rest. Record the mass and measure the new length of the spring. The extension is the difference from the natural length to the new length.

If the spring is stretched too far, it can permanently deform. So it's important to keep checking that the spring still goes back to its original shape.

3) Repeat this process until you have enough measurements (no fewer than six).

Extension is the change in length due to an applied force...

Make sure you know how to calculate the extension of a spring — it's the difference between the stretched length and the original, unstretched length. The extension when no force is acting on a spring should always be zero — unless the spring has been permanently deformed.

Turning Effects

When forces act around a fixed point called a pivot they have turning effects called moments.
We use these effects all the time in everyday life — e.g. when we use door handles or spanners...

Forces Can Cause Objects to Rotate About a Pivot

 The moment of a force is a measure of its turning effect.

The size of the moment of the force is given by:

$$\text{moment (Nm)} = \text{force (N)} \times \frac{\text{perpendicular distance (m)}}{\text{from the pivot}}$$

$$M = Fd$$

The perpendicular distance is the distance from the pivot that forms a right angle with the line of action of the force applied.

1) The force on a spanner causes a turning effect or moment on the nut. A larger force would mean a larger moment.

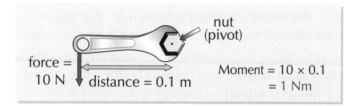

force = 10 N   distance = 0.1 m   nut (pivot)   Moment = 10 × 0.1 = 1 Nm

2) Using a longer spanner, the same force can exert a larger moment because the distance from the pivot is greater.

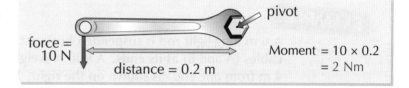

force = 10 N   distance = 0.2 m   pivot   Moment = 10 × 0.2 = 2 Nm

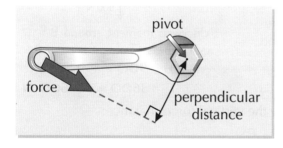

pivot   force   perpendicular distance

3) To get the maximum moment (or turning effect) you need to push at right angles (perpendicular) to the spanner.

4) Pushing at any other angle means a smaller moment because the perpendicular distance between the line of action and the pivot is smaller.

EXAMPLE:

A door is pushed with a force of 30 N at a perpendicular distance of 1.2 m from its hinge.

a) Calculate the moment of the force on the door.

b) If the force applied is halved, but the distance remains the same, what happens to the moment?

a) Put the numbers into the formula. $M = Fd = 30 \times 1.2 = 36$ Nm

b) Change the calculation so that the force is halved.

$M = Fd = 15 \times 1.2 = 18$ Nm
So halving the force halves the moment.

The moment of a force = force × distance...

Think of the extra force you need to use to open a door by pushing it near the hinge compared to pushing by the handle — the distance from the pivot is less, so you need more force to get the same moment.

Principle of Moments

Once you can calculate moments, you can work out if a seesaw is balanced. Useful thing, Physics.

A Question of **Balance** — Are the **Moments Equal?**

The principle of moments says that if an object is balanced then:
total anticlockwise moments = total clockwise moments

EXAMPLE:

A person weighs 300 N and sits 2.1 m from the pivot of a seesaw. If you weigh 700 N, where should you sit to balance the seesaw?

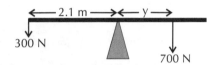

Ignore the weight of the seesaw — its centre of gravity (p.20) is on the pivot, so it doesn't have a turning effect.

For the seesaw to balance:
Total anticlockwise moments = total clockwise moments

anticlockwise moment = clockwise moment
$300 \times 2.1 = 700 \times y$
$y = 0.90$ m

1) In seesaws, the forces are acting downwards. But you may come across situations where the forces are acting upwards.

2) If a light rod is being supported at both ends, the upwards force provided by each support won't always be the same.

3) If a heavy object is placed on the rod, the support that's closer to the object will provide a larger force.

"Light" means you can ignore the weight in your calculations. In general, if they don't tell you the weight, you can ignore it.

EXAMPLE:

A 6 m long light rod is suspended horizontally by two cables (A and B) at its ends. A 900 N weight is placed 4 m from one end, as shown on the right. Work out the tension in cable A, T_A, and the tension in cable B, T_B.

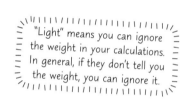

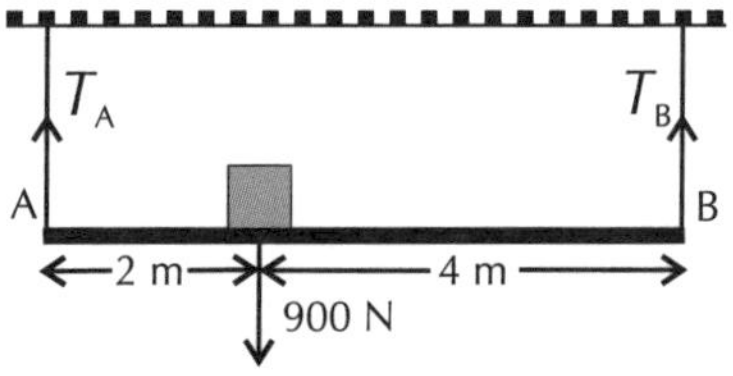

1) The weight is balanced by the tension forces in the cables. To work out the forces, start at one end and treat that end as a pivot, so you can work out the upward force at the other end.

clockwise moment around B =
anticlockwise moment around B
$T_A \times 6 = 900 \times 4$
$T_A = 3600 \div 6 = 600$ N

2) Then you can work out the force in B as we know the vertical forces balance:

900 N $= T_A + T_B$ so $T_B = 900 - T_A$
$= 900 - 600 = 300$ N

And if the Moments are **Not Equal...**

1) If the total anticlockwise moments do not equal the total clockwise moments, there will be a resultant moment — so the object will turn.

2) This propeller isn't balanced — the clockwise moment ($40 \times 1 = 40$ Nm) is greater than the anticlockwise moment ($20 \times 1 = 20$ Nm), so it will rotate clockwise.

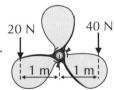

There Can be **Several Forces** Acting on **Each Side** of a Pivot

1) Don't be alarmed if you come across situations where there are two forces acting on one side of a pivot. For example, two children sitting on the right-hand side of a seesaw (a clockwise moment).

2) In this case, you'd just work out the moment created by the weight of each child and add them together to give you the total clockwise moment.

Supplement (left margin)

Supplement (right margin)

Forces in Equilibrium

If an object's motion isn't changing in any way, and it isn't rotating either, it is in equilibrium.

Two Conditions Must be met for an Object to be in Equilibrium

 KEY TERM — An object is in equilibrium if there is no resultant force on it and no resultant moment on it.

1) If there is no resultant force on the object (see page 9), the object will either be at rest or moving at a constant speed (p.11).

2) If there is no resultant moment, the total clockwise moment must equal the total anticlockwise moment about any pivot (see previous page).

3) A uniform beam balanced on a pivot will be in equilibrium. There will be no resultant force or moment acting on it.

The centre of gravity (p.20) of the beam must be exactly over the pivot so that the weight of the beam doesn't cause a moment.

You Can Investigate Moments on Objects in Equilibrium

1) Hanging a mass from a balanced beam creates a downward force on the beam. This force is equal to the weight, or $W = mg$ (p.5).

2) The force creates a turning effect about the pivot. The moment of the force is given by $M = Fd$ (p.17), with d being the perpendicular distance of the mass from the pivot.

3) There's an experiment you can do to show there is no resultant moment on an object in equilibrium:

Finding the Moments on a Beam in Equilibrium

1) Rest a beam on a pivot until it balances.

2) Whilst supporting the beam, hang a known mass on the left-hand side of the beam, at a fixed distance, e.g. 20 cm.

3) Hang a second mass on the right-hand side of the beam. Move this mass along the beam until it is balanced.

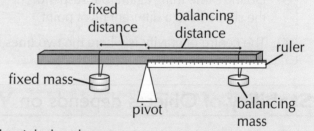

4) Measure the distance between the pivot and the right-hand mass.

5) Calculate the clockwise and anticlockwise moments acting on the beam using $M = Fd$.

6) Remove the right-hand mass.

7) Using a different mass each time, repeat steps 3-6.

You can record your results in a table. Here is an example of some results you might get:

A 2 N weight is placed at a fixed distance of 0.2 m from the left-hand side of the pivot. This gives a moment of 2 × 0.2 = 0.4 Nm in the anticlockwise direction. This is balanced by the weights and distances shown in the table:	Weight on right-hand side (N)	Distance from pivot (m)	Clockwise moment (Nm)
	1	0.4	1 × 0.4 = 0.4
	2	0.2	2 × 0.2 = 0.4
	3	0.13	3 × 0.13 = 0.39
	4	0.1	4 × 0.1 = 0.4

The clockwise moment each time should equal the anticlockwise moment (allowing for experimental error). This supports the principle of moments (see p.18).

Centre of Gravity

The entire mass of an object can be thought of as being concentrated at a point called its centre of gravity.

The **Centre of Gravity** Hangs **Below** the **Point of Suspension**

KEY TERM — The centre of gravity of an object can be thought of as the point through which the weight of the object acts.

1) A freely suspended object will swing until its centre of gravity is vertically below the point of suspension. This is because the object's weight acts at a perpendicular distance from the pivot, creating a moment.

2) The object will come to rest in a position where its centre of gravity is directly below the pivot. This is because in this position there's no moment — the pivot is in line (parallel) with the direction of the force.

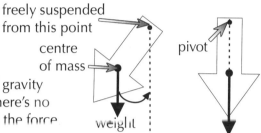

freely suspended from this point

centre of mass

pivot

weight

You can do an **Experiment** to Find the **Centre of Gravity**

You can perform an experiment to determine the position of the centre of gravity of a flat shape (a plane lamina).

To Find the Centre of Gravity of a Flat Shape

1) Suspend the shape and a plumb line from the same point, and wait until they stop moving.

2) Draw a line along the plumb line.

3) Do the same thing again, but suspend the shape from a different pivot point.

4) The centre of gravity is where the two lines cross.

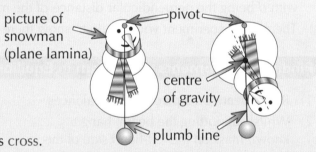

picture of snowman (plane lamina)

pivot

centre of gravity

plumb line

Stability of Objects depends on **Where** the **Centre of Gravity** is

1) An object will be stable (harder to tip over) if it has a low centre of gravity and a wide base area.

2) The higher the centre of gravity, and the smaller the base area, the less stable the object will be.

3) It's all to do with moments. If you tilt an object by pushing it at the top, the object's centre of gravity will no longer be directly over the point where the object is in contact with the ground (which acts as a pivot). This results in a turning effect, or moment.

4) If the object has a wide base and a low centre of gravity, this moment will probably just cause the object to fall back onto its base.

5) However, if the object has a small base area and a high centre of gravity, the moment is more likely to cause the object to topple.

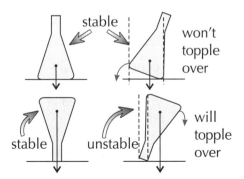

stable

won't topple over

stable   unstable

will topple over

A suspended object swings until its centre of gravity is below the pivot

So there you go — now you know how to find the centre of gravity of any irregularly-shaped object in a few easy steps. And remember, the position of the centre of gravity determines how stable an object is.

Momentum

A large rugby player running very fast is going to be a lot harder to stop than a small one out for a Sunday afternoon walk — that's momentum for you. Momentum is something all moving objects have.

Both **Mass** and **Velocity** Affect Momentum

 KEY TERM Momentum is defined as mass × velocity.

1) The greater the mass of an object and the greater its velocity, the more momentum the object has.
2) Momentum is a vector quantity (see page 9) — it has size and direction.
3) The unit of momentum is kg m/s.
4) You can work out momentum using: $p = mv$

p is the symbol for momentum.

EXAMPLE:

A 50 kg cheetah is running at 28 m/s. Calculate its momentum.

Substitute the mass and velocity into the momentum formula.

$p = mv = 50 \times 28 = 1400$ kg m/s

Momentum **Before** = Momentum **After**

 KEY TERM The principle of conservation of momentum states the total momentum before an event is equal to the total momentum after the event, as long as no external forces act.

EXAMPLE:

Two skaters approach each other, collide and move off together as shown. Calculate the velocity that they move off with after the collision.

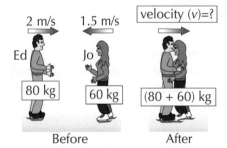

Before   After

1) Choose which direction is positive. Here we'll use to the right as positive.
2) Total momentum before collision = Ed's momentum + Jo's momentum
3) Total momentum after collision = momentum of Ed and Jo together
4) Set momentum before equal to momentum after, and rearrange to find the velocity, v.

Momentum before = $(80 \times 2) + (60 \times (-1.5))$
= 70 kg m/s

Momentum after = $140 \times v$

$140v = 70$, so $v = 70 \div 140$
$v = 0.5$ m/s to the right

If the momentum before an event is zero, then the momentum after is also zero. E.g. in an explosion, the momentum before is zero. After the explosion, the pieces fly off in different directions, so that the total momentum cancels out to zero.

See the next page for an example of momentum cancelling out to zero.

 EXAM TIP ## Momentum questions may need you to analyse a scenario...

Make sure you read any momentum questions carefully. You need to identify what the objects and momentum were before the interaction, and what they are after the interaction. The question may not be a scenario you're familiar with, so you'll need to work out what's going on.

Supplement

Impulse

Momentum is conserved in collisions, when external forces aren't acting. But when a force does act on an object it causes its momentum to change. Bigger forces cause faster momentum changes.

Forces Cause Changes in Momentum

When a resultant force acts on an object, it causes a change in momentum.

 KEY TERM — Impulse is the size of the force multiplied by the length of time it acts for. It equals the change of momentum of the object on which the force acts.

impulse (Ns) = force (N) × time(s) = change in momentum (kg m/s) | $F\Delta t = \Delta(mv)$

So a resultant force that is applied over a long time period produces a greater change in momentum than the same force over a short time period — i.e. it has a greater impulse.

 **EXAMPLE:**

A ping pong ball is hit with a paddle, which applies a force of 30 N for a time period of 5.0 ms. What is the impulse applied to the ball?

1) Convert the time to s.   5.0 ms = 0.005 s

2) Use the formula for impulse.   Impulse = Ft = 30 × 0.005 = 0.15 Ns

This example uses the principle of conservation of momentum along with the impulse equation:

 **EXAMPLE:**

A gun fires a bullet as shown.
a) At what speed does the gun recoil (move backwards)?
b) Find the force exerted on the gun if it is accelerated for 0.10 seconds.

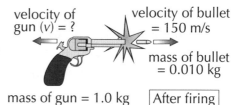

velocity of gun (v) = ?   velocity of bullet = 150 m/s

mass of bullet = 0.010 kg

mass of gun = 1.0 kg   After firing

a) Calculate the momentum of the bullet after firing. p_B = 0.010 × 150 = 1.5 kg m/s

Find the momentum of the gun after firing. p_G = 1.0 × v = v

The total momentum before firing the gun is zero. This is equal to the total momentum after firing.

Momentum before = momentum after
$$0 = p_B + p_G$$
$$0 = 1.5 + v$$

Rearrange for the velocity of the gun, v. The minus sign shows the gun is travelling in the opposite direction to the bullet. $v = -1.5$ m/s

So the gun moves backwards at 1.5 m/s.

b) The momentum of the gun before firing is zero. mu = 1.0 × 0 = 0 kg m/s

Find the momentum of the gun after firing. mv = 1.0 × −1.5 = −1.5 kg m/s

Rearrange the above equation for force.
$$F = \Delta(mv) \div \Delta t = (mv - mu) \div t$$
$$= (-1.5 - 0) \div 0.10 = -1.5 \div 0.10$$
$$= -15 \text{ N}$$

Changes in Momentum

When a force acts on an object, it causes the object to change momentum.
The bigger the force, the faster the change in momentum. And the reverse is true too.

Change in Momentum Over Time

1) You know that when a non-zero resultant force acts on a moving object
(or an object that can move), it causes its velocity to change (p.11).
This means that there is a change in momentum.

2) You also know that $F = ma$ and that a = change in velocity ÷ change in time.

3) So $F = m \times \frac{\Delta v}{\Delta t}$, which can also be written as:

Change in momentum (kg m/s)

Force (N) ⎯⎯⎯ $$F = \frac{\Delta (mv)}{\Delta t}$$ or (because $p = mv$) $$F = \frac{\Delta p}{\Delta t}$$

Change in time (s)

4) You might recognise this equation from the previous page, as the equation used to calculate impulse. If you multiply both sides of the equation above by 'Δt', you end up with:

$$F\Delta t = \Delta (mv)$$

5) The force causing the change is equal to the rate of change of momentum.

6) A larger force means a faster change of momentum.

7) Likewise, if someone's momentum changes very quickly (like in a car crash),
the forces on the body will be very large and more likely to cause injury.

8) This is why cars are designed to slow people down over a longer time when they have a crash
— the longer it takes for a change in momentum, the smaller the rate of change of momentum,
and so the smaller the resultant force. Smaller forces mean the injuries are likely to be less severe.

 KEY TERM | The resultant force is equal to the rate of change of momentum.

**A car of mass 1500 kg slows from 10 m/s to 0 m/s in 20 s.
What is the resultant force on the car?**

1) Calculate the change in momentum.

$\Delta (mv) = (1500 \times 10) - (1500 \times 0)$
$= 15\,000 - 0 = 15\,000$ kg m/s

2) Divide this by the time taken to slow down, to find the resultant force.

$F = \Delta (mv) \div \Delta t = 15\,000 \div 20 = 750$ N

Many safety features decrease rate of change of momentum...

 Knowledge of the connection between force and the rate of change of momentum has allowed us to develop a range of safety features designed to minimise injury in crashes and collisions. This is a clear example of science being applied to develop useful new technologies and devices.

Warm-Up & Exam Questions

Don't lose momentum now — you've almost made it to the end of the topic.
Have a go at these questions and you'll be done before you know it.

Warm-Up Questions

1) State the formula linking force, extension and spring constant.
2) True or false? The shorter the perpendicular distance between a force and the pivot, the greater the moment of the force.
3) State the principle of moments.
4) What conditions must be met in order for a system to be in equilibrium?
5) Briefly describe how you could find the centre of gravity of an irregular plane lamina.
6) Calculate the momentum of a 2.5 kg rabbit running through a garden at 10 m/s.
7) Give the formula which links impulse and change of momentum.

Exam Questions

1 The diagram shows four objects. The centre of gravity of each object is marked with a cross. Which object is **least** stable?

A | B | C | D

 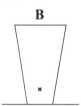 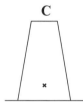 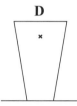

[Total 1 mark]

2 A door has a horizontal door handle. To open the door, its handle needs to be rotated clockwise. The arrows in the diagrams show the direction and position of forces exerted on the handle. The forces are all equal. In which diagram is the moment largest?

A | B | C | D

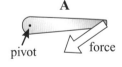 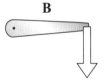 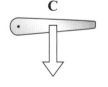

[Total 1 mark]

3 A uniform beam with a block placed at one end is rested on a pivot as shown in **Figure 1**. The block's weight provides a downwards force and the beam is in equilibrium. The full length of the beam is 18 m and the weight of the beam is 300 N.

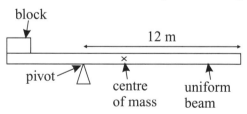

Figure 1

(a) Find the distance from the pivot to the centre of gravity.

[1]

(b) (i) The block is removed from the end of the beam. State the direction that the moment acts in.

[1]

(ii) Calculate the moment of the weight of the beam about the pivot, in Nm.

[2]

[Total 4 marks]

Exam Questions

4   A student is investigating how a spring extends when masses
     are hung from it. **Figure 2** shows the student's apparatus.

   The extension of the spring and the total weight of the masses and hook
   are recorded each time a mass is added to the bottom of the spring.

   A graph of the student's results is shown in **Figure 3**.

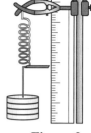

Figure 2

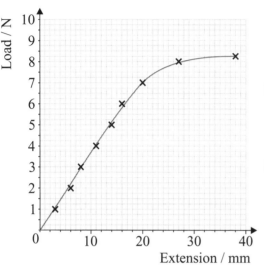

Figure 3

   (a)   When a load of 3 N is applied to the spring
        the length of the spring is measured as 51.4 cm.
        Calculate the natural length of the spring.

        [2]

   (b)   The spring constant is equal to the gradient of the
        graph up to the limit of proportionality.

        Calculate the spring constant in N/mm

        [1]
        [Total 3 marks]

5   A 65 kg stuntperson jumps from a balcony onto an inflated airbag.
     Her speed is 14 m/s just before she hits the airbag. She is stopped
     in a time of 1.3 seconds (after which her momentum is zero).

   (a)   Calculate the momentum of the stuntperson just before she hits the airbag and give the unit.

        [2]

   (b)   Calculate the average resultant force in N acting
        on the stuntperson as she is stopped by the airbag.

        [2]
        [Total 4 marks]

6   **Figure 4** shows three weights on a light plank, resting on a pivot. Weight A is 2 N and sits
     20 cm to the left of the pivot. Weight B exerts an anticlockwise moment of 0.8 Nm.

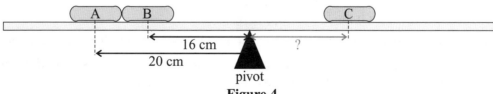

Figure 4

   (a)   Calculate the anticlockwise moment in Nm exerted by weight A.

        [2]

   (b)   The system is currently balanced. Weight C has a weight of 8 N.
        Calculate the distance of weight C from the pivot in metres.

        [3]
        [Total 5 marks]

Supplement

Revision Summary

That was a wild ride through forces and motion but thankfully that's all for Section 1. Time to test yourself.
- Try these questions and tick off each one when you get it right.
- When you've done all the questions for a topic and are completely happy with it, tick off the topic.

Speed, Distance and Time (p.1-4) ☐

1) What's the formula relating the average speed, total distance and time taken for a moving object?
2) What is meant by a negative acceleration?
3) What does a straight, horizontal line show on a distance-time graph?
4) How do you find the speed of an object from a distance-time graph?
5) What does a straight, horizontal line show on a speed-time graph?
6) How could you find the distance travelled by an object from its speed-time graph?
7) What does the gradient represent for a speed-time graph?

Mass, Weight and Density (p.5-6) ☐

8) What's the difference between mass and weight?
9) What's the formula relating an object's weight, its mass and the strength of the gravitational field?
10) What is the relationship between the density, mass and volume of a substance?
11) Briefly describe how to find the density of a liquid.

Resultant Forces, Motion and Friction (p.9-12) ☐

12) How do you find the resultant of two forces acting in opposite directions?
13) What's the difference between a vector quantity and a scalar quantity?
14) What will happen to the velocity of a moving object if a non-zero resultant force acts on it?
15) True or false? An object that changes direction is accelerating.
16) What effect does drag have on motion?

Elasticity and Springs (p.15-16) ☐

17) Sketch a typical load-extension graph.
18) Describe a simple experiment you could do to investigate the link between force and extension of a spring.

Moments, Equilibrium and Centre of Gravity (p.17-20) ☐

19) How does the moment of a force vary with the perpendicular distance from the pivot at which the force is applied?
20) If a seesaw is balanced, what can you say about the clockwise and anticlockwise moments?
21) A light rod is hung horizontally from two cables, one at each end. A mass is placed on the rod next to the left-hand end. Which cable will provide the largest supporting force?
22) What name is given to the point through which all of an object's weight acts?

Momentum and Impulse (p.21-23) ☐

23) What's the relationship between momentum, mass and velocity?
24) What is the principle of conservation of momentum?
25) What are the units for impulse?
26) What is the formula relating force to change in momentum?

Energy Stores and Energy Transfers

I hope you're feeling lively, because this section is all about energy...

Energy Exists in Energy Stores

Energy can be transferred between and held in different energy stores. There are seven you need to know:

Kinetic — anything moving has energy in this store.

Gravitational potential — anything that will fall (or would if it wasn't supported).

Chemical — anything that can release energy by a chemical reaction, e.g. food, fuels.

Elastic (or strain) — anything stretched, like springs, rubber bands, etc.

Nuclear — atomic nuclei release energy from this store in nuclear reactions.

Electrostatic — e.g. two charges that attract and repel each other.

Internal (or thermal) — any object — the hotter it is, the more energy it has in this store (see p.51).

Energy can be Transferred in Different Ways

1) Energy can be transferred between objects and transferred from one energy store to another.

2) Energy can be transferred in four main ways:

Mechanically — work is done (p.31) by a force acting on an object, e.g. pushing, pulling, stretching or squashing.

Electrically — work is done by an electric current flowing (see page 102).

By waves — energy being transferred by waves (e.g. light and other electromagnetic waves, see page 87, sound and other waves), e.g. light transfers energy from the Sun to Earth.

By heating (see p.58) — energy being transferred from a hotter object to a colder object, e.g. heating a pan of water on a hob.

There is a Principle of Conservation of Energy

There are plenty of different energy stores, but energy always obeys the principle below:

KEY TERM

The Principle of Conservation of Energy states that energy can be stored, transferred from one store to another, or dissipated — but it can never be created or destroyed.

Dissipated is a way of saying that the energy is spread out and lost to the surroundings.

In other words, when an energy transfer takes place, the same amount of energy comes out as was put in.

However, not all of the energy is transferred usefully. Whenever something happens that causes energy to be transferred, some energy is wasted. This often involves energy being transferred to the internal energy stores of the objects and the surroundings.

REVISION TIP

No matter what store it is in, it's all energy...

There are a lot of energy stores and transfers to remember. Cover this page and keep scribbling down the energy stores and types of transfer until you know them all. Then you can start applying what you've learned to work out what energy transfers take place in different situations...

Examples of Energy Transfers

More! More! Tell me more about energy transfers please! OK, since you insist:

You Need to be Able to **Describe Energy Transfers**

Here are some examples of energy transfers in every day situations:

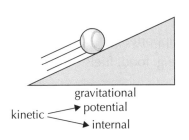
gravitational
kinetic → potential
→ internal

A BALL ROLLING UP A SLOPE:
Energy is transferred mechanically by gravity from the kinetic energy store of the ball to its gravitational potential energy store. Some energy is also transferred mechanically to the internal energy stores of the ball, slope and surroundings (due to friction). The total energy transferred to the gravitational potential and internal energy stores equals the energy transferred away from the kinetic energy store of the ball.

A BAT HITTING A BALL:
Some of the energy in the bat's kinetic energy store is transferred mechanically to the kinetic energy store of the ball. The rest of the energy is wasted — some is transferred mechanically to the internal energy store of the bat and the ball. The remaining energy is transferred to the internal energy stores of the surroundings by sound waves.

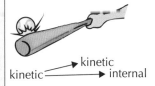
kinetic → kinetic → internal

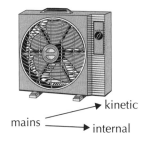
mains → kinetic
→ internal

AN ELECTRIC FAN:
Energy is transferred electrically from the mains to the kinetic energy store of the fan's blades and then mechanically to the kinetic energy store of the air. Some energy is also wasted, as it is transferred to the internal energy stores of the motor and electrical circuit in the fan, as well as to the surroundings by heating and by waves (both sound waves and electromagnetic waves).

A BUNSEN BURNER:
In a lit Bunsen burner, the combustion reaction releases the energy in the chemical energy store of the natural gas. The energy is transferred by heating and by waves (infrared radiation, p.58) to the internal energy stores of the surroundings. Some energy is also transferred away by waves as light and is dissipated.

chemical → internal

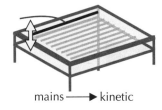
mains → kinetic

A RIPPLE TANK (see p.68):
Energy is transferred electrically from the mains to the kinetic energy store of the dipper, moving it up and down. The dipper's motion causes water particles to move up and down, creating a water wave that transfers energy through the water. Energy is wasted as it's transferred to the internal energy stores of the circuit, water and surroundings.

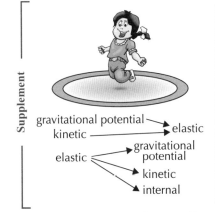
gravitational potential
kinetic → elastic
gravitational potential
elastic → kinetic
→ internal

A CHILD BOUNCING ON A TRAMPOLINE:
As the child falls towards the trampoline, she has energy in her kinetic and gravitational potential energy stores (p.29). As the child lands on the trampoline, the trampoline material stretches down and decreases her speed until she stops. Energy is transferred mechanically from the kinetic and gravitational potential energy stores of the child to the elastic energy store of the trampoline. As the child bounces back up, energy is transferred mechanically back from the elastic energy store to the child's kinetic and gravitational potential energy stores. Some energy is also mechanically transferred to the internal energy stores of the trampoline and surroundings.

Kinetic and Gravitational Potential Energy Stores

Time to focus on two of the most common energy stores — kinetic and gravitational potential.

Movement Means Energy in an Object's Kinetic Energy Store

1) Anything that is moving has energy in its kinetic energy store.

Energy is measured in joules (J).

2) The amount of energy in the kinetic energy store of an object depends on the object's mass and speed. The greater its mass and the faster it's going, the more energy it has in its kinetic energy store.

3) There's a formula for the amount of energy in the kinetic energy store of an object:

Kinetic energy (J) — $E_k = \frac{1}{2}mv^2$ — (Speed)^2 (m/s)^2

Mass (kg)

$\frac{1}{2}mv^2$ means $\frac{1}{2} \times m \times v^2$.

 **EXAMPLE:** **A car with a mass of 2500 kg is travelling at 20 m/s. Calculate the amount of energy in its kinetic energy store.**

$E_k = \frac{1}{2}mv^2 = \frac{1}{2} \times 2500 \times 20^2 = 500\ 000$ J

Raised Objects Store Energy in G.P.E Stores

1) Lifting an object in a gravitational field (p.5) causes energy to be transferred to the gravitational potential energy store of the object. The higher the object is from the ground, the more energy it has in its gravitational potential energy store.

2) The energy in an object's gravitational potential energy store depends on the object's mass, its height and the strength of the gravitational field the object is in.

3) You can use this equation to find the change in energy in an object's gravitational potential energy store when its height above the ground changes.

The 'Δ' symbol means 'change in'. It's the Greek letter delta.

Change in gravitational potential energy (J) — $\Delta E_p = mg\Delta h$ — Change in height (m)

Mass (kg)

Gravitational field strength (N/kg)
$g = 9.8$ N/kg on Earth

Falling Objects Transfer Energy

1) When something, e.g. a ball, is dropped from a height, it's accelerated by gravity. The gravitational force causes an energy transfer.

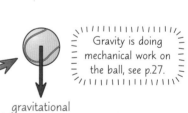

Gravity is doing mechanical work on the ball, see p.27.

2) As it falls, some of the energy in the object's gravitational potential energy store is transferred to its kinetic energy store.

gravitational force

3) If there is no air resistance, then:

Energy lost from the g.p.e. store = Energy gained in the kinetic energy store

4) In real life, air resistance (p.12) acts on almost all falling objects. It causes some of the energy from the object's gravitational potential energy and kinetic energy stores to be transferred to other energy stores, e.g. the internal energy stores of the object and the surroundings.

This is an example of the conservation of energy principle (p.27) in action.

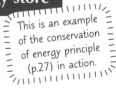 **REVISION TIP** ## You need to learn the equations for KE and GPE...

Think of the delta symbol like a hill. Climbing up a hill increases the energy in your gravitational potential energy store, so the equation with a Δ gives you gravitational potential energy.

Warm-Up & Exam Questions

These questions give you chance to use your knowledge about energy types and transfers.

Warm-Up Questions

1) Which energy store is energy transferred to when an object starts moving?
2) Give two methods of energy transfer.
3) State the principle of the conservation of energy.
4) State the equation that links the energy in an object's kinetic energy store with its mass and speed.

Exam Questions

1   Which of these objects has energy in its elastic energy store?

☐   **A**   A burning piece of coal.

☐   **B**   A skydiver falling from an aeroplane.

☐   **C**   A stretched spring.

☐   **D**   A stone rolling down a hill.

[Total 1 mark]

2   **Figure 1** shows a golf ball on flat ground before and after it was hit by a golf club. There is a sound as the club hits the ball. The ball is initially at rest, and moves off to the right after it is hit by the club.

Before   After

Figure 1

Describe the two energy transfers that cause the observations described above when the golf club hits the ball. Explain how you know these energy transfers have taken place.

[Total 2 marks]

3   **Figure 2** shows a roller coaster cart with a mass of 105 kg, rolling along a horizontal track at 2.39 m/s.

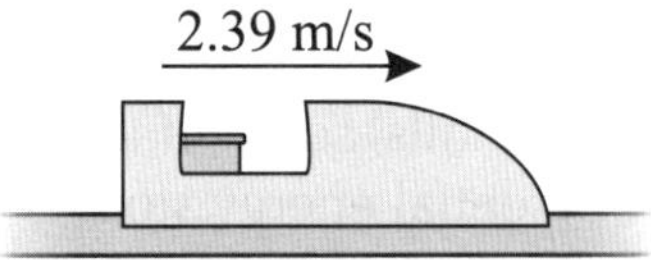

2.39 m/s

Figure 2

(a)   Calculate the energy in the kinetic energy store of the cart, in J.

[2]

(b)   The cart reaches a downhill slope in the track with a vertical height of 20.2 m.
It rolls down the slope with no driving force other than the force due to gravity.

(i)   Calculate the energy lost from the gravitational potential energy store of the cart as it rolls down the slope, in J.

Use g = 9.8 N/kg.

[2]

(ii) Assuming no resistive forces act against the cart, state the amount by which the energy in the kinetic energy store of the cart changes between the top and bottom of the slope. Explain your answer.

[2]

[Total 6 marks]

Supplement

Work

Work (like a lot of things) means something slightly different in physics to what it means in everyday life...

'Work Done' is Just 'Energy Transferred'

 Work done is equal to energy transferred.

1) You've seen on p.27 that there are two types of work done, mechanical and electrical.

2) To make something move, some sort of force needs to act on it.
The thing applying the force needs a source of energy (like fuel or food).

3) The force does 'work' to move the object and energy is transferred mechanically to the object (see page 27) — this is mechanical work done.

4) Electrical work done is when energy is transferred when a charge moves through a potential difference (p.102).

5) Whether energy is transferred usefully (e.g. lifting a load) or is wasted (see page 33), work is still done.

> For example, when you push something along a rough surface (like a carpet) you are doing work against frictional forces. Energy is being transferred to the kinetic energy store of the object because it starts moving, but some energy is also being transferred to the internal energy stores of the object and the surface due to the friction. This causes the temperature of the object and the surface to increase. (Like rubbing your hands together to warm them up.)

There's a Formula to Learn for Mechanical Work Done

Mechanical work done is equal to the force doing the work multiplied by the distance moved. Since work done is equal to energy transferred, you can write this equation as:

Mechanical work done = Force × Distance moved = Energy transferred mechanically

This formula only works if the force is in exactly the same direction as the movement.

FORCE

Distance

$W = Fd = \Delta E$

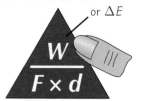

or ΔE

$$\dfrac{W}{F \times d}$$

Whether the force is friction or weight or tension in a rope, it's the same equation. To find how much work has been done in joules, you just multiply the force in newtons by the distance moved in metres.

 **EXAMPLE:**

Some people pull an old tractor tyre 5 m over flat ground. They pull with a total force of 340 N. Find the work done.

Just stick the numbers you've been given into the equation for work.

$W = F \times d$
$= 340 \times 5 = 1700$ J

Work is done when a force acts over a distance...

Whenever a force acts on an object, and causes the object to move in the direction of the force, work is being done. And if 'work is done', that means 'energy is transferred' — they're the same thing. Make sure you can recognise when this is happening, so an energy question won't take you by surprise in the exams.

Power

The more powerful a device is, the more energy it will transfer in a certain amount of time.

Power is the 'Rate of Doing Work' — i.e. How Much per Second

1) Power is a measure of how quickly work is being done.
   As work done = energy transferred, you can define power like this:

 Power is the work done, or the energy transferred, per unit time.

2) So, the power of a machine is the rate at which it transfers energy.

3) The unit of power is the watt (W). 1 W = 1 J of energy transferred per second (J/s).
   If an electric drill has a power of 700 W, this means it can transfer 700 J of energy every second.

For example, a 900 W microwave oven will transfer more energy in a fixed period of time than a 700 W microwave oven.

This also means the 900 W microwave oven will transfer a set amount of energy faster than a 700 W microwave oven.

To Calculate Power you Divide Energy by Time

$$\text{Power} = \frac{\text{Energy transferred}}{\text{Time taken}}$$

$$P = \frac{\Delta E}{t}$$

Since energy transferred is equal to work done you can also write it as:

$$P = \frac{W}{t}$$ — Work done (J)

 **A motor transfers 4.8 kJ of useful energy in 2 minutes. Find its power output.**

1) Convert the values into the correct units.
   You need your values to be in J and s.

2) Then just substitute the values into the formula.

energy = 4.8 kJ = 4800 J

time = 2 minutes = 120 s

$P = \Delta E \div t$
$= 4800 \div 120 = 40$ W

4.8 kJ of useful
energy transferred in 2 minutes

A large device doesn't always mean a large power...

Power isn't just about the amount of energy transferred, it's how fast it transfers the energy. A device that transfers a small amount of energy very quickly could have the same power as a device that transferred a huge amount of energy over a very long time. Now use your brain power to get more revision done...

Efficiency

Devices have energy transferred to them, but only transfer some of that energy to useful energy stores. Wouldn't it be great if we could tell how much they usefully transfer? That's where efficiency comes in.

Energy Transfers Involve Some Wasted Energy

1) Useful devices and processes are only useful because they can transfer energy.
2) But some of the input energy is wasted by being transferred to an energy store that isn't useful — usually internal energy stores (see page 27).
3) The less energy that is 'wasted', the more efficient the device or process is said to be.

 The efficiency of a process or device is a measure of the proportion of the input energy that is transferred usefully.

4) Efficiencies will usually be stated as percentages, e.g. 75%.
5) Due to conservation of energy (p.27), the total input energy ALWAYS equals the total output energy.
6) If a device is 75% efficient, this means it transfers 75% of its input energy usefully and wastes 25% of its input energy. The higher a device or process's efficiency, the less energy it wastes.
7) No real device or process is 100% efficient, some energy will always be wasted.

You can Calculate Efficiency from Energy and Power

1) The efficiency for any device or process can be worked out using this equation:

$$\text{Efficiency} = \frac{\text{useful energy output}}{\text{total energy input}} \times 100\%$$

2) You might not know the energy inputs and outputs, but you can still calculate its efficiency as long as you know the power inputs and outputs (see page 32):

$$\text{Efficiency} = \frac{\text{useful power output}}{\text{total power input}} \times 100\%$$

You can ignore the percentage sign when you rearrange and substitute values in these equations. It doesn't change the maths, it just tells you the efficiency should be a percentage.

 **A blender is 70% efficient. It has a total input power of 600 W. Calculate the useful power output.**

1) Rearrange the efficiency equation for useful power output.
2) Stick in the numbers you're given.

useful power output = (efficiency ÷ 100) × total power input
= (70 ÷ 100) × 600
= 0.70 × 600
= 420 W

 ## The higher the efficiency, the less energy wasted...
If you're asked to calculate efficiency in the exam, you should give it as a percentage unless you're told otherwise. You may see efficiency given as a decimal, instead of a percentage (e.g. 0.25 instead of 25%). To convert the decimal to a percentage, multiply by 100 and stick on a %.

Flow Diagrams and Sankey Diagrams

Energy moving from one store to another can be represented using diagrams showing where it's coming from and going to. It really makes things clearer if you make one.

You can **Draw Flow Diagrams** to Show Energy Transfers

Diagrams can make it easier to see what's going on when energy is transferred.
The flow diagram below shows the energy transferred when a ball is thrown upwards, taking air resistance into account. The boxes represent stores and the arrows show transfers:

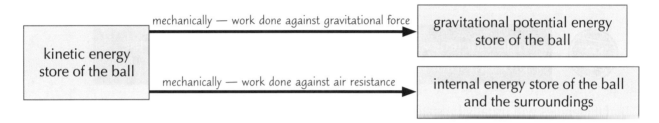

Sankey Diagrams show the Amount of Energy to Each Store

The idea of Sankey diagrams is to make it easy to see at a glance how much of the input energy is being usefully transferred compared with how much is being wasted.

The thicker the arrow, the more energy it represents — so you see a big thick arrow going in, then several smaller arrows going off it to show the different energy transfers taking place.

You can have either a little sketch (like the one on the right) or a properly detailed diagram where the width of each arrow is directly proportional to the number of joules it represents.

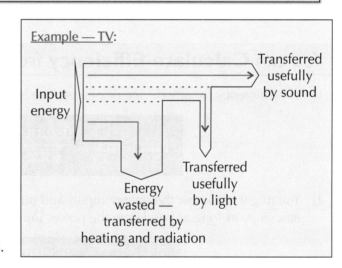

Example — Sankey Diagram for a **Simple Motor**:

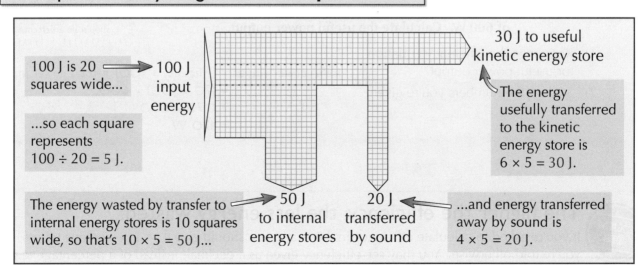

Pressure

I'm sure you're familiar with exam pressure, but pressure is an important concept in physics too.

When a **Force** acts on a **Surface**, there is a **Pressure**

 KEY TERM Pressure is the force per unit area.

1) Pressure can be calculated using this equation:

2) Pressure is usually measured in pascals, Pa (or kilopascals, kPa). 1 pascal is defined as 1 N/m².

3) The larger the area a force is applied over, the lower the pressure the force creates.

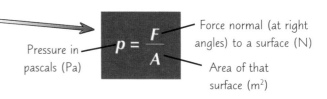
Pressure in pascals (Pa)
$$p = \frac{F}{A}$$
Force normal (at right angles) to a surface (N)
Area of that surface (m²)

The soles of snowshoes have very large areas, which 'spread out' your weight (the force). This reduces the pressure exerted on the ground and stops you sinking into snow as you walk.

High-heeled shoes have a small area in contact with the ground, so they increase the pressure exerted on the ground, which can damage some types of flooring.

4) Fluids (liquids and gases) cause a pressure.

As the particles in a gas or liquid move around, they collide with surfaces and other particles and exert a force. These collisions create an overall force at right angles to each surface. Pressure is force per unit area, so this means the particles exert a pressure.

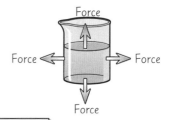
Force
Force
Force
Force

Pressure in a **Liquid** Depends on **Depth** and **Density**

1) For a given liquid, the density is uniform (the same everywhere) and it doesn't vary with shape or size. The density of a gas can vary though.

To refresh your memory on density, take a look back at page 6.

2) The more dense a given liquid is, the more particles it has in a certain space. This means there are more particle collisions, so the pressure is higher.

3) As the depth below the surface of the liquid increases, the number of particles above that point increases. The weight of these particles adds to the pressure felt at that point, so liquid pressure increases with depth.

4) You can calculate the change in pressure between different depths in a liquid using:

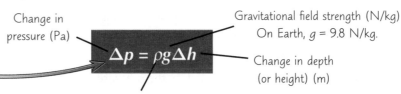
Change in pressure (Pa)
Gravitational field strength (N/kg) On Earth, g = 9.8 N/kg.
$$\Delta p = \rho g \Delta h$$
Change in depth (or height) (m)
Density of the liquid (kg/m³) (the symbol is the Greek letter 'rho')

 **EXAMPLE:**

Calculate the change in pressure between a point 35 m below the surface of a pool of water and a point 10 m below the surface. The density of water is 1000 kg/m³.

1) First find the change in depth.

$\Delta h = 35 - 10 = 25$ m

2) Then substitute the values into the equation to find the change in pressure.

$\Delta p = \rho g \Delta h = 1000 \times 9.8 \times 25$
$= 245\ 000$ Pa
(or 245 kPa)

Supplement

Warm-Up & Exam Questions

Do some work by answering these questions and transfer some knowledge from your brain...

Warm-Up Questions

1) How much energy is transferred when 160 J of work is done to move a plant pot?
2) What is the unit of power?
3) What is meant by the efficiency of a device or process?
4) Define the term pressure.
5) Name two variables that affect the pressure at a point beneath the surface of a liquid.

Exam Questions

1 Which of these statements correctly describes power?

☐ **A** Power is the total work done by an object.

☐ **B** Power is the rate at which energy is transferred.

☐ **C** Power is the total energy transferred to an object.

☐ **D** Power is the minimum work done to an object to cause it to move.

[Total 1 mark]

2 Three students, A, B and C, each push a box the same distance across a flat surface. Each student pushes the box in the same direction that it moves.

(a) To move the box, student A did 500 J of work, student B did 450 J of work, and student C did 620 J of work. Who applied the largest force to the box? Explain your answer.

[2]

(b) The box contains two electrical devices, X and Y. Device X has an efficiency of 60% and device Y has an efficiency of 85%. If both devices were supplied with the same amount of energy, which would waste more energy? Explain your answer.

[1]

[Total 3 marks]

3 **Figure 1** shows a simple hydraulic system containing a liquid.

In a hydraulic system, a force is applied to a liquid using a piston. The pressure is transmitted from one piston to another through the liquid.

The liquid cannot be compressed, so the pressure is the same at all points in the liquid.

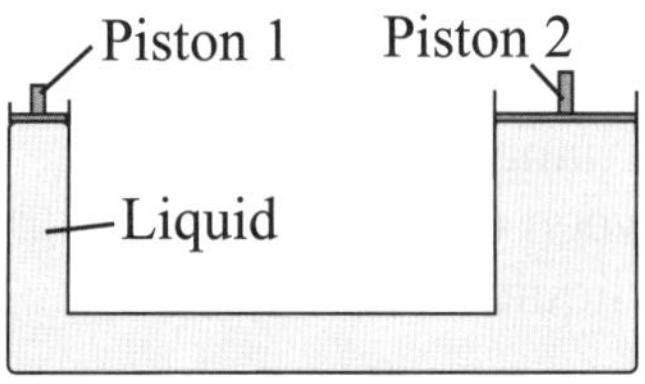

Figure 1

(a) A force of 175 N is applied to the liquid by piston 1, which has a cross-sectional area of 0.25 m². Calculate the pressure created in the liquid by piston 1.

[2]

(b) Piston 2 has a cross-sectional area of 1.3 m². Calculate the force acting on piston 2 due to the liquid.

[2]

[Total 4 marks]

Exam Questions

4 The manufacturer of a toy crane creates a Sankey diagram to show the energy transfers involved when the crane is in operation, as shown in **Figure 2**.

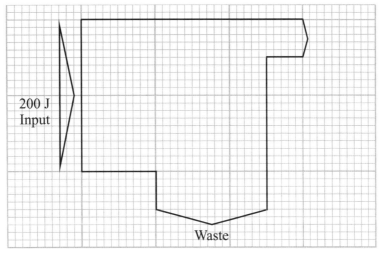

200 J Input

Waste

Figure 2

(a) Calculate the value represented by each small square.

[1]

(b) Calculate how much energy, in J, is transferred usefully by the toy crane for every 200 J of energy supplied.

[1]

[Total 2 marks]

5 Torch A transfers 1200 J of energy per minute. 480 J of energy is transferred away usefully by light waves. 720 J is wasted and transferred to the internal energy stores of the torch and its surroundings.

(a) Calculate the efficiency of torch A.

[2]

(b) Torch B transfers 540 J of energy away usefully by light each minute.
Calculate the output power of torch B.

[2]

(c) Torch B has an efficiency of 55%. Calculate the input power of torch B.

[2]

(d) Each torch is powered by an identical battery. A student claims that the battery in torch B will discharge (run out of energy and need replacing) faster than in torch A because it transfers more energy away as light each minute. Explain whether or not you agree with the student.

[1]

[Total 7 marks]

6 A student holds a ball just under the surface of a bucket full of water. He lets the ball go, and it sinks to the bottom of the bucket, as shown in **Figure 3**.
The ball has a diameter of 8 cm. The water is 50 cm deep.
Water has a density of 1000 kg/m³.
The gravitational field strength is 9.8 N/kg.
Calculate the change in pressure on the bottom of the ball from its initial position to its final position.

[Total 3 marks]

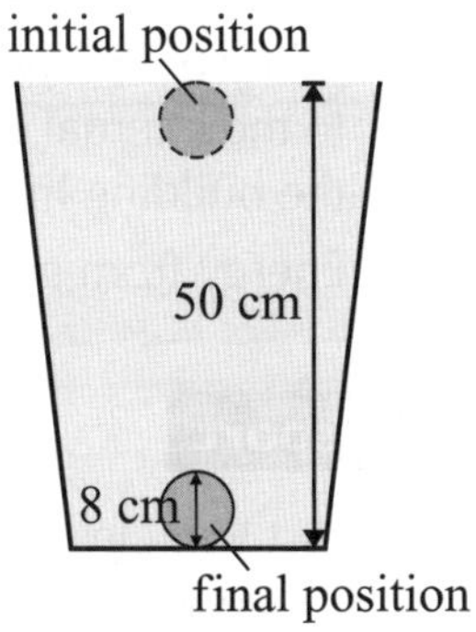

initial position

50 cm

8 cm

final position

Figure 3

Energy Resources

There are lots of energy resources available on Earth. They are either renewable or non-renewable resources.

Non-Renewable Energy Resources Will Run Out One Day

A non-renewable energy resource is an energy resource that cannot be made at the same rate as it's being used, so it will one day run out.

Non-renewable energy resources are fossil fuels and nuclear fuel (e.g. uranium and plutonium).
Fossil fuels are natural resources that form underground over millions of years.
The three main fossil fuels are:

1) Coal   2) Oil   3) (Natural) gas

Renewable Energy Resources Will Never Run Out

A renewable energy resource is an energy resource that is being, or can be, made at the same rate (or faster) than it's being used, so it will never run out.

Renewable energy resources are:

1) The Sun (Solar)   4) Hydroelectricity   6) Tides
2) Wind   5) Biofuels   7) Geothermal
3) Water waves

Energy Resources can be Used for Heating and Transport

1) Energy resources all serve as sources of energy, but we need to convert that energy into the energy stores that we want for a particular use.

2) Fuels (e.g. fossil fuels and biofuels) have energy in their chemical energy stores that can usually be burned to transfer that energy into internal energy stores. This energy can then be used in these stores, or transferred to other useful energy stores.

3) We use energy resources in many different ways. One of the most important uses of energy resources is generating electricity (more on that coming up on the next page). Here are a couple of others:

Heating

1) When you stand near a hot object and you can feel the heat from it, what you're actually feeling is energy being transferred from that object's internal energy store to yours.

2) We can burn fuels to directly heat us or our surroundings (e.g. a coal fire).

3) Many buildings have central heating systems. A fuel (e.g. gas) is often burned to transfer energy to the internal energy store of the water in the heating system. The hot water is pumped around the building in pipes. Energy is transferred from the water to the surroundings by heating.

4) Energy from geothermal resources (p.43) and the Sun can also be used to heat water.

Transport

In most vehicles, fuel is burned in an engine to release the energy in its chemical energy store. This energy is transferred to other stores (e.g. internal energy stores) before being transferred to the kinetic energy store of the vehicle (so it moves).

Generating Electricity from Fuels

Energy resources like fossil fuels and nuclear fuels can be use to generate electricity. Now let's find out how...

Fossil Fuels can be Burned to Drive Turbines in Power Stations

One of the most common methods of generating electricity is to use one of the three fossil fuels (coal, oil and gas) in big power stations. The power stations that use each fuel are all very similar. The typical features of a fossil fuel power station are shown below.

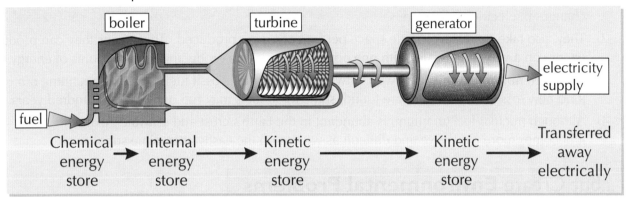

In a fossil fuel power station:

1) The fossil fuel is burned, causing energy to be transferred from its chemical energy store by heating.

2) The energy is transferred to the internal energy store of water and heats it. It changes state to become water vapour and steam.

3) The water vapour and steam turn a turbine, transferring some of the energy mechanically from the internal energy store of the steam to the kinetic energy store of the turbine.

Some fossil fuel power stations just heat air rather than water. Then the hot air is used to turn the turbine.

4) As the turbine revolves, so does the generator, which produces an electric current (see p.102). The energy is transferred away electrically from the power station.

You can also burn biofuels to produce electricity in the same way (see page 42).

There are some big advantages and disadvantages to generating electricity using fossil fuels (see p.40).

Nuclear Power Stations have Nuclear Reactors instead of Boilers

1) A nuclear power station has most of the same features as those shown above.

2) The difference is that the fuel (e.g. uranium) undergoes a nuclear reaction called nuclear fission rather than being burned. So instead of a boiler, nuclear power stations have nuclear reactors:

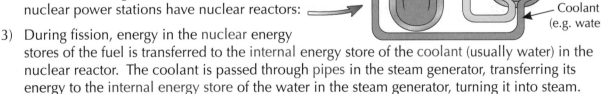

3) During fission, energy in the nuclear energy stores of the fuel is transferred to the internal energy store of the coolant (usually water) in the nuclear reactor. The coolant is passed through pipes in the steam generator, transferring its energy to the internal energy store of the water in the steam generator, turning it into steam.

4) But after that, the process is very similar to generating electricity using fossil fuels. The steam drives a turbine, which turns a generator, which produces electricity.

Turbines and generators are key...

Make sure you really understand that bit about how turning a turbine ends up generating electricity (including the energy transfers involved). With that memorised, you're halfway to telling the examiner how we get energy from fossil fuels, nuclear, biofuels, wind, geothermal, tides and hydroelectric — the only exception is solar power. Read on for more on these energy resources.

Non-Renewable Resources

We still use a lot of non-renewable resources, even though they damage the environment...

Non-Renewables are Reliable and Available at the Moment...

1) Fossil fuels and nuclear fuel are readily available energy resources — there are enough fossil and nuclear fuels to meet current demand. This means power stations always have fuel in stock and can generate a reliable electricity supply. This also means that the power stations can respond quickly to changes in electricity demand.

2) They also take up relatively little space per unit of power produced. This means they can produce energy on a very large scale, with one power station alone producing large amounts of energy.

3) However, non-renewable fuels won't always be available. Fossil fuels are slowly running out. If no new fossil fuel resources are found, some fossil fuels may run out within a hundred years.

4) Although nuclear fuel (uranium) is abundant in the Earth's crust and seawater, extracting it becomes more expensive and difficult as we use up the easily accessible supplies.

...but Create Environmental Problems

1) Coal, oil and gas release carbon dioxide (CO_2) into the atmosphere when they're burned. All this CO_2 adds to the greenhouse effect, and contributes to global warming.

2) Burning coal and oil also releases sulfur dioxide, which causes acid rain. This can be harmful to trees and soils and can have far-reaching effects in ecosystems (habitats and the organisms that live in them).

Acid rain can be reduced by taking the sulfur out before the fuel is burned, or by cleaning up the emissions.

3) Views can be spoiled by fossil fuel power stations, and coal mining can have a huge effect on the landscape, especially 'open-cast mining'.

4) Oil spillages cause serious environmental problems, affecting mammals and birds that live in and around the sea.

Nuclear fuels are often mined, processed and transported by machines powered by fossil fuels, which do release greenhouse gases into the atmosphere.

5) Nuclear fuel has to be processed before you can use it, which causes pollution. Although generating electricity using nuclear fuel produces very little of the pollutants produced by fossil fuel power stations, the nuclear waste it produces is very dangerous (p.144) and difficult to dispose of.

6) Nuclear power stations always carry a risk of a major catastrophe, like the Fukushima disaster in Japan.

Nuclear Fusion Might Be a Better Option

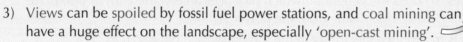

1) We currently use nuclear fission to generate electricity in nuclear power stations (p.39).

2) Nuclear fusion is another nuclear reaction that releases energy. Compared to fission, it releases more energy from a given mass of fuel, produces less nuclear waste and fuel is unlimited and easily produced.

3) Scientists are researching ways of using nuclear fusion to generate electricity on a large scale.

4) But they haven't been able to create the conditions needed for nuclear fusion (very high temperatures and pressures) without using more energy than the fusion would release.

Supplement

The big advantage of non-renewables is how reliable they are...

... the big disadvantages are that they'll run out and using them harms the planet. Many countries around the world are trying to reduce the amount of non-renewable fuels they use, and instead use renewable energy resources for their energy needs. There's more on renewable energy resources coming up on the next page...

Solar Power

The Sun isn't just good for making our days bright and warm. It can be a powerful renewable energy resource for heating and generating electricity, thanks to some useful bits of technology.

Supplement

A Lot of the Energy on Earth Originally Came from the Sun

1) The energy in most energy resources (basically everything except geothermal, nuclear and tidal power) started off as energy released in the Sun.

2) Energy is released in the Sun by nuclear fusion (see p.138). This energy is transferred away from the Sun by electromagnetic radiation (p.87) and reaches the Earth.

3) This energy heats the planet and its atmosphere, which causes wind and waves.

4) Sunlight provides energy for plants (through photosynthesis) — animals then eat those plants for energy. So the energy stored in energy resources made from plants and animals (e.g. biofuels and fossil fuels) originally came from the Sun.

5) We can also use the energy from the Sun directly, using solar cells and solar panels. This is called solar power.

Supplement

Solar Cells — Expensive but Not Much Environmental Damage

Solar cells generate electric currents directly from sunlight. Often solar cells are attached together to form a solar panel.

1) Solar cells are often the best source of energy to charge batteries in calculators and watches which don't use much electricity.

2) Solar power is often used in remote places where there's not much choice (e.g. the Australian outback) and to power electric road signs and satellites.

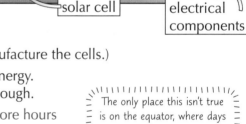

3) There's no pollution. (Although the factories do use quite a lot of energy and produce some pollution when they manufacture the cells.)

4) In sunny countries solar power is a very reliable source of energy. Solar power can still be cost-effective in cloudy countries though.

5) Solar power is only available in the daytime. Places with more hours of sunlight have more solar power available to them. The availability is higher in summer than winter in most places as the days are longer.

The only place this isn't true is on the equator, where days are always 12 hours long.

6) Sadly, you can't increase the power output when there is extra demand.

7) Compared to other energy resources, solar cells produce little power per unit of space taken up. So they are often used to generate electricity on a relatively small scale. To produce energy on a larger scale, they are used as part of 'solar farms', where lots of solar panels are laid out over a big area in one location and are used to generate a relatively large amount of electricity.

Solar Power can also use Energy from the Sun for Heating

Solar water heating panels are more simple than solar cells — they're basically just black water pipes inside a glass box.

The glass lets energy transferred by light, infrared and other electromagnetic waves from the Sun in. The energy is then absorbed by the black pipes and heats up the water. This hot water can then be used in a building's central heating system to heat it.

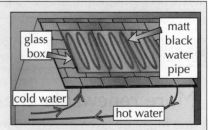

Like with solar cells, the initial set up cost can be fairly high, but there are few ongoing costs. They're mostly only used for small-scale heating and any environmental downsides are small.

Biofuels and Wind Power

Just like the other renewable energy resources, the wind and biofuels will not run out...

Biofuels are Made from Plants and Waste

Biofuels are a renewable energy resource created from plant products or animal dung. They can be solid, liquid or gas, and can be burned to produce electricity or run cars in the same way as fossil fuels.

They have Pros...

1) Generating electricity using biofuels is theoretically carbon neutral (the overall change in CO_2 in the atmosphere is zero), in which case it wouldn't contribute to global warming. However, there is some debate about whether biofuels really are carbon neutral, as it's only really true if you keep growing plants at the same rate that you're burning biofuels.

> When plants grow, they absorb CO_2 from the atmosphere — the amount of CO_2 released by burning biofuels is equal to the amount absorbed by the plants you grow to make it.

2) Biofuels are a fairly reliable and available energy resource — it's easy to have biofuels constantly available as crops take a relatively short time to grow and different crops can be grown all year round. Biofuels are continuously produced and stored for when they are needed.

... and Cons

1) You need a lot of space for crops per unit of power produced, so generating energy on a large scale is limited by having enough land. Some people worry that growing crops specifically for biofuels will mean there isn't enough space or water to meet the demands for crops that are grown for food.

2) In some regions, large areas of forest have been cleared to make room to grow biofuels, resulting in lots of species losing their natural habitats. This also means there's less plant-life to remove carbon dioxide (CO_2) from the atmosphere. The decay and burning of this vegetation also increases CO_2 and methane emissions, which contributes to global warming.

Wind Power — Lots of Wind Turbines

The Sun is the source of wind energy. As it heats the Earth and atmosphere, the temperature changes cause winds. Wind power involves putting lots of wind turbines (windmills) up in exposed places, e.g. on coasts.

1) Each turbine has a generator inside it — the rotating blades turn the generator and produce electricity.

2) There's no pollution (except for a bit when they're manufactured).

3) But they do spoil the view. You need a huge number of wind turbines to replace one coal-fired power station and the wind turbines would cover a lot more ground — which would have a big effect on the scenery.

4) And they can be noisy, which can be annoying for people living nearby.

5) Their availability depends on there being a suitable location to install them given the above factors.

6) They're not always reliable. The turbines will also stop working when the wind stops or if the wind is too strong, so they can't generate electricity all the time. And it's impossible to increase supply if there's extra demand.

7) There's no permanent damage to the landscape — if you remove the turbines, you remove the noise and the view returns to normal.

8) Wind power can be used on a large scale, with huge 'wind farms' made up of many turbines. They can also be used on a small scale, e.g. a single turbine can provide electricity to a single home.

More renewable energy resources to learn...

EXAM TIP You might be given a scenario in the exam and asked to recommend a type of energy resource to use. Go through the requirements given and compare them to the advantages and disadvantages you know about each energy resource to lead you to the right answer.

Geothermal and Hydroelectric Power

Here are some more examples of renewable energy resources — geothermal and hydroelectric.
These ones are a bit more reliable than wind and solar, read on to find out why...

Geothermal Power — Energy from Underground

Geothermal power uses energy in the internal energy
stores of rocks underground.

1) This is only available in volcanic areas where
   hot rocks lie quite near to the surface.
   The source of much of the energy is the
   slow decay of various radioactive elements,
   including uranium, deep inside the Earth.

2) This is a very reliable source of energy, as the
   geothermal energy resource is always there.

3) It also has very few environmental problems — it
   can release some CO_2 from underground, but it
   releases much less than a fossil fuel power station.

4) Geothermal energy can be used on a
   large scale to generate electricity, or
   on a small scale to heat buildings directly.

5) The main drawbacks with geothermal energy
   are that there aren't very many suitable locations
   for power stations and that the cost of building
   a power station is often high compared
   to the amount of energy it produces.

Hydroelectric Power Uses Falling Water

Hydroelectric power generates electricity from the energy in the kinetic energy stores of falling water.

1) Hydroelectric power usually requires the flooding of a valley by building a big dam to create
   a reservoir. Rainwater is caught in the reservoir, and water is allowed to flow through the dam
   through turbines. This turns the turbines, which drives generators and generates electricity.

2) It doesn't directly produce any pollution, but there is a big impact on the environment. The
   flooding of the valley causes rotting vegetation (which releases methane and carbon dioxide) and
   a loss of habitat for animal species. It can also cause the loss of people's homes. The reservoirs
   can also look unsightly when they dry up. Putting hydro-electric power stations in remote valleys
   tends to reduce their impact on humans.

3) A big advantage is it can provide an
   immediate response to an increased
   demand for electricity, by allowing
   more water to flow from the reservoir.

4) There's no problem with reliability
   except in times of drought.

5) Availability depends on having a
   suitable site to create a dam.

6) It can be used to generate electricity on
   a small scale (e.g. in remote areas) or on
   a large scale (e.g. the Three Gorges Dam in China).

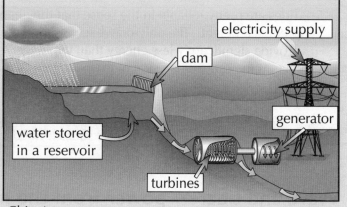

Wave Power and Tidal Barrages

Rivers and seas aren't just pretty, we can also use them to generate electricity...

Wave Power — Lots of Little **Wave-Powered Turbines**

1) You need lots of wave-powered turbines located around the coast to produce a reasonable amount of electricity. Like with wind power (p.42) the moving turbines are connected to a generator which produces electricity.

2) There is no pollution. The main problems are disturbing the seabed and the habitats of marine animals, spoiling the view and being a hazard to boats.

3) They are fairly unreliable, since waves tend to die out when the wind drops.

4) Wave power is only available in coastal locations.

5) Wave power is never likely to provide energy on a large scale, but it can be very useful on small islands.

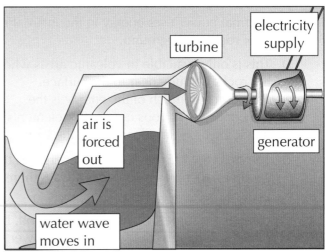

Tidal Barrages — Using the **Sun and Moon's Gravity**

1) Tides are used in lots of ways to generate electricity. A common method is to build a tidal barrage.

2) Tidal barrages are big dams built across river estuaries (where a river flows into the sea), with turbines in them. As the tide comes in, it fills up the estuary. The water is then allowed out through turbines at a controlled speed. The turbines drive generators which generate electricity.

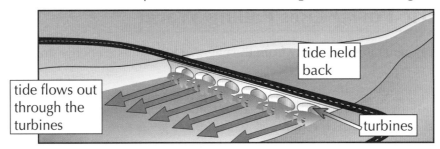

3) Tides are produced by the gravitational pull of the Sun and Moon.

4) There is no pollution. The main problems are preventing free access by boats, spoiling the view and altering the habitat of the wildlife, e.g. wading birds and sea creatures who live in the sand.

5) Tides are pretty reliable in the sense that they happen twice a day without fail, and always near to the predicted height. The only drawback is that the height of the tide is variable so lower (neap) tides will provide significantly less energy than the bigger (spring) tides. They also don't work when the water level is the same either side of the barrage — this happens four times a day because of the tides.

6) In terms of availability, tidal power can only be used in some estuaries.

7) Even in a suitable estuary, the power produced per square metre of space taken up by the barrage is low compared to other resources, so it's limited to producing energy on a relatively small scale.

Wave and tidal — power from the motion of the ocean...

The first large-scale tidal barrages started being built in the 1960s, so tidal power isn't a new thing. Wave power is still pretty experimental though. Make sure you know the differences in how they work.

Warm-Up & Exam Questions

You must be getting used to the routine by now — the warm-up questions get you, well, warmed up, and the exam questions give you some idea of what you'll have to cope with on exam day.

Warm-Up Questions

1) Name three non-renewable energy resources.
2) What does it mean if an energy resource is 'renewable'?
3) Give two ways in which using coal as an energy resource causes environmental problems.
4) Describe how electricity can be generated from a geothermal energy resource.

Exam Questions

1 Which of the following energy resources doesn't generate electricity by turning a turbine?

☐ **A**   fossil fuels

☐ **B**   nuclear fuel

☐ **C**   solar

☐ **D**   geothermal

[Total 1 mark]

2 In some coastal regions, electricity is generated from waves using wave-powered turbines. Which of the following statements about wave-powered turbines is true?

☐ **A**   They generate a reliable amount of electricity all the time.

☐ **B**   One wave-powered turbine generates electricity on a very large scale.

☐ **C**   They produce pollution when generating electricity.

☐ **D**   They can disturb the habitats of marine animals.

[Total 1 mark]

3 In a nuclear power station, water is heated to produce steam.

(a) Name the reaction that releases the energy stored in the nuclear energy stores of nuclear fuel.

[1]

(b) (i) One argument for building more nuclear power stations is that generating electricity from nuclear fuel does not directly contribute to global warming. Explain why this is the case.

[1]

(ii) Give **two** ways in which using nuclear fuel to generate electricity causes harm to the environment.

[2]

[Total 4 marks]

Exam Questions

4   Electricity is generated using the hydroelectric dam shown in **Figure 1**. Water is held back behind the dam before being allowed to flow out through turbines to produce electricity.

Figure 1

(a) Describe the energy transfers involved when water is used to produce electricity in this way.

[3]

(b) Hydroelectric power stations don't produce any carbon dioxide when generating electricity. Give **two** ways that using hydroelectric power stations to generate electricity damages the environment.

[2]

(c) Sea tides can also be used to generate electricity using tidal barrages. Give **two** advantages of generating electricity using tidal barrages.

[2]

[Total 7 marks]

5   The energy stored in biofuels originally came from the Sun.

(a) Name the process that releases energy in the Sun.

[1]

(b) Describe the energy transfers involved when biofuels are used to generate electricity.

[3]

(c) Compare the environmental impact of burning biofuels to power vehicles instead of using fuels made from fossil fuels.

[3]

[Total 7 marks]

6   A family want to install solar panels on their home to generate electricity. They have 8 m² of space on their roof for the solar panels. They use 34 000 000 J of energy per day. A 1 m² solar panel has an output of 200 J of energy each second in good sunlight.

(a) Calculate the minimum number of 1 m² solar panels required to cover the family's daily energy use, assuming there are 5 hours of good sunlight in a day.

[4]

(b) Determine, using your answer from (a), whether the family can install enough solar panels to provide all of the energy they use, assuming there are 5 hours of good sunlight every day.

[1]

(c) In reality, the number of hours of good sunlight in a day varies based on the weather and time of year. Discuss the reliability of energy from solar panels compared to energy from a local coal-fired power station.

[3]

[Total 8 marks]

Revision Summary

Well, that's that for Section 2 — this is when you find out how much you've actually learned.
- Try these questions and tick off each one when you get it right.
- When you've done all the questions under a heading and are completely happy with it, tick it off.

Energy Stores and Energy Transfers (p.27-29) ☐

1) Write down four stores of energy.
2) What store is energy transferred to when you compress a spring?
3) True or false? Energy cannot be destroyed.
4) Describe the energy transfers that occur when a ball rolls down a hill.
5) If the energy in an object's kinetic energy store increases, what happens to its speed?
6) Give the equation for finding the change in energy in an object's gravitational potential energy store.

Work, Power, Efficiency and Pressure(p.31-35) ☐

7) How is work done related to energy transferred?
8) Give an example of a force doing work.
9) Give the formula for calculating the mechanical work done by a force.
10) Which will transfer more energy in a minute: a 500 W device or a 650 W device?
11) How much energy is transferred to a 50 W device in 1 second?
12) True or false? The more energy a device wastes, the more efficient it is.
13) Give the equation that relates efficiency to total power input and useful power output.
14) True or false? In a Sankey diagram drawn to scale, the width of the input energy
    is equal to the combined width of all the output energy arrows.
15) State the equation linking pressure, force and area.
16) Describe how the pressure in a liquid varies with the density of the liquid.
17) True or false? Pressure in a liquid decreases with depth.

Energy Resources and their Uses (p38-44) ☐

18) Name four renewable energy resources.
19) What is the difference between renewable and non-renewable energy resources?
20) Explain why using fossil fuels to generate electricity is reliable.
21) Give one environmental benefit of using nuclear fuel instead of fossil fuels to generate electricity.
22) Explain why geothermal power is considered to be a fairly reliable energy resource.
23) True or false? Wind can only be used to generate electricity on a small scale.
24) True or false? Hydroelectric power stations have no effect on the environment.
25) Give one environmental impact of using tidal power to generate electricity.

The Kinetic Particle Model

The kinetic particle model states that everything is made up of lots of tiny identical particles...

You can Describe the States of Matter Using the Particle Model

1) In the kinetic particle model, all matter is made up of particles. You can think of the particles as being tiny balls.

2) Different materials have different types of particles such as atoms, molecules, ions or electrons.

3) The three states of matter are solid (e.g. ice), liquid (e.g. water) and gas (e.g. water vapour).

4) You can explain the ways that matter behaves in these states using the kinetic particle model.

Solids

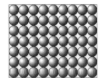

1) The particles are held very close together in a fixed, regular arrangement.

2) The particles can't move past each other — they only vibrate about their fixed positions. They have much less energy than particles in other states of matter.

3) There are strong forces that act between the particles. These forces stop the particles from moving much and keep them in their fixed arrangements. The forces between particles are also known as bonds.

Liquids

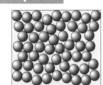

1) The particles are close together, but further apart than in a solid.

2) The particles can move past each other, and form irregular arrangements.

3) This is because the forces between the particles are weaker than in a solid.

4) The particles have more energy than particles in a solid, and move around each other in random directions at low speeds.

Gases

1) Gas particles are mostly far apart from each other. They have more energy than the particles in a solid or a liquid.

2) The particles move in random directions and at high speeds.

3) The particles are able to move so freely because there are almost no forces between the particles in a gas.

Liquids and gases are both fluids. A fluid is any substance that can flow.

You can use the Particle Model to Explain Properties of Matter

Shape and Flow

Solids can't flow. They have a fixed size and shape.

Liquids and gases can flow, so they will always take the shape of the container they're in. Liquids and gases can flow because their particles can move past each other.

The particles in a solid can't move past each other because the forces between them are much stronger.

Compressibility

Gases can be compressed, but liquids and solids cannot.

This is because gas particles are so far apart, they can easily be pushed closer together. Liquid and solid particles are already so close together that they can't be pushed closer.

Volume

Solids and liquids have a fixed volume, but gases will expand to have the same volume as the container they're in.

This is because the strong forces between particles in a solid or liquid keep the particles close together. There are almost no forces between gas particles.

Density

Solids are generally more dense than liquids, and liquids are generally more dense than gases.

Remember, density is mass per unit volume (p.6). The distances between the particles in a liquid are larger than in a solid, so there will be fewer particles in a particular volume. This is true when you compare a gas to a liquid too — the particles are further apart in a gas than a liquid, so there is less mass per unit volume.

Brownian Motion

You can see the effects of the kinetic particle model in action with Brownian motion...

Microscopic Particles in a Fluid Move in Random Directions

1) Microscopic particles of solid can become suspended in a fluid
   — this means they are mixed throughout the fluid.
   For example, pollen grains can become suspended in water,
   and smoke particles can become suspended in the air.

2) The microscopic particles of solid move within the fluid, even when
   the fluid itself isn't moving. The microscopic particles move
   in random directions, taking a zigzag-shaped path.

3) Using a microscope and a bright lamp you can see
   pollen grains suspended in water moving in this way.

4) You'll see the pollen grains as spots of bright light,
   because they reflect the light from the lamp.

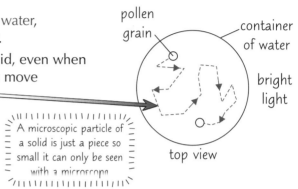

A microscopic particle of a solid is just a piece so small it can only be seen with a microscope.

Brownian Motion Provides Evidence for the Particle Model

1) The kinetic particle model can be used to explain the zigzag motion of the microscopic particles of solid.

2) According to the model, a fluid is made up of many small particles.
   These particles are so small that you can't see them, even with a standard microscope.

3) When the microscopic particles of solid, which are larger and more massive, are suspended
   in a fluid (e.g. pollen grains in water), the fluid particles collide with the particles of solid.
   These collisions may change the speed and direction of the particles of solid, which are much larger
   than the fluid particles, making them move in random directions. This is Brownian motion.

4) For example, here's the path of a smoke particle suspended in air:

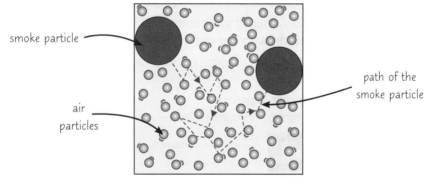

5) The particles that make up gases and liquids (e.g. atoms or molecules)
   are much smaller than a microscopic solid (e.g. a smoke particle).

Brownian Motion Involves Changes in Momentum

1) Small, light fluid molecules are able to move microscopic
   particles of solid much more massive than themselves.

2) This is because the fluid molecules have a large speed,
   which means they have a relatively large momentum.

3) When they collide with a microscopic particle, they undergo a large change in momentum.
   This means they apply a large force to the particle (p.22) — this force causes the particle to move.

Need to remind yourself about momentum? Have a look on page 21.

Random, zigzag motion is a sign that everything's made of particles...

Brownian motion gives evidence to support the kinetic particle model, because if matter wasn't made from
particles, microscopic particles suspended in fluids wouldn't be bombarded by anything and so wouldn't
change direction. For them to move in random directions there must be particles to give them a push.

Supplement

Gas Pressure

Handily, you can explain pressure (see page 35) in terms of the kinetic particle model of matter too...

Pressure is Created when Particles Collide with Container Walls

1) Imagine a gas trapped inside a sealed container of a fixed size. The gas particles collide with the container walls and exert a force on them, creating pressure (p.35).

2) The gas pressure is the total force exerted by all the particles in the gas on a unit area of the container walls.

3) If the force per unit area exerted by the particles increases, the gas pressure will increase.

4) If the force per unit area exerted by the particles decreases, the gas pressure will decrease.

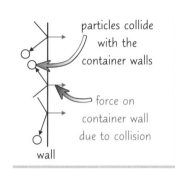

particles collide with the container walls

force on container wall due to collision

wall

At a Constant Volume, Gas Pressure will Increase with Temperature

1) Increasing the temperature of a gas will mean the gas particles move faster (see p.51).

2) For a gas with a constant volume (e.g. in a sealed, rigid container), the total force exerted on the container walls by the gas will increase because:
   • the particles will collide more often with the walls of the container.
   • they will each exert a larger force on the container.

3) This means the pressure will be higher.

4) Similarly, if you decrease the temperature, the particles move slower and the pressure decreases.

At a Constant Temperature, Decreasing Volume will Increase Pressure

1) Decreasing the volume of a container of gas means that the gas particles have less room to move. The particles will therefore collide with the container walls more often.

If you increase the volume, the particles will collide with the wall less often and the pressure will decrease.

2) That means there will be a greater overall force exerted on the walls and the pressure will increase.

3) You can use this equation to find changes in volume and pressure at a constant temperature:

$$pV = \text{constant}$$

Where p = pressure, V = volume.

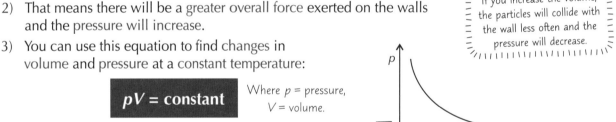

4) This graph shows this relationship.

 **EXAMPLE:**

A gas has a pressure of 200 kPa and a volume of 0.08 m³. The pressure is increased to 500 kPa, while the temperature is constant. What is the gas's new volume?

1) Since pV = constant, you can equate pV in the initial conditions ($p_1 V_1$) to pV in the final conditions ($p_2 V_2$).

$$p_1 V_1 = p_2 V_2$$
$$200 \times 0.08 = 500 \times V_2$$
$$16 = 500 \times V_2$$

2) Then just substitute in the values, and rearrange for V_2.

$$V_2 = \frac{16}{500} = 0.032 \text{ m}^3$$

More particle collisions means a higher gas pressure...

When you're revising this, try to picture what is happening to the gas particles whizzing around their container. Remember — the frequency of collisions and the force of the collisions is what causes the total force on the container. The higher the total force, the higher the pressure will be.

Changes of State and Internal Energy Stores

To change a substance's state, you need a change in the energy in the internal energy stores of the particles.

Heating Transfers Energy to Internal Energy Stores

1) The particles that make up a substance all have energy in their kinetic energy stores (see p.27).

2) The higher the temperature of a substance, the more energy its particles have in these stores.

3) The total energy of all the particles in a substance is the energy in the substance's internal energy store.

4) When you heat a substance, you transfer energy to the particles of the substance
— so you will always increase the energy in the internal energy store of the substance.

5) When energy is transferred by heating, either energy will be transferred to the kinetic energy stores of the particles or the energy will be used to change the state of the substance.

Note only one of these can happen at once — if a substance is changing state, its temperature will stay constant.

6) The temperature of a substance can be measured in Kelvin (K) or degrees Celsius (°C). You can convert between these units with this equation:

$$T \text{ (in K)} = T \text{ (in °C)} + 273$$

7) If you decrease the temperature of a substance, you could theoretically reach a point where particles have the minimum possible energy in their kinetic energy stores and the temperature of a substance cannot get any lower. This temperature is called absolute zero and occurs at –273 °C (0 K).

Energy is Transferred when a Substance Changes State

1) There are different names for different changes of state.

- melting — solid to liquid
- solidification — liquid to solid
- boiling — liquid to gas
- condensation — gas to liquid

A liquid can also become a gas via evaporation (see next page).

2) When a substance is changing state, it does not change temperature, even if you're heating it.

3) That's because the energy in the internal energy store of the substance will change, but the energy in the kinetic energy stores of the particles will not.

4) The temperature at which a substance changes between two states depends on the substance.

5) The temperature at which a substance boils is called its boiling point. Similarly, the melting point is the temperature at which a substance melts.

6) For water at standard atmospheric pressure, the melting point is 0 °C and the boiling point is 100 °C.

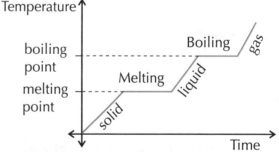

Substances Condense or Solidify when Particles Lose Energy

1) As substances cool, energy is transferred away from them
— they lose energy from their internal energy store.

2) Condensation occurs at the same temperature as the substance boils (its boiling point).

3) As a gas is cooled to this temperature, the energy in the kinetic energy stores of the gas particles decreases. Once the temperature of the gas reaches the boiling point, the gas begins to change state. Energy continues to be transferred away from the substance, causing the particles to move closer together.

4) The forces between the particles become stronger as the particles move closer to each other.

5) This process continues until the substance becomes a liquid.

6) A similar process happens when a liquid solidifies. When a liquid that's being cooled reaches the melting point temperature, the liquid particles move closer together.

7) Again, the forces between the particles become stronger as they move closer together.

8) Eventually the particles form a fixed, regular arrangement — the substance has solidified.

Evaporation

There are two processes by which a liquid can turn into a gas — boiling (p.51) and evaporation.

Evaporation is a Special Example of Changing State

1) Evaporation is when more-energetic particles escape from a liquid's surface and become gas particles.

2) In both boiling and evaporation, liquids become gases, although the two processes are very different.

Process	Description	Temperature the process occurs at
Boiling	Bubbles of gas form in the boiling liquid. The bubbles rise to the surface of the liquid and the gas escapes.	The boiling point of the substance.
Evaporation	Individual particles escape from the surface of the liquid. No gas bubbles are formed.	Temperatures below the boiling point of the substance.

3) In evaporation, particles near the surface of a liquid can escape and become gas particles if:

- They're travelling in the right direction to escape the liquid (i.e. towards the surface).
- They have enough energy in their kinetic energy stores (they're travelling fast enough). This is so they can overcome the attractive forces of the other particles in the liquid.

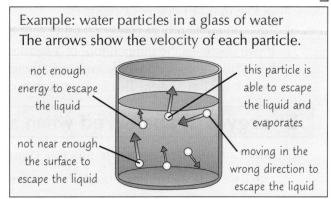

Example: water particles in a glass of water
The arrows show the velocity of each particle.

not enough energy to escape the liquid

this particle is able to escape the liquid and evaporates

not near enough the surface to escape the liquid

moving in the wrong direction to escape the liquid

4) Increasing the following factors will increase the rate of evaporation of a liquid.

1) **Temperature** — The higher the temperature, the higher the average energy in the kinetic energy stores of the particles (p.51). This means more particles have enough energy in their kinetic energy stores to escape the liquid.

2) **Surface area** — The larger the area of a liquid's surface, the more particles will be near the surface. More particles will be in the correct position and have enough energy to escape.

3) **Air movement** — If the air is moving over the liquid's surface, particles that escape from the liquid won't be able to drop back into the liquid because they'll be carried away.

Evaporation has a Cooling Effect

1) The particles with the most energy in their kinetic energy stores are usually the ones that escape from a liquid during evaporation.

2) Evaporation causes the temperature of the liquid to decrease — it cools down.

3) This is because as liquid evaporates, the average energy in the kinetic energy stores of the remaining particles in the liquid decreases.

4) This cooling effect can be passed on to anything in contact with the liquid.

5) As the liquid cools, energy will be transferred to the liquid from an object in contact with it by a heating process. Because energy is transferred away from the object, the object cools down.

6) This is what happens when you sweat — as the water from the sweat on your skin evaporates, it cools you down.

Evaporation depends on energy in kinetic energy stores...

However, simply being energetic isn't enough — particles need to be moving in the right direction, too. They won't manage to escape the liquid and evaporate if they're travelling away from the surface.

Warm-Up & Exam Questions

It's time again to test what you've learnt from the last few pages. Have a go at these...

Warm-Up Questions

1) Describe the particles in a liquid in terms of their arrangement and movement.
2) What is Brownian motion?
3) True or false? For a gas held at a fixed volume, as temperature decreases, pressure decreases.
4) What is 12°C in Kelvin?
5) State the conditions necessary for particles near the surface of a liquid to escape by evaporation.

Exam Questions

1   Temperature is often measured in degrees Celsius.

(a)   State the temperature, in degrees Celsius, of absolute zero.

[1]

(b)   In terms of energy, describe what happens to particles at absolute zero.

[1]
[Total 2 marks]

2   A heater is used to change a substance from a solid to a liquid.

(a)   (i)   Give the name of this process.

[1]

(ii)   What happens to the temperature of the substance during this process?

[1]

(b)   The heater is removed. Some of the liquid becomes a gas due to evaporation.
(i)   Name another process by which a liquid becomes a gas.

[1]

(ii)   Suggest **one** way the rate of evaporation of the liquid could be increased.

[1]

(iii) Explain why the remaining liquid cools down as some of the liquid evaporates.

[3]
[Total 7 marks]

3   A scientist has a canister of gas. The canister is a sealed container with a fixed volume.

(a)   Use the kinetic particle model to describe how gas particles create pressure in the canister.

[3]

(b)   Describe what would happen to the pressure of the gas within the canister if its temperature increased. Explain your answer using the kinetic particle model.

[4]

(c)   The scientist used the gas in the canister to inflate a balloon. The inflated, sealed balloon contained 0.034 m³ of gas at a pressure of 98 kPa. The balloon was then compressed to 0.031 m³.
The temperature of the gas inside it remained constant.
Calculate the air pressure inside the balloon after the compression.

[2]
[Total 9 marks]

Specific Heat Capacity

Now for another term which sounds a lot scarier than it actually is...

Specific Heat Capacity is the Energy Needed to Heat a Material

 KEY TERM Specific heat capacity is the amount of energy needed to raise the temperature of 1 kg of a substance by 1 °C.

1) When an object is heated to increase its temperature, energy is being transferred to the kinetic energy stores of its particles, increasing the average energy in these stores.

2) It takes more energy to increase the temperature of some materials than others. E.g. you need 4200 J to warm 1 kg of water by 1 °C, but only 139 J to warm 1 kg of mercury by 1 °C.

3) The specific heat capacity of a material relates the amount of energy transferred when you heat a certain mass of it to the change in its temperature.

4) Bodies that need to gain lots of energy to warm up also release a lot of energy when they cool down.

5) Specific heat capacity is a material constant. This means that any sample of a specific material will have the same specific heat capacity.

6) Below is the equation for specific heat capacity.

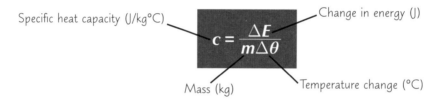

Specific heat capacity (J/kg°C)　　Change in energy (J)

$$c = \frac{\Delta E}{m\Delta \theta}$$

Mass (kg)　　Temperature change (°C)

 **EXAMPLE:** **It takes 12 000 J of energy to heat a 3.00 kg brick from 15 °C to 20 °C. What is the specific heat capacity of the brick?**

1) First find the change in temperature ($\Delta \theta$) in °C.

$\Delta \theta = 20 - 15 = 5$ °C

2) Now substitute this value, along with the values for mass and change in energy, into the formula.

$c = \dfrac{\Delta E}{m\Delta \theta}$

$= \dfrac{12\ 000}{3.00 \times 5}$

$= 800$ J/kg°C

 **EXAMPLE:** **How much energy is needed to heat 2.00 kg of water from 10 °C to 100 °C? The specific heat capacity of water is 4200 J/kg°C.**

1) First find the change in temperature ($\Delta \theta$) in °C.

$\Delta \theta = 100 - 10 = 90$ °C

2) Then rearrange the equation for specific heat capacity to find energy transferred.

$c = \dfrac{\Delta E}{m\Delta \theta}$ ... so... $\Delta E = cm\Delta \theta$

3) Now substitute the values for change in temperature, mass and specific heat capacity into the formula.

$\Delta E = cm\Delta \theta$

$= 4200 \times 2.00 \times 90$

$= 756\ 000$ J

Specific heat capacity tells you how hard it is to heat something up...

In addition to telling you the energy needed to increase the temperature of each kg by 1 °C, specific heat capacity also tells you the energy released from 1 kg of an object for every degree it cools down.

Measuring Specific Heat Capacity

Now it is time to get practical and learn how to measure specific heat capacities yourself...

You can Find the **Specific Heat Capacity** of a **Substance**

Here are two experiments you can do to find the specific heat capacity of a liquid or a solid.

In both experiments, you should keep the substance you're investigating in a thermally insulated container to reduce the amount of energy that's transferred to the surroundings.

Liquids

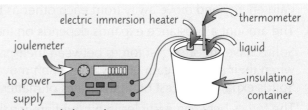

1) Use a mass balance to measure the mass of the insulating container. Fill the container with liquid (e.g. water) and measure the mass again. The difference in mass is the mass of the liquid in the container.

2) Set up the experiment as shown. Place an insulating lid on the container during the experiment. This will minimise the energy transferred from the liquid to the surroundings during heating, and stop any liquid evaporating from your container.

3) Measure the initial temperature of the liquid, then turn on the heater. Make sure the power is fairly low, so that the liquid is heated gradually. This will stop the liquid around the heater heating up much faster than the rest of the liquid, which may give you misleading results.

4) When the liquid's temperature has increased by e.g. ten degrees, switch off the power and record this temperature increase and the energy transferred to the liquid (from the joulemeter).

5) You can then calculate the specific heat capacity of the liquid by substituting your values into the specific heat capacity equation $c = \Delta E \div m\Delta\theta$ (see p.54).

6) Repeat the whole experiment at least five times, then find the average specific heat capacity.

Solids

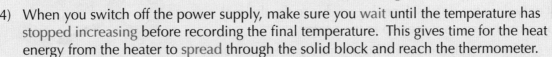

1) For this version of the experiment, you'll need to use a block of the material you're investigating. Make sure it has two holes in it for the heater and thermometer.

2) The rest of the method is exactly the same as the method above for a liquid.

3) Again, make sure you heat the block slowly, so that energy isn't being transferred to the block faster than it can be transferred through it.

4) When you switch off the power supply, make sure you wait until the temperature has stopped increasing before recording the final temperature. This gives time for the heat energy from the heater to spread through the solid block and reach the thermometer.

Your Experimental **Specific Heat Capacity** Value May be **Too Large**

The energy transferred that you record in your experiment is likely to be larger than the actual amount of energy transferred to the substance to cause its temperature change. This is because:

1) Not all of the energy measured by the joulemeter will be transferred to the substance.

2) Some of the energy supplied will be lost from the substance as it is being heated (even if you used insulation). Some energy will also be lost in the circuitry of the immersion heater itself.

This means your value for specific heat capacity will also be larger than the true value.

Think about how you could improve your experiments...

You need to be able to evaluate the method used for an investigation and suggest improvements to make the results more accurate. For example, if you saw a method for this practical using a beaker to hold the liquid, you could suggest changing it to a thermally insulated container.

Thermal Expansion

The vast majority of substances get bigger as their temperature increases...

Substances **Expand** as they get **Hotter**

1) When most substances are heated, they get bigger — this is called thermal expansion.

2) This happens for every state of matter (solids, liquids and gases) as long as the surrounding pressure isn't changing.

Remember, temperature is a measure of the average kinetic energy of the molecules in a substance.

3) Thermal expansion happens because the particles in the substance gain energy and move away from each other as the temperature of the substance increases.

4) The amount a substance expands depends on the forces of attraction between its particles.

5) Solids have the strongest forces between their particles, so even when their particles gain energy, they can't move very far apart. Solids expand the least of all the states of matter.

6) The forces between particles in a liquid are weaker than in a solid, so the particles in a liquid can move further apart. This means liquids normally expand more than solids.

7) There are almost no forces between the particles in a gas, so they're able to move furthest when they gain energy through heating. Gases expand the most of all the states of matter.

Thermal Expansion has **Uses** and **Drawbacks**

Thermal expansion comes up all the time in day-to-day life. Here are some examples:

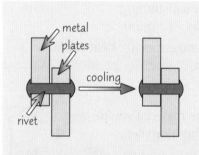

1) If you heat a metal rod, it will get longer. When it cools, it will get shorter again.

2) Rivets use this in order to secure objects (e.g. metal plates) together.

3) The rivet starts off as a very hot metal rod that is threaded through holes in the plates. It is then hammered down, so its ends are flat against the surfaces of the plates.

4) As the rivet cools down, its length decreases, so the flattened ends of the rivet pull the two plates together tightly.

1) When a solid ring is heated, it undergoes thermal expansion. Not only does the ring itself get bigger due to the thermal expansion, but so does the gap in the centre.

2) This is why you can loosen the lid of a jar by running it under hot water. The jar lid heats up and expands, increasing the diameter of the lid, and making it easier to remove from the jar.

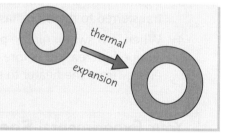

1) If an object tries to expand, and can't (due to being fixed in place), it experiences forces that could damage the object.

2) If this happened with materials that make up buildings or bridges, it could have nasty results.

3) 'Expansion joints' can be used to prevent this. They fasten pieces of a bridge or building together while leaving a small gap where the pieces meet. Then, when the bridge or building gets hot, it can expand into this gap without causing damage.

4) The opposite situation can also be a problem. Power lines are made to sag slightly, rather than hang tight between pylons, because if they contracted in the cold they could snap, or damage the pylons.

5) Power lines sag more on hot days, as they've undergone thermal expansion and have got longer.

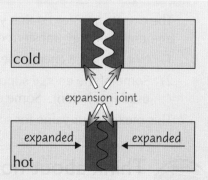

Warm-Up & Exam Questions

Time to test yourself on specific heat capacity and thermal expansion. There's no escaping it — get going.

Warm-Up Questions

1) What is the specific heat capacity of a material?
2) True or false? The specific heat capacity is different for different masses of the same material.
3) True or false? Only solids undergo thermal expansion.
4) Why do gases expand more than liquids and solids when heated?

Exam Questions

1   A group of engineers are repairing an old steam train.

The outer ring on a wheel needs replacing.
It must fit very tightly around the rest of the wheel
when it is fitted in order to operate properly.
Figure 3 shows the wheel and outer ring at 20 °C.

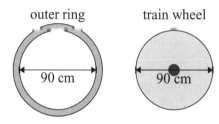

Figure 3

The engineers heat the outer ring to a high temperature before attempting to fit it.
Explain how this will help them to fit the wheel correctly.

[Total 3 marks]

2   Different materials have different specific heat capacities.

(a)   36 000 J of energy is transferred to a 0.5 kg concrete block.
The block increases in temperature from 20 °C to 100 °C.
Calculate the specific heat capacity of the concrete block.

[2]

(b)   71 600 J of energy is transferred away from 0.2 kg of oil as it cools from a high temperature
to a temperature of 20 °C. The specific heat capacity of the oil is 1790 J/kg°C.
What was the starting temperature of the oil?

[2]

[Total 4 marks]

3   A student uses the equipment listed below to investigate the specific heat capacity of a liquid.

- Insulated flask with lid
- Mass balance
- Joulemeter
- Thermometer
- Power supply
- Immersion heater

(a)   Describe how the student could find the mass of a sample of liquid.

[1]

(b)   State the other two quantities that the student would need
to measure in order to find the specific heat capacity of the liquid.

[1]

(c)   Explain why the insulated flask with lid is needed for this investigation.

[2]

[Total 4 marks]

Thermal Energy Transfers by Radiation

When an object is heated, there's a thermal energy transfer. This can happen via three thermal processes — this page is all about energy transfer by thermal radiation...

There are **Three Types** of **Thermal Energy Transfer**

1) Thermal energy transfers (p.27) involve energy being transferred from one thermal energy store to another. They can happen by conduction, convection or radiation.

2) Conduction (p.61) and convection (p.62) require particles to transfer the energy, i.e. energy can only be transferred in these ways through a medium. This is known as energy transfer by heating.

3) Energy transfer by thermal radiation is the transfer of energy by infrared electromagnetic waves.

4) Infrared waves (or infrared radiation) are part of the electromagnetic spectrum (see page 87). Like all electromagnetic waves, they don't need a medium to travel through.

Every Object **Absorbs** and **Emits Infrared Radiation**

1) All objects are continually emitting and absorbing infrared radiation.

2) Infrared radiation is emitted from the surface of an object.

3) An object that's hotter than its surroundings emits more infrared radiation than it absorbs (e.g. a cup of tea left on a table). Energy is being transferred away from the object's thermal energy store at a higher rate than it is being received by the object, so the object cools down.

4) Similarly, an object that's cooler than its surroundings absorbs more infrared radiation than it emits (e.g. a cold glass of water on a sunny day). Energy is being received by the object's thermal energy store at a higher rate than it is being transferred away from the object, so the object warms up.

The hot chocolate (and the mug) is warmer than the air around it, so it gives out more infrared radiation than it absorbs, which cools it down.

5) For an object at constant temperature, energy is being transferred away from the object's thermal energy store at the same rate that it is being received by the object.

6) Some colours and surfaces absorb and emit radiation better than others too.

7) For example, a black surface is better at absorbing and emitting radiation than a white one, and a dull surface is better at absorbing and emitting radiation than a shiny one.

8) However, shiny surfaces are better at reflecting radiation compared to dull ones.

Infrared Emission Depends on **Temperature** and **Surface Area**

1) The higher the surface temperature of an object, the more infrared radiation it emits in a given time — so the higher the rate of energy transferred away from the object.

2) The bigger the surface area of an object, the more infrared waves that can be emitted from (or absorbed by) the surface. This increases the rate of energy transferred from (or received by) the object.

3) Devices that need to maximise the amount of infrared radiation they emit often have 'fins'. Fins are thin, flat parts that have a larger surface area. They help to increase the total surface area over which the device can emit radiation.

Cooling fins on engines increase surface area to speed up cooling.

4) They help to maximise the rate of thermal energy transfer away from the device by infrared radiation, to help control the temperature of the device.

Energy transfer by radiation happens constantly...

REVISION TIP

Dull, darkly-coloured surfaces are much better at absorbing AND emitting radiation than pale-coloured shiny ones. If you need help remembering, think of wearing a tight black T-shirt on a summer's day — you'll be a lot warmer in that than if you wore a white one instead...

Investigating Energy Transfer by Radiation

Time for some more practicals. In this first one, you'll meet a fun, new piece of kit called a Leslie cube. Read on to find out more about how you can use this equipment to investigate infrared radiation emissions.

You Can Investigate **Emission** with a **Leslie Cube**

A Leslie cube is a hollow, watertight cube made of metal (often aluminium). The four vertical faces of the cube have different surfaces (for example, dull black paint, dull white paint, shiny metal and dull metal). You can investigate the amount of infrared radiation emitted by the different surfaces:

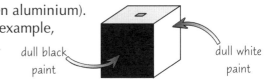
dull black paint
dull white paint

1) Place an empty Leslie cube on a heatproof mat.
2) Boil water in a kettle and fill the Leslie cube with boiling water.
3) Wait for the cube to warm up, then hold a thermometer against each of the four vertical faces of the cube. You should find that all four faces are the same temperature.

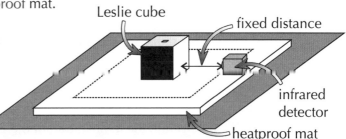
Leslie cube
fixed distance
infrared detector
heatproof mat

4) Hold an infrared detector a set distance (e.g. 10 cm) away from one of the cube's vertical faces, and record the amount of infrared radiation it detects in a given time.
5) Repeat this measurement for each of the cube's vertical faces. Make sure you position the detector at the same distance from the cube each time.
6) You should find that you detect more infrared radiation from the black surface than the white one, and more from the matt surfaces than the shiny ones.
7) As always, do the experiment more than once, to make sure your results are repeatable (p.167).

You Can Investigate **Absorption** with **Melting Wax**

The amount of infrared radiation absorbed by an object also depends on the object's surface. You can do an experiment to show this, using a Bunsen burner and some candle wax.

1) Set up the equipment as shown on the right. Two ball bearings are each stuck to one side of a metal plate with solid pieces of candle wax. The other sides of these plates are then faced towards the flame. The plates are placed the same distance away from the flame.

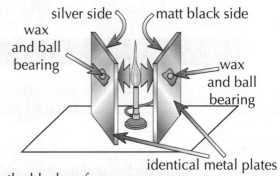
silver side
matt black side
wax and ball bearing
wax and ball bearing
identical metal plates

2) The sides of the plates that are facing towards the flame each have a different surface colour — one is matt black and the other is silver.
3) The ball bearing on the black plate will fall first as the black surface absorbs more infrared radiation — transferring more energy to the wax by radiation. This means the wax on the black plate melts before the wax on the silver plate.

PRACTICAL TIP

Carry out your practicals carefully...

And that means both being careful when collecting data, and careful when dealing with potential hazards. Watch out when you're pouring or carrying hot water, and make sure any equipment has cooled down enough before you start handling it after your experiment is done.

Supplement

Earth and Radiation

The Sun is about 150 million km away from Earth and transfers energy to us by infrared radiation...

Radiation Affects the Earth's Temperature

The overall temperature of the Earth depends on the amount of IR radiation it reflects, absorbs and emits.

1) During the day, lots of radiation (like light) is transferred to the Earth from the Sun and absorbed. This causes an increase in local temperature.

2) At night, less radiation is being absorbed than is being emitted, causing a decrease in the local temperature.

3) Overall, the temperature of the Earth stays fairly constant.

Some radiation is reflected by the atmosphere, clouds and the Earth's surface.

Some radiation is emitted by the atmosphere, clouds and surface.

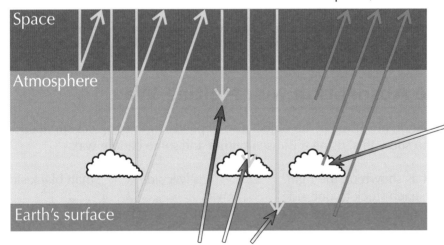

Some of the radiation emitted by the surface is reflected or absorbed (and later emitted) by the clouds.

Some radiation is absorbed by the atmosphere, clouds and the Earth's surface.

4) Changes to the atmosphere can cause a change to the Earth's overall temperature. If the atmosphere starts to absorb more radiation without emitting the same amount, the overall temperature will rise until absorption and emission are equal again.

Absorbed radiation means a rise in temperature...

Greenhouse gases, such as carbon dioxide, are good absorbers of radiation. That's why adding more of them to the atmosphere causes the Earth's atmosphere to warm up as more radiation is absorbed by the atmosphere and less is emitted back into space. This is the mechanism behind global warming.

Conduction

Here's more about thermal energy transfers — this time we're dealing with conduction.

Materials Can be Good or Bad Conductors of Heat

1) Conduction is a type of thermal energy transfer where energy is transferred through a material.
2) Energy spreads out from the point where the object is heated, until the whole object is warmer.
3) How fast the energy can be transferred depends on how good a thermal conductor the material is.
4) A good thermal conductor will transfer energy quickly, while a bad thermal conductor (a thermal insulator) will do so slowly. Liquids and gases are poor thermal conductors.
5) You can experience this on a cold day — a thermal conductor feels colder than a thermal insulator at the same temperature because the thermal conductor transfers energy away from your skin rapidly.
6) Most metals are good thermal conductors. Thermal insulators include plastics, most fabrics and wood.
7) There are lots of solids that conduct thermal energy better than thermal insulators, but they still don't do this as well as good thermal conductors.

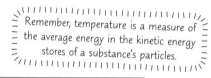
Remember, temperature is a measure of the average energy in the kinetic energy stores of a substance's particles.

Conduction Occurs Mainly in Solids

KEY TERM

Conduction is the process where vibrating particles transfer energy from their kinetic energy stores to those of neighbouring particles.

1) In a solid, the atoms or molecules are held tightly together in a lattice. So when one particle vibrates, it collides with other particles nearby and the vibrations quickly pass from particle to particle.

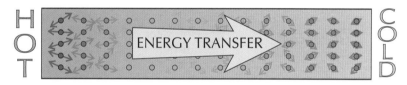

2) These atomic or molecular lattice vibrations continue throughout the solid and gradually some of the energy is passed all the way through, causing a rise in temperature at the other side of the solid. It's then usually transferred to the internal energy store of the surroundings (or anything else touching the object).
3) In liquids and gases, the atoms or molecules are further apart from each other, so fewer collisions take place and the vibrations are passed along much more slowly. This is why liquids and gases are bad thermal conductors.
4) Metals conduct heat so well because the electrons are delocalised (free to move) inside the metal.

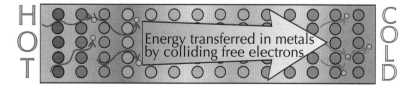

5) At the hot end the electrons move faster and collide with metal ions and other free electrons, transferring energy. These metal ions and free electrons then pass on their extra energy to other electrons, and so on.
6) Because the electrons can move freely, this is obviously a much faster way of transferring the energy through the metal than just slowly passing it between vibrating neighbouring particles.
7) This is why heat travels so quickly through metals.

Convection

Two down one to go — here's convection...

Convection — **Liquids** and **Gases** Only

1) The particles in gases and liquids are free to move about. This allows them to transfer energy by convection, which is a much more effective process than conduction in liquids and gases.

 KEY TERM Convection is the process where more energetic particles of a substance move from a hotter region to a cooler region — and transfer energy as they do.

2) This is how immersion heaters in kettles, hot water tanks and convector heaters work.

3) Convection simply can't happen in solids because the particles can't move (apart from vibrating — see page 48).

The **Immersion Heater** Example

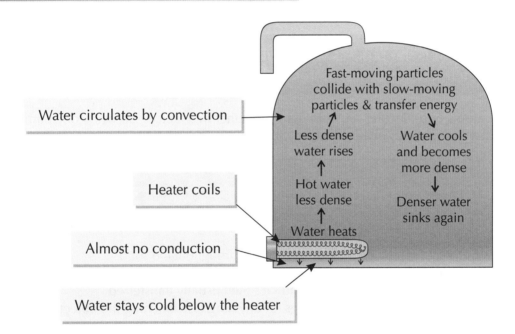

Water circulates by convection

Heater coils

Almost no conduction

Water stays cold below the heater

Fast-moving particles collide with slow-moving particles & transfer energy

Less dense water rises

Hot water less dense

Water heats

Water cools and becomes more dense

Denser water sinks again

1) Energy is transferred from the heater coils to the internal energy store of the water by conduction.

2) The water near the coil heats up and undergoes thermal expansion (p.56), becoming less dense.

3) This reduction in density means that hotter water tends to rise above the denser, cooler water.

4) As the hot water rises, the colder water sinks towards the heater coils.

5) This cold water is then heated by the coils and rises — and so it goes on. You end up with convection currents going up, round and down, circulating the energy.

6) Because the hot water rises (because of the lower density), you only get convection currents in the water above the heater. The water below it stays cold because there's almost no conduction.

In convection, particles move from hotter areas to cooler areas...

... taking their energy with them. Don't get this confused with conduction, where the particles can't move from their fixed positions, but vibrate more and transfer energy to neighbouring particles.
Have a flick back to the previous page if you need to remind yourself about conduction.

Investigating Conduction and Convection

Another page of practicals — this time for conduction and convection...

You Can **Demonstrate** the Properties of **Good** and **Bad** Conductors

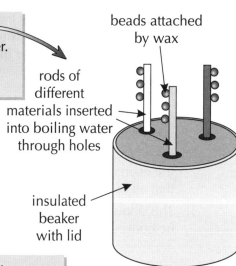

beads attached by wax

rods of different materials inserted into boiling water through holes

insulated beaker with lid

1) For this experiment you'll need rods made from different materials. They should all have the same length and diameter. Attach identical beads at regular intervals near to the ends of rods using identical blobs of wax.

2) Fill an insulated beaker with boiling water and add an insulated lid with holes for the rods. Stand the rods in the beaker of water, as shown in the diagram.

3) As time goes on, energy is transferred along the rods by conduction and the temperature increases along the rods.

4) As the temperature increases along the rods, the wax holding the beads in place will gradually melt and the beads will fall, starting with the beads closest to the water. This illustrates conduction.

5) The beads will take different lengths of time to fall off each rod. This demonstrates the effectiveness of each material as a thermal conductor. The sooner all the beads fall from a rod, the better conductor that rod is.

You Can See **Convection Currents** Using **Coloured Crystals**

1) Place some purple potassium permanganate crystals in a beaker of cold water. Aim to put the crystals to one side of the beaker.

2) Using a Bunsen burner, gently heat the side of the beaker with the crystals at the bottom.

3) As the temperature of the water around the potassium permanganate crystals increases, they begin to dissolve, forming a bright purple solution.

4) This purple solution is carried through the water by convection, and so traces out the path of the convection currents in the beaker.

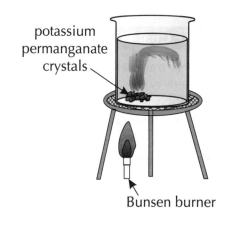

potassium permanganate crystals

Bunsen burner

PRACTICAL TIP

Remember basic laboratory safety...

These might not seem the most dangerous experiments ever, but there are still a few precautions you should take. For example, the apparatus, water and ends of at least some of the rods will get hot. Using potassium permanganate also comes with risks, so follow all safety advice.

Thermal Energy Transfer Examples

We use the different types of thermal energy transfers in many different ways...

Thermal Energy Transfers have Many Applications

We make use of thermal energy transfers in our day-to-day lives in many different ways.
You've already seen how we maximise radiation to help cool down devices (p.58), and how
convection heats a tank of water in an immersion heater (p.62). Here are some other examples:

Kitchen Pan

1) A kitchen pan is made of metal, as metal is a good thermal conductor.
2) Heat is applied to the bottom of the pan and the energy spreads through it by conduction, so that all of the metal is at the same temperature.
3) This allows food placed on it to be cooked evenly and at the same rate.

Toaster

1) Toasters contain electrical wires which get hot, glow and emit infrared radiation.
2) The infrared radiation transfers energy to the internal energy stores of the food in the toaster (e.g. slices of bread) to heat it up.

House Radiators

1) Despite what their name might suggest, radiators heat up rooms mainly by forming convection currents.
2) Hot, less dense air by the radiator rises and denser, cooler air in the room sinks.
3) This causes a flow of hot air throughout the room, which heats it up.

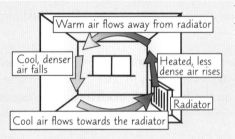

Warm air flows away from radiator

Cool, denser air falls

Heated, less dense air rises

Radiator

Cool air flows towards the radiator

Radiators can sometimes be called 'convectors' or 'convector heaters'.

Some Devices using Energy Transfers can be more Complex

In the examples above, only one main type of thermal energy transfer takes place during their use. Here are some examples of things where more than one type of energy transfer is important:

Wood or Coal Fire

1) Energy transferred by a fire spreads out in all directions by radiation — this is the heat you feel when you're next to a fire.
2) Energy is also transferred by heating through convection.
3) The hot air directly above the fire is less dense than the surrounding air and so it rises.
4) A convection current is set up, just like with a radiator.

Car Radiators

1) Car radiators help cool down car engines.
2) Energy is transferred away from the engine by passing a liquid coolant (usually water with added chemicals) over the engine through metal pipes.
3) Heat from the engine is transferred into the metal pipes and coolant by conduction.
4) The heated coolant is pumped away from the engine to the radiator.
5) Energy is transferred from the coolant to the surface of the cooling fins by conduction.
6) The thin metal pipes and cooling fins transfer the energy away from their surfaces mainly by radiation, but also conduction to the outside air and convection of the air.

Supplement

Supplement

Warm-Up & Exam Questions

Now it's time to test how much of this information you've actually absorbed by answering a few questions.

Warm-Up Questions

1) True or false? When thermal energy is transferred by radiation, the thermal energy must be transmitted through a solid medium.
2) What is the relationship between an object's surface temperature and the rate of infrared radiation emission?
3) Why does the local temperature on Earth decrease at night?
4) Explain how energy is transferred through a solid by conduction.
5) Give an example of a device which uses convection.

Exam Questions

1   A car radiator is used to reduce the temperature of the engine.

  (a)   Part of the radiator is made up of metal pipes containing a liquid coolant. The coolant becomes hot when it passes through the pipes next to the hot engine. State the type of thermal energy transfer involved in transferring energy to the thermal energy store of the coolant.

[1]

  (b)   The hot coolant is then pumped away from the engine and made to flow through thin metal fins. State the main type of thermal energy transfer involved in transferring energy away from the surface of the fins.

[1]

[Total 2 marks]

2   A teacher is carrying out an experiment to demonstrate convection. She has a rectangular glass tube with some purple potassium permanganate crystals in one of the bottom corners. She fills the tube with water, and heats the corner containing the permanganate crystals, as shown in **Figure 1**.

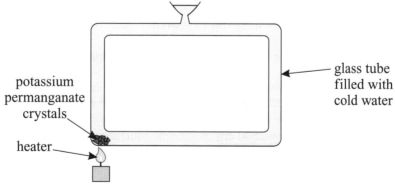

potassium permanganate crystals

glass tube filled with cold water

heater

Figure 1

  (a)   Copy the diagram above and draw **two** arrows to show the movement of the water in the tube.

[1]

  (b)   Explain why the water in the tube moves in the way that you have shown in part (a).

[3]

[Total 4 marks]

Exam Questions

3   A student is investigating the rate at which infrared radiation is emitted by different surfaces using a Leslie cube, as shown in **Figure 2**.

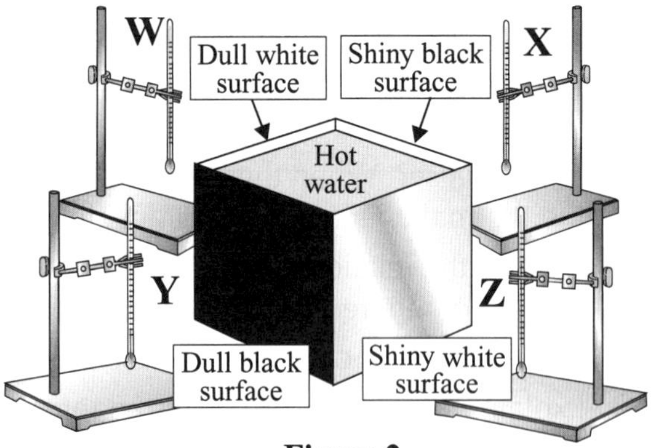

The student records how long it takes the temperature on each thermometer to increase by 5 °C.

(a)   Suggest **one** thing the student should do to make the experiment a fair test.

[1]

Figure 2

(b)   Which thermometer would you expect to increase by 5 °C the fastest?

☐ **A**   W

☐ **B**   X

☐ **C**   Y

☐ **D**   Z

[1]

(c)   The water used in the experiment was initially at boiling point, 100 °C.
The experiment is repeated using water at 60 °C.
Predict how this would affect the results. Explain your prediction.

[2]

[Total 4 marks]

4   A chef is working in a kitchen.

(a)   The chef uses oven gloves made from insulating fabric to remove hot objects from the oven. State the type of thermal energy transfer that is reduced by the oven gloves, and explain how it is reduced.

[2]

The chef removes two steel baking trays from the oven.

(b)   Explain, in terms of particle motion, how energy is conducted through steel.

[2]

Figure 3 shows the baking trays. They have the same mass, but are different sizes.

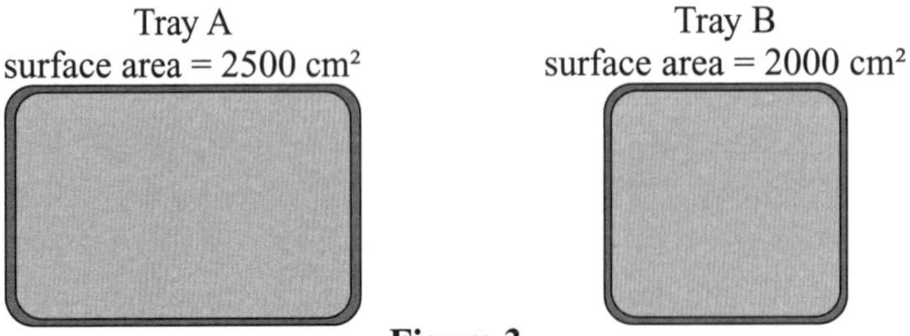

Tray A
surface area = 2500 cm²

Tray B
surface area = 2000 cm²

Figure 3

(c)   Suggest why baking tray A will cool down faster than baking tray B. Explain your answer.

[2]

[Total 6 marks]

Supplement

Revision Summary

Don't let all that stuff about gas pressures in Section 3 put too much pressure on you. Try these questions to see if you've really got to grips with all of that stuff about states of matter and the kinetic particle model.

- Try these questions and tick off each one when you get it right.
- When you've done all the questions under a heading, and are completely happy with it, tick it off.

Matter and Particle Motion (p.48-50) ☐

1) What are the three states of matter?
2) Which states of matter can flow?
3) True or false? Only solids be compressed.
4) True or false? Particles suspended in a fluid will move in random, zigzag paths.
5) Explain how a gas in a sealed container exerts a pressure on the walls of the container.
6) A sealed container of gas is kept at a constant temperature.
   The volume of the container is increased. What happens to the pressure of the gas? Explain why.
7) For a fixed mass of gas at a constant temperature,
   what is the relationship between pressure and volume?

Changes of State and Internal Energy (p.51-52) ☐

8) What happens to the energy in the kinetic energy stores of the particles in a substance
   when its temperature increases?
9) What is meant by the energy in the internal energy stores of a substance?
10) Name the change of state that occurs when a gas turns into a liquid.
11) Explain what happens to particles in a substance during evaporation.
12) How does the motion of air across the surface of a liquid affect the rate of evaporation?

Specific Heat Capacity and Thermal Expansion (p.54-56) ☐

13) True or false? It takes the same amount of energy to increase the temperature
    of any object by 1 °C.
14) Why are experimentally determined specific heat capacities
    likely to be larger than the true value?
15) Which state of matter expands the most due to thermal expansion?
16) Give one example of thermal expansion in everyday life.

Thermal Energy Transfers (p.58-64) ☐

17) Name the three methods of thermal energy transfer.
18) Compare the infrared radiation absorption and emission rates
    for an object at a constant temperature.
19) How could you use a Leslie cube to investigate infrared radiation emitted by different surfaces?
20) Explain why the overall temperature of the Earth stays fairly constant.
21) Describe how the energy transferred from a heating element to the water in an immersion
    heater tank is spread evenly throughout the water in the tank. What is this process called?
22) Describe the energy transfers that take place in a car radiator.

Section 4 — Properties of Waves

General Wave Properties

Waves transfer energy from one place to another without transferring any matter (stuff).

Waves Transfer Energy in the Direction they are Travelling

1) Waves happen when a vibration (or other oscillation) travels out from its starting point.

2) The direction a wave travels in is called the direction of propagation.

3) When waves travel through a medium, the particles of the medium oscillate and transfer energy between each other. BUT overall, the particles stay in the same place — only energy is transferred, not matter.

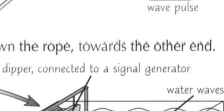

direction of motion

wave pulse   direction of motion

wave pulse

4) For example, if you drop a twig into a calm pool of water, ripples form on the water's surface. The ripples don't carry the water (or the twig) away with them.

5) You can demonstrate waves using a rope. Hold one end, get a friend to hold the other, and hold it tight between you.

6) If you wiggle one end quickly, you will see a wave pulse travel down the rope, towards the other end. Keep wiggling and you'll see a continuous wave.

7) You can also demonstrate waves using water in a ripple tank. The wave pattern can be seen more clearly if a lamp is positioned so light shines down through the ripple tank. This casts shadows of the waves on a screen (or the floor) below the tank.

dipper, connected to a signal generator

water waves

ripple tank

8) You can also demonstrate waves using springs (see next page).

Waves have Amplitude, Wavelength and Frequency

There are some key properties of a wave that you need to learn.

 KEY TERM The amplitude of a wave is the maximum displacement of a point on the wave from its undisturbed position.

 KEY TERM The wavelength is the distance between the same point on two adjacent waves (e.g. between the trough of one wave and the trough of the wave next to it).

 KEY TERM Frequency is the number of complete waves passing a certain point per second. Frequency is measured in hertz (Hz). 1 Hz is 1 wave per second.

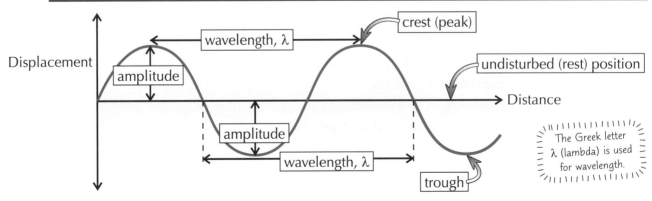

Displacement

wavelength, λ

crest (peak)

amplitude

undisturbed (rest) position

Distance

amplitude

wavelength, λ

trough

The Greek letter λ (lambda) is used for wavelength.

The only thing a wave transfers is energy...

That's one fact that's key to understanding waves. Here's another example — if you strum a guitar string and create sound waves, the sound waves don't carry the air away from the guitar and create a vacuum.

Transverse and Longitudinal Waves

All waves are either transverse or longitudinal. Read on to find out more...

Transverse Waves Have Perpendicular Vibrations

 In transverse waves, the vibrations are perpendicular (at 90°) to the direction in which the wave is propagated.

A spring wiggled from side to side gives a transverse wave:

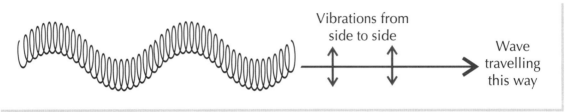

Vibrations from side to side

Wave travelling this way

Most waves are transverse, including:

1) All electromagnetic radiation, e.g. light (page 87).
2) Seismic S-waves (secondary earthquake waves).
3) Ripples and waves in water.
4) A wave on a rope.

Longitudinal Waves Have Parallel Vibrations

 In longitudinal waves, the vibrations are parallel to the direction in which the wave is propagated.

If you push the end of a spring, you get a longitudinal wave.

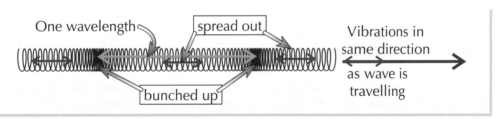

One wavelength

spread out

bunched up

Vibrations in same direction as wave is travelling

Other examples of longitudinal waves are:
1) Sound waves in air, ultrasound (see page 94).
2) Seismic P-waves (primary earthquake waves).

Wave Speed is the Speed a Wave Travels

 The wave speed is the speed at which energy is being transferred (or the speed the wave is moving).

The wave equation applies to all waves:

Wave speed (m/s) — $v = f\lambda$ — Wavelength (m) / Frequency (Hz)

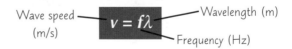

 **A radio wave has a frequency of 1.2×10^7 Hz. Find its wavelength. (The speed of radio waves in air is 3.0×10^8 m/s.)**

1) To find λ, you need to rearrange the equation $v = f\lambda$. $\lambda = v \div f$
2) Substitute in the values for v and f to calculate λ. $= (3.0 \times 10^8) \div (1.2 \times 10^7) = 25$ m

Warm-Up & Exam Questions

Now to check what information's actually been transferred to your brain over the last two pages...

Warm-Up Questions

1) A twig is dropped on a pool of water and creates water ripples. Explain why a leaf on the surface of the pool will stay where it is, rather than being carried away by the ripples.
2) What are the units of frequency?
3) Give one example of a longitudinal wave.
4) State the equation that relates wave speed, frequency and wavelength.

Exam Questions

1   **Figure 1** shows a graph of a water wave.

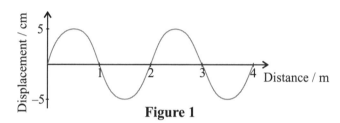

Figure 1

(a) State whether water waves are transverse or longitudinal.

[1]

(b) Give the amplitude of this wave.

[1]

(c) Find the wavelength of this wave.

[1]

[Total 3 marks]

2   **Figure 2** shows ripples on the surface of some water in a ripple tank. Each shadowed line is the crest of a wave. The signal generator producing the ripples is set to a frequency of 12 Hz. A student measures the distance between the first and last visible ripple as 18 cm, as shown in **Figure 2**.

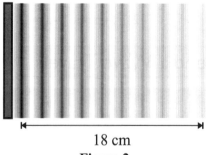

18 cm
Figure 2

(a) Determine the wavelength of the water ripples.

[1]

(b) Calculate the speed of the ripples in the water.

[2]

[Total 3 marks]

Reflection

You should be pretty familiar with the idea of reflection. Of course, there's a bit more to it than you'd think.

Reflection is when a Wave Bounces Back

1) Reflection happens when waves bounce off a surface. All waves can be reflected.

2) You can draw ray diagrams, like the one on the right, to show the path that waves travel along. Rays are always drawn as straight lines. There's more on ray diagrams on page 72.

3) The normal is an imaginary line that's perpendicular (at right angles) to the surface at the point of incidence (the point where the wave hits the boundary). The normal is usually shown as a dotted line.

4) The angle of incidence is the angle between the incoming wave and the normal. The angle of reflection is the angle between the reflected wave and the normal.

5) The law of reflection applies to every reflected wave:

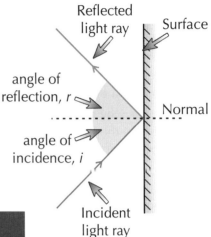

 KEY TERM — The law of reflection states that the angle of incidence always equals the angle of reflection.

You Can Show Reflection Using Water Waves

1) Reflection happens for all types of waves. You can see this for yourself using water waves. To do this, you'll need to set up a ripple tank.

2) First, fill the ripple tank with water. Then set up the dipper so its tip is just below the surface of the water.

3) Next connect the dipper to a signal generator. You can set the generator to a frequency, and the dipper will dip in and out of the water at that frequency. This creates water waves of the same frequency.

4) Set the signal generator to a frequency that produces clear water waves in the ripple tank.

5) Then stop the signal generator, and place a flat barrier into the tank at an angle to the dipper, as shown in the diagram below. Then turn the signal generator back on.

dipper dips in and out of the water, producing ripples

to signal generator

water

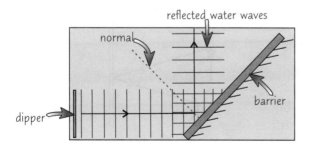

6) When water waves hit the barrier, they are reflected by it.

7) The angles the incident and reflected waves make with the normal always match each other — this is the law of reflection in action.

EXAM TIP — ## The law of reflection applies to all reflected rays...

... if you know the angle of incidence then you know the angle of reflection — simple as that. In the exam you can use a pencil to draw diagrams (such as ray diagrams like the ones on the next few pages). So make sure you've got a nice sharp one with you, and an eraser too.

Mirror Images

You'll probably have gathered from years of looking in mirrors that they form images of whatever's in front of them. Read on to find out how exactly they do it...

Reflection can be used to Form Optical Images

1) Visible light is a transverse wave (see page 69), like all electromagnetic waves (p.87).

2) Reflection of visible light is what allows us to see most objects. Light bounces off them into our eyes.

3) When parallel light rays reflect from an even surface (one which is smooth and shiny like a plane mirror) they're all reflected at the same angle and you get a clear reflection.

4) This is why mirrors form images of the objects in front of them. The ray diagram on the right shows how an optical image is formed in a plane mirror.

5) The image produced by a mirror is:

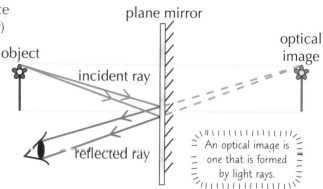

An optical image is one that is formed by light rays.

- the same size as the object and upright.
- the opposite side of the mirror from the object.
- the same distance from the mirror as the object.

Mirrors form Virtual Images

1) A virtual image is formed when the rays of light forming the image are diverging (spreading out).

2) This means the light from the object appears to be coming from a completely different place.

3) When you look in a mirror you see a virtual image of your face — the object (your face) appears to be behind the mirror.

4) For the exams, you'll have to be able to draw simple ray diagrams of light being reflected by a plane mirror like the one above. Here's how to draw a ray diagram of how a plane mirror forms a virtual image.

You might also need to make some measurements or calculations based on ray diagrams. Make sure you have your protractor handy.

1) First, draw the virtual image. Don't try to draw the rays first. Remember, the image is the same size as the object and it's as far behind the mirror as the object is in front.

2) Next, draw a reflected ray going from the top of the virtual image to the top of the eye. Draw a solid line for the part of the ray between the mirror and eye, and a dotted line for the part of the ray between the mirror and virtual image.

3) Now draw the incident ray going from the top of the object to the mirror. The incident and reflected rays follow the law of reflection — but you don't actually have to measure any angles. Just draw the ray from the object to the point where the reflected ray meets the mirror.

4) Now you have an incident ray and reflected ray for the top of the image. Do steps 2 and 3 again for the bottom of the eye — a reflected ray going from the top of the image to the bottom of the eye, then an incident ray from the object to the mirror.

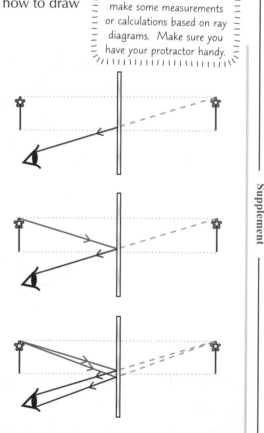

Supplement

Refraction

If a wave isn't reflected off a material, it'll either be absorbed by the material, or transmitted into it. If the wave is transmitted, it may be refracted. But before we get to that, you need to know about wavefronts.

Two or More Waves Moving Together Have Wavefronts

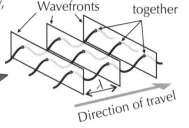

Points on each wave vibrating together

1) Often when we talk about waves approaching an obstacle or boundary, there are multiple waves moving together in the same direction.

2) In this case it's useful to talk about wavefronts. Wavefronts are imaginary planes that cut across all the waves, connecting the points on adjacent waves which are vibrating together.

3) The distance between each wavefront is equal to one wavelength, i.e. each wavefront is at the same point in the cycle.

Refraction — Waves Changing Direction at a Boundary

KEY TERM — Refraction is when a wave changes direction when it crosses a boundary between two materials at an angle to the normal. This happens because the wave changes speed.

1) How much a wave is refracted when it hits a boundary at a given angle depends on how much the wave speeds up or slows down. This usually depends on the densities of the two materials.

2) If a wave crosses a boundary and slows down it will bend towards the normal. If it crosses into a material and speeds up it will bend away from the normal.

3) The wavelength of a wave changes when it is refracted, but the frequency stays the same.

4) If the wave is travelling along the normal it will change speed (and wavelength), but it's NOT refracted.

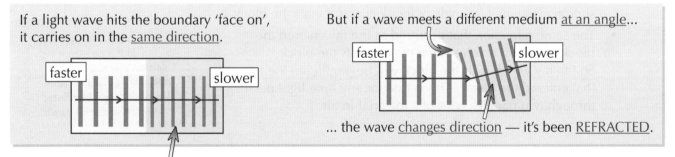

If a light wave hits the boundary 'face on', it carries on in the same direction.

But if a wave meets a different medium at an angle...

... the wave changes direction — it's been REFRACTED.

The wavefronts being closer together shows a change in wavelength (and so a change in speed).

You Can Show Refraction Using Water Waves

Just like reflection, you can demonstrate refraction using water waves in a ripple tank (p. 68).

Place a block into the tank at one end, so that water in part of the tank is a different depth to the rest. Make sure the waves produced by the dipper will hit the shallower water at an angle, as shown in the diagram.

When water waves hit the boundary between the deeper and shallower water, they refract towards the normal. This is because water waves travel more slowly in shallow water than in deep water.

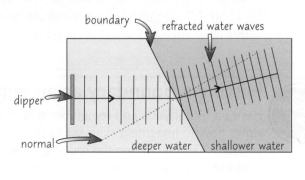

Investigating Refraction of Light

You can do experiments to investigate how light behaves when it travels through different materials. For these experiments, you'll need a ruler, a protractor and a nice sharp pencil...

You Can Use **Transparent Materials** to Investigate **Refraction**

1) Place a transparent rectangular block on a piece of paper and trace around it. Use a ray box or a laser to shine a ray of light at an angle to the middle of one side of the block.

2) Trace the incident ray and the light ray that emerges on the other side of the block.

3) Remove the block and, with a straight line, join up the incident ray and the emerging ray to show the path of the refracted ray through the block.

4) Draw normals at the points where the light ray entered and exited the block.

5) Use a protractor to measure the angle between the incident ray and the normal (the angle of incidence, i) and the angle between the refracted ray and the normal (the angle of refraction, r).

6) Then repeat these measurements for the emerging ray. Here, the 'incident ray' is the ray inside the block, and the 'refracted ray' is the ray emerging from the block.

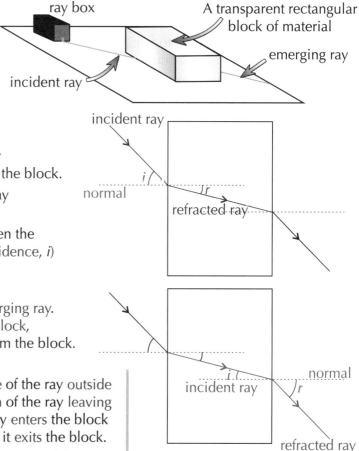

- You should find that the angle of incidence of the ray outside the block is equal to the angle of refraction of the ray leaving the block. The angle of refraction as the ray enters the block should also equal its angle of incidence as it exits the block.

- The same refraction that occurred as the ray entered the block occurs in reverse when the ray exits the block. So the ray which exits the block will be parallel to the ray that entered the block. This is true for any time light passes through two parallel sides of a material in air.

You can do this experiment with different shaped transparent blocks, e.g. a triangular block. The results would be different because the sides aren't parallel.

Different Materials Refract Light by **Different Amounts**

The boundaries between different substances refract light by different amounts. You can investigate this by looking at how much light is refracted by when it passes from air into different materials.

1) Repeat the experiment above using rectangular blocks made from different materials, keeping the incident angle the same throughout.

2) You should find that the angle of refraction changes for different materials — this difference is due to the speed that light travels in different materials (see previous page).

REVISION TIP

Hitting a boundary at an angle leads to refraction...

Here's a hint if you can't remember which way a wave bends when it enters a new material and slows down. Imagine a skier skiing from some nice smooth snow onto some rough ground at an angle. The ski hitting the rough ground first slows down first, so it moves a shorter distance than the other ski. This means the skier turns towards the ski that hits the rough patch first.

Refractive Index

Make sure you're happy with the last few pages before going on, because there's more refraction coming...

Every Transparent Material Has a **Refractive Index**

1) The refractive index of a transparent material tells you how fast light travels in that material.

> **KEY TERM**
>
> The refractive index of a material, n, is the ratio of the speed of light in a vacuum to the speed of light in the material.

2) Light travels slower in glass than in water, so the refractive index of glass is higher than the refractive index of water. It's around 1.5 in glass and around 1.33 in water.

3) The speed of light in air is about the same as in a vacuum, so the refractive index of air is 1.00 (to 2 d.p.).

4) For a ray of light passing from air into a material, the angle of incidence, angle of refraction and refractive index of the material are all linked by the equation:

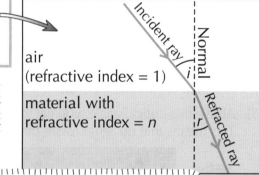

air (refractive index = 1)

material with refractive index = n

$$n = \frac{\sin i}{\sin r}$$

This formula actually works for the boundary between any two materials. Just let n equal the speed of light in the first material divided by the speed of light in the second.

5) So if you know any two of n, i or r, you can work out the missing one.

Remember, if a wave is travelling along (or parallel to) the normal when it crosses a boundary between materials, it doesn't refract.

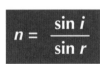 **EXAMPLE:**

A beam of light travels from air into water. The angle of incidence is 23°. The refractive index of water is 1.33. Calculate the angle of refraction to the nearest degree.

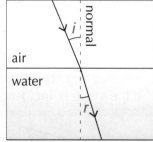

1) Rearrange the equation.

$$\sin r = \frac{\sin i}{n}$$

2) Then substitute the values in.

$$\sin r = \frac{\sin 23°}{1.33} = 0.29....$$

3) Use the inverse function of sine to find r.

$$r = \sin^{-1}(0.29...) = 17.08....$$
$$= 17° \text{ (to the nearest degree)}$$

The higher the refractive index, the slower light travels...

When finding the angles from the refractive index equation, remember to apply the <u>inverse sine function</u>. If your answer is less than 1, you probably haven't done it (or the settings on your calculator are wrong)...

Internal Reflection

It's not just a case of one or the other when it comes to reflection and refraction.
A lot of the time, when a wave hits a boundary, both happen at once.

Internal Reflection Occurs when a Wave **Tries to Leave** a Material

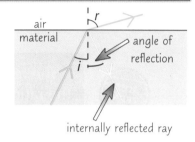

1) Whenever waves hit a boundary between materials, some of the waves may be reflected, even if the rest of the waves are transmitted into the new material.

2) So, when a ray of light tries to exit a material, some of the ray may be reflected back into the material. This is called internal reflection.

3) The reflected part of the ray still obeys the law of reflection — angle of incidence = angle of reflection.

4) There are many everyday examples of internal reflection. E.g. mirrored sunglasses reflect some of the light that hits them, which is why you can see a reflection when you look at someone wearing them. But they also let some light pass through to the wearer's eyes — otherwise you wouldn't be able to see anything when you put them on.

Total Internal Reflection is when **No Light Leaves** a Material

1) As you've seen on page 73, if light speeds up when going from one material to another, it bends away from the normal (e.g. when travelling from glass into air).

2) If you keep increasing the angle of incidence (i), the angle of refraction (r) gets closer and closer to 90°.

3) As the angle of refraction gets closer to 90°, more light is internally reflected.

4) Eventually i reaches a critical angle (c) for which $r = 90°$. The light is refracted right along the boundary.

5) Above this critical angle, you get total internal reflection. This means that no light crosses the boundary — it's all reflected back into the material.

> The critical angle is the angle of incidence on a boundary that will cause the angle of refraction to be 90°. An angle of incidence greater than the critical angle will cause total internal reflection.

6) You can easily demonstrate total internal reflection using a semicircular block.

7) The incident light ray is aimed at the curved edge of the block so that it always enters at right angles to the edge. This means it doesn't bend as it enters the block — only when it leaves from the straight edge.

8) If you vary the angle of incidence, you should find that...

If the angle of incidence (i) is...

Remember — the angle of incidence and the angle of reflection are equal, and always measured from the normal.

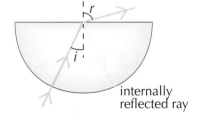

internally reflected ray

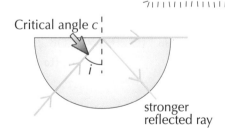

Critical angle c

stronger reflected ray

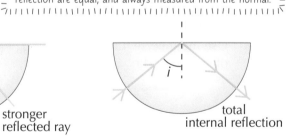

total internal reflection

...less than the critical angle:

Most of the light passes out but a little bit of it is internally reflected.

...equal to the critical angle:

The emerging ray comes out along the surface. There's quite a bit of internal reflection.

...greater than the critical angle:

No light comes out. It's all internally reflected, i.e. total internal reflection.

More on Internal Reflection

Total internal reflection has some great applications, and one of these is very glamorous indeed...

Diamonds and Optical Fibres Use Total Internal Reflection

1) Diamonds are cut in a way that makes use of total internal reflection. A correctly-cut diamond reflects almost all the light that hits it back upwards, so that none is lost out the sides or the bottom. This makes the diamond sparkle.

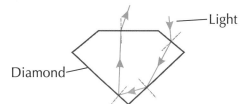

Light

Diamond

2) Optical fibres are made of plastic or glass, and consist of a central core surrounded by cladding with a lower refractive index.

3) The core of the fibre is so narrow that light signals passing through it always hit the core-cladding boundary at angles higher than *c* — so the light is always totally internally reflected.

4) It only stops working if the fibre is bent too sharply.

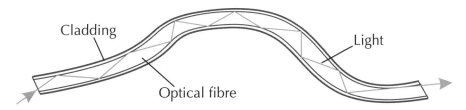

Cladding

Light

Optical fibre

5) Optical fibres are used in telecommunications:

> Optical fibres are used in telephone cables and broadband internet cables. Data can be encoded in pulses of light, which are then passed down the optical fibre. Optical fibres tend to provide better quality signals than traditional phone and internet cables.

You Can Use a Formula to find Critical Angles

You can find the critical angle, *c*, of a material to air boundary using this equation:

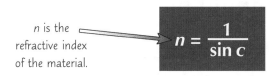

n is the refractive index of the material.

$$n = \frac{1}{\sin c}$$

The higher the refractive index, the lower the critical angle. For water, *c* is 49°.

Diamonds are forever...

... and now you know that some of their appeal is to do with total internal reflection. When you're explaining something about internal reflection, you'll need to be comfortable using the specific terms correctly — make sure you learn all the definitions, e.g. total internal reflection, critical angle, refractive index...

Supplement

Diffraction

If you thought reflection and refraction were good, you'll just love diffraction. If you didn't find them interesting then I'm afraid it's tough luck — you need to know about all three of them.

Diffraction — Waves **Spreading Out**

 Diffraction is when waves spread out as they 'bend round' obstacles.

1) All waves diffract when they pass through a gap or pass an obstacle, but it's not always easy to observe.
2) One way you can observe diffraction is by using water waves in a ripple tank.
3) Set up the ripple tank (like on page 68), but place a barrier in the water, as shown below on the left. When you set the waves going, you should see them bend around the edge of the barrier as they pass.
4) Then add another barrier, so there is a small gap between them, as shown below on the right. You should see the waves spread out at both sides as they pass through the gap.

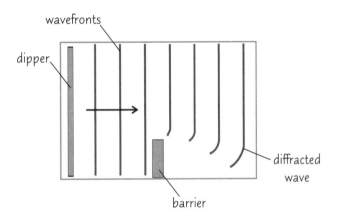

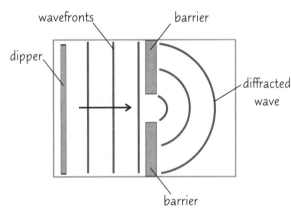

Diffraction Depends on **Wavelength**

1) The amount of diffraction around an edge depends on the wavelength of the wave.
2) In general, the bigger the wavelength, the more it will diffract around an edge.
3) The amount of diffraction through a gap depends on the size of the gap relative to the wavelength of the wave.
4) The narrower the gap, or the longer the wavelength, the more the wave spreads out.
5) Waves diffract most when the width of the gap is of the same order of magnitude as the wavelength of the wave — i.e. they're about the same size.
6) Light has a very small wavelength (about 0.0005 mm), so to be diffracted it needs a really small gap.

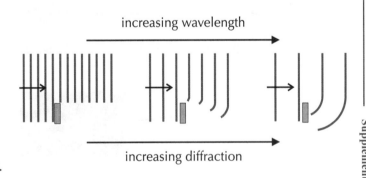

Gap much wider than wavelength

Little diffraction

Gap a bit wider than wavelength

Diffraction only at edges

Gap the same as wavelength

Maximum diffraction

Supplement

Warm-Up & Exam Questions

Now to check what's actually stuck in your mind over the last eight pages...

Warm-Up Questions

1) State the law of reflection.
2) What causes light to refract when it enters a new medium?
3) True or false? A wave entering a new medium along the path of the normal won't be refracted.
4) State the equation that links the refractive index, the angle of incidence and the angle of refraction.
5) What is total internal reflection?
6) Give an everyday example of total internal reflection.
7) Describe how a water wave in a ripple tank behaves as it passes the edge of an obstacle.

Exam Questions

1   Some water waves pass through a gap, and undergo diffraction. The size of the gap is equal to the wavelength of the water waves. Which of the images below shows the diffracted waves?

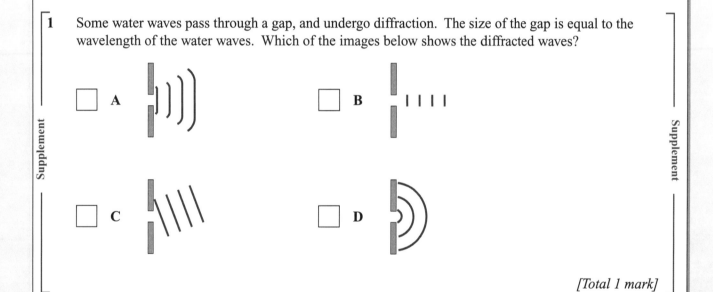

[Total 1 mark]

2   **Figure 1** shows an incomplete ray diagram of a student using a plane mirror to look at a pencil positioned behind a screen.

(a) The angle of incidence of the ray shown on the diagram is 20°. What will be the angle of reflection?

[1]

(b) Describe the size and position of the image of the pencil produced by the mirror.

[2]

(c) Copy and complete the ray diagram in **Figure 1** to show how an image of the pencil is formed by the mirror.

[3]

[Total 6 marks]

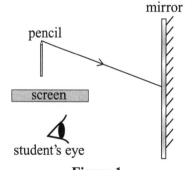

Figure 1

Exam Questions

3 A semicircular acrylic block is placed in water. Light passes through the block into the water. The critical angle (*c*) of the acrylic-water boundary for the light is 63.2°.

(a) State what is meant by the critical angle for a boundary.

[1]

(b) A ray of light meets the acrylic-water boundary at an angle of incidence of 75°. Describe what will happen to the ray of light at the boundary.

[1]

Supplement

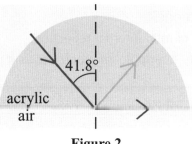

Figure 2

(c) **Figure 2** shows a ray of light hitting the boundary between the same acrylic block and the air. Calculate the refractive index of the acrylic.

[3]

[Total 5 marks]

Supplement

4 A student is investigating refraction through a transparent, rectangular block. The student aims a beam of light at a side of it, as shown in **Figure 3**. The light travels more slowly in the block than in air.

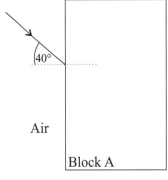

Air

Block A

Figure 3

(a) What is the name of the angle labelled 40° in **Figure 3**?

[1]

(b) Describe the path of the light through the block.

[3]

(c) The student now aims the beam of light at a side of the block at an angle of 30° to the normal. The angle of refraction is 11°. Determine the refractive index of the block.

[2]

[Total 6 marks]

Converging and Diverging Lenses

This bit is about how light acts when it hits a lens. Be ready for lots of diagrams on the next four pages.

Converging Lenses bring Parallel Rays to a Focus

Lenses form images by refracting light (p.73) and changing its direction.
A common type of lens is the converging (or convex) lens.

1) A converging lens bulges outwards.
   It causes rays of light parallel to the
   principal axis to be brought together (converge).

2) The principal axis of a lens is a straight line
   passing through the middle of the lens.

3) The principal focus (or focal point) of a converging lens
   is where rays hitting the lens parallel to the axis all meet.

4) There is a principal focus on each side of the lens.
   The distance from the centre of the lens to the
   principal focus on either side is called the focal length.

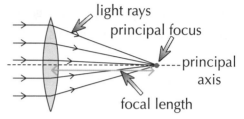

Rays actually refract twice as they pass through a lens — once as they enter and once as they leave. But you only need to worry about thin lenses. With these, you can think of the rays as refracting once in the centre of the lens.

There are Three Rules for Refraction in a Converging Lens...

1) An incident ray parallel to the axis refracts through the lens
   and passes through the principal focus on the other side.

2) An incident ray passing through the centre of the lens
   carries on in the same direction.

3) An incident ray passing through the principal focus
   refracts through the lens and travels parallel to the axis.

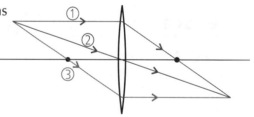

Diverging Lenses Make Parallel Rays Spread Out

1) A diverging (or concave) lens caves inwards.
   It causes rays of light parallel to the
   principal axis to spread out (diverge).

2) The principal focus of a diverging lens is the
   point where rays hitting the lens parallel to the
   axis appear to all come from. If you extend the
   rays coming from the lens backwards, they all
   appear to meet up at a point behind the lens.

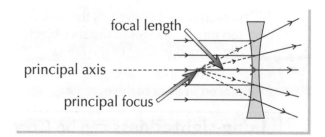

Focus on learning the three rules for converging lenses...

Those rules will come up again on p.83 (and p.84 if you're doing the Extended course). They're all you need to draw a ray diagram involving a converging lens, no matter where the object is and what the image looks like — so they're pretty important. And make sure you know your 'converging' from your 'diverging' too.

Images and Vision

That's one page on lenses done, so there's just a few more to go... You need to know the two types of image that can be produced by a lens and how they are different.

Lenses can Produce **Real** and **Virtual** Images

Images are formed at points where all the light rays from a certain point on an object appear to come together.

There are two types of images that can be formed by lenses:

A real image is formed when the light rays actually come together to form the image. The image can be projected on a screen, because the light rays actually meet at the place where the image seems to be.

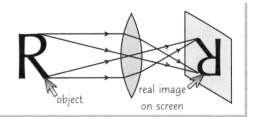

A virtual image is formed when the light rays appear to be coming from a completely different place to where they're actually coming from. When you extend the rays backwards, they meet at the point where the image is formed.

The light rays don't actually come together at the point where the image seems to be, so it cannot be projected on a screen.

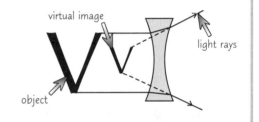

Lenses can Correct **Sight Problems**

Eyes contain converging lenses which focus light to form a real image on the retina at the back of the eyeball. This image is then interpreted by the brain.

However, if the image is formed in front of or behind the retina, it will appear blurry. This can be corrected by putting lenses in front of the eyes, either in spectacles (glasses) or as contact lenses.

Short-sightedness can be Corrected using **Diverging** Lenses

1) Short-sighted people are unable to focus on distant objects.

2) The focusing system in the eye is too powerful — it converges the rays too much. Images of distant objects are formed in front of the retina.

3) To correct this, a diverging lens is placed in front of the eye.

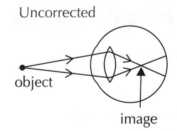

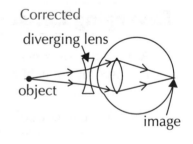

Long-sightedness can be Corrected using **Converging** Lenses

1) Long-sighted people are unable to focus clearly on near objects.

2) The focusing system in the eye is too weak — it can't converge the rays enough. Images of near objects are formed behind the retina.

3) To correct this a converging lens is placed in front of the eye.

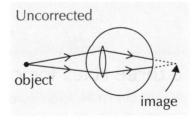

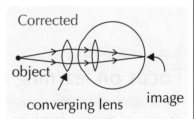

Images and Ray Diagrams

You need to be able to draw ray diagrams for converging lenses and describe the images formed.

You Need to be able to **Describe Images**

You need to be able to describe the images that are produced by a lens.
There are three details you need to give about the image:

1) You need to describe the size of the image — say if it is enlarged (bigger than the object), the same size as the object, or diminished (smaller than the object).

2) You need to describe the image's orientation — say if it is upright, or inverted (upside down).

Real images produced by converging lenses are always inverted.

3) You also need to say whether the image is real or virtual (p.82).

Draw a **Ray Diagram** for an **Image** Through a **Converging Lens**

Here's how to draw a ray diagram for the formation of a real image by a converging lens using the three rules you saw on p.81.

1) Pick a point on the top of the object. Draw a ray going from the object to the lens parallel to the axis of the lens.

2) Draw another ray from the top of the object going right through the middle of the lens.

3) The incident ray that's parallel to the axis is refracted through the principal focus (at focal length F) on the other side of the lens. Draw a refracted ray passing through the principal focus.

4) The ray passing through the middle of the lens doesn't bend.

5) Mark where the rays meet. That's the top of the image.

6) Repeat the process for a point on the bottom of the object. When the bottom of the object is on the axis, the bottom of the image is also on the axis.

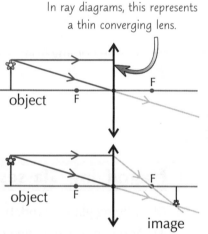

In ray diagrams, this represents a thin converging lens.

If you really want to draw a third incident ray passing through the principal focus on the way to the lens, you can (refract it so that it goes parallel to the axis). But you won't need it to know where and how big the image is.

Distance from the Lens Affects the **Image**

1) An object at 2F will produce a real, inverted image the same size as the object, and at 2F.

2) Between F and 2F it'll make a real, inverted image bigger than the object, and beyond 2F.

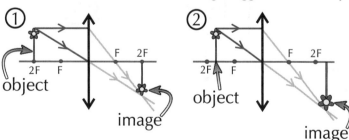

Converging lenses can produce virtual images, depending on where the object is. If you're doing the Extended course, see the next page for more.

Use the converging lens refraction rules to draw ray diagrams...

The first rule you need is that rays parallel to the principal axis refract to pass through the principal focus. The second rule needed is that rays passing through the lens' centre don't change direction. See page 81 for the rules. And then practise, practise, practise. It's the only way.

Magnifying Glasses

How close an object is to a thin converging lens affects the size and position of the image it creates. It's because of this that magnifying glasses work.

Converging Lenses can also make Virtual Images

1) An object nearer than F will make a virtual image that is upright, enlarged (bigger than the object) and on the same side of the lens as the object.

2) You need to be able to draw a ray diagram to show the formation of a virtual image by a thin converging lens. Here's how:

1) Follow the same steps as on the last page, but you'll find the two refracted rays never meet. Instead you need to extend the refracted rays back through the object's side of the lens as dotted lines.

2) The virtual image is formed where the two dotted lines cross — this is where the light appears to be coming from when you view the image.

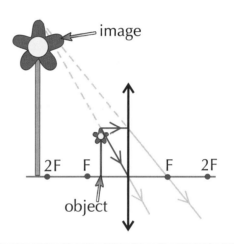

Magnifying Glasses Use Converging Lenses

Magnifying glasses work by creating a magnified virtual image in the way described above.

1) You can use any thin converging lens as a magnifying glass.

2) The object being magnified must be closer to the lens than the focal length.

3) The closer the object is to the lens, the bigger the image will appear.

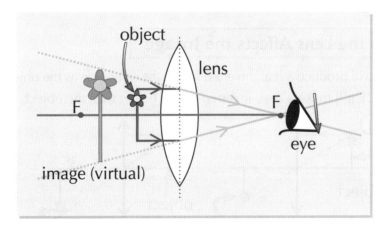

Use a ruler to draw the rays in the exam...

Also, read the instructions carefully — if they tell you to label your image with a particular letter, then do so. If you draw your two rays from the top of the object, they'll either cross and show you where the top of the image is, or they'll never meet, and you'll have to trace them back.

Dispersion

White light is actually a mix of every colour of light. A rainbow's what happens when it gets split apart...

White Light is made up of Seven Different Colours

1) White light is a mixture of all the different colours of light, which all have different frequencies.

2) It can be split up into a spectrum — where each colour flows into another. This is what happens in a rainbow.

3) We usually split the spectrum into 7 distinct colours: red, orange, yellow, green, blue, indigo and violet.

You need to be able to list the colours of light in order of frequency and wavelength.

4) Red light has the lowest frequency, and violet light has the highest frequency. Frequency increases as you go along the spectrum from red to violet.

5) Red light has the longest wavelength, and violet light has the shortest wavelength. Wavelength decreases as you go along the spectrum from red to violet.

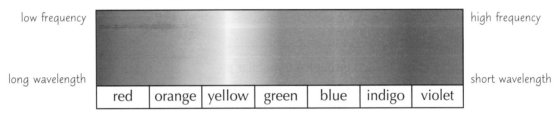

low frequency / high frequency

long wavelength / short wavelength

| red | orange | yellow | green | blue | indigo | violet |

Triangular Prisms Disperse White Light

1) Different frequencies (colours) of light travel at different speeds in glass, so they refract by different amounts.

2) This is known as dispersion, and it can cause light made of multiple frequencies (e.g. white light) to spread out.

3) For example, when white light passes through a triangular prism, you get a rainbow:

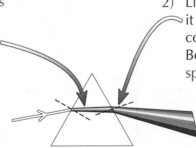

1) The light bends towards the normal as it enters the prism, as glass is denser than air. Different frequencies (colours) of light bend by different amounts — red bends the least, violet bends the most.

2) Light bends away from the normal as it leaves the prism. Again, different colours bend by different amounts. Because of the prism's shape, this spreads the frequencies out even more.

3) On the far side of the prism, you see a spectrum (rainbow).

You don't get a rainbow like this with a rectangular block because it has parallel boundaries, so although the different colours bend by different amounts when they enter the block, they bend back in the opposite direction when they leave it. So the rays emerge parallel.

4) Most light is made up of a mixture of different frequencies. The only light that won't be dispersed by a triangular prism is monochromatic light.

KEY TERM — Monochromatic light is made up of waves that all have the same frequency.

Supplement

Red light has the lowest frequency of visible light...

... and violet light has the highest. Make sure you know the colours of light in order of increasing frequency.

Warm-Up & Exam Questions

It's best to make sure this topic is really clear now, or you'll regret it when you get to the exams...
So here are lots of questions on lenses and light. Go on, answer them — you know you want to.

Warm-Up Questions

1) What is the principal focus of a converging lens?
2) What happens to a light ray that passes through the centre of a thin converging lens?
3) What happens to light rays passing through a thin diverging lens parallel to the principal axis?
4) True or false? A virtual image can be projected onto a screen.
5) [S] Where does an object need to be placed for a thin converging lens to form a virtual image of it?
6) Name all the colours that make up white light.

Exam Questions

1 A student passes a ray of white light through a triangular prism, so that it splits into a colour spectrum.

(a) Which of the following colours of light has the highest frequency?

☐ **A** green ☐ **B** blue

☐ **C** indigo ☐ **D** yellow

[1]

(b) Describe why white light is split into a colour spectrum when it passes through the prism.

[3]

[Total 4 marks]

2 Copy and complete the diagram in **Figure 1** to show how a real image of the object is formed by a thin converging lens. The principal foci of the lens are labelled *F*.

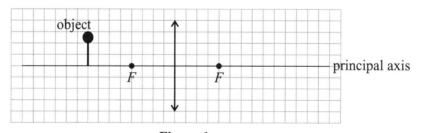

Figure 1

[Total 3 marks]

Supplement

3 **Figure 2** shows light rays from an object entering the eye of a person with short-sightedness.

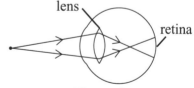

Figure 2

(a) Describe how the person's lens causes short-sightedness, and the effect it will have on their vision.

[2]

(b) Describe how a lens could be used to correct the person's vision.

[1]

[Total 3 marks]

Electromagnetic Waves and Their Uses

EM waves are great — there's so much you can do with them. Here's a good look at the uses of EM waves.

There are **Seven Types** of **Electromagnetic (EM) Waves**

1) Electromagnetic (EM) waves with different wavelengths have different properties. They're grouped into seven types by their wavelength (but the types actually merge to form a continuous spectrum).

RADIO WAVES	MICRO-WAVES	INFRA-RED	VISIBLE LIGHT	ULTRA-VIOLET	X-RAYS	GAMMA RAYS
1 m – 10^4 m	10^{-2} m (1 cm)	10^{-5} m (0.01 mm)	10^{-7} m	10^{-8} m	10^{-10} m	10^{-12} m

Wavelength

INCREASING FREQUENCY AND DECREASING WAVELENGTH

2) All types of EM radiation are transverse waves.

3) They all travel at the same high speed through a vacuum.

4) This speed is 3.0×10^8 m/s. EM waves travel at roughly this speed in air as well.

Since $v = f\lambda$ (p.69) and all the EM waves travel at the same speed, the longer the wavelength, the lower the frequency, and the shorter the wavelength, the higher the frequency.

Radio Waves are Used for **Radio** and **TV**, **Astronomy** and **RFID**

1) Radio waves are used for radio and TV transmissions.

2) How they travel from the transmitter to the receiver depends on their wavelength. Long-wave (1 – 10 km), short-wave (10 – 100 m) and TV/FM (10 cm – 10 m) are all used differently.

3) Radio astronomers use radio telescopes to detect radio waves from distant galaxies. The radio waves tell them about the composition and motion of bodies in outer space.

4) RFID (radio frequency identification) involves the transfer of data using radio waves. RFID tags allow objects to be identified, e.g. library books, animals, car keyfobs. RFID was first used in World War II to identify planes.

Short-wave signals reflect off the ionosphere

Ionosphere

Long-wave signals bend around the Earth.

FM radio and TV signals must be in line of sight — they have very short wavelengths

5) Bluetooth® uses short-wave radio waves to transmit data between devices. These waves can pass through walls, but weaken as they do so. This reduces interference between devices which are using Bluetooth® at the same time.

Microwaves are Used for **Phones** and **Cooking**

There's more on using microwaves in communications on the next page.

1) Mobile phone (or cell phone) calls also travel as microwaves from your phone to the nearest transmitter. Communications microwaves are low intensity — they don't transfer much energy per unit area.

2) Wireless internet and mobile phones use microwaves because only a short aerial is needed to transmit and receive microwaves. This is essential if devices need to be easy to carry around. Microwaves are able to pass through some walls, making them suitable for mobile devices.

3) Microwaves of a much higher intensity are used in microwave ovens. They transfer their energy to water molecules in food, causing them to vibrate. This leads to the food heating.

4) These high intensity microwaves can be dangerous to people exposed to them — they cause internal heating of body cells that absorb them.

REVISION TIP

You need to remember the seven types of EM waves...

...and you need to remember them in order. A mnemonic can make this easier. My favourite is: Raging Martians Invaded Venus Using X-ray Guns. But you can make up your own if you prefer.

Satellite Communications

Electromagnetic radiation is vital for communications — one important type is
satellite communications, which makes use of microwaves to relay information.

Satellite Communication Mainly Uses Microwaves

1) Satellite communications (including satellite phones and satellite TV signals) use microwaves.
2) Satellites orbit the Earth high above it, and signals can be sent
   to and received from them using transmitters and receivers on Earth.
3) There are two main types of satellite used for communications:

Low Orbit Satellites

1) Low orbit satellites sweep relatively low over
   the Earth (usually closer than 1000 km).
2) Since they're fairly close to the Earth, they move quite fast
   (see page 150) — orbits often take less than 2 hours.
3) Because they are close to Earth and orbit quickly, you need multiple satellites
   working together to maintain constant coverage everywhere.

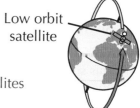

Low orbit satellite

Geostationary Satellites

1) Geostationary satellites have a high orbit (thousands of km)
   over the Earth's equator and orbit once every 24 hours.
2) This means they stay at the same point above the Earth because
   they orbit at the same speed as the Earth turns.
3) Because of this, they're ideal for communications as it's easy to point
   transmitters and receivers at them. Also, they can transfer signals
   from one side of Earth to the other in a fraction of a second.

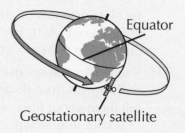

Equator

Geostationary satellite

4) Satellite phones use both of these types of satellite,
   while satellite television uses geostationary satellites.
5) Satellite phones send microwave signals to artificial satellites above the Earth.
   They also receive microwave signals transmitted by the satellites.
6) The advantage of satellite phones over normal mobile phones (cell phones) is that they work
   all over the planet. They're not limited to areas covered by normal mobile phone masts
   — so they're often used on boats or on trips to remote areas.
7) Satellite television data is transmitted by microwave signals
   from a large antenna on the ground to the receiver dish of
   a geostationary satellite in space.
8) The satellite then transmits the data directly to satellite dishes
   on the roofs of individual homes. It's known as direct broadcast
   satellite television since a signal goes straight from the satellite to each house's dish. The satellite
   dishes always point in the same direction, because the satellite is always in the same place in the sky.

Microwaves are pretty useful...

As well as the different applications on the previous page, microwaves allow us to make use
of satellites. Make sure you know the two types of satellite on this page and what we use them for.

More Uses of Electromagnetic Waves

Infrared radiation is another very useful EM wave. You can use it to cook your dinner, catch criminals in the dark, and change the TV channel without getting up from your favourite chair.

Infrared Radiation Can be Used to Monitor Temperature...

1) Infrared (IR) radiation is given out by all hot objects — the hotter the object, the more IR radiation it gives out (p.58).

2) This means that infrared sensors can be used to monitor temperature.

3) Infrared sensors can be used by intruder alarms. People emit much more infrared radiation than empty rooms or the general environment, so intruders will be detected as a change in infrared radiation.

4) If a change in infrared radiation is detected, an alarm sounds or a security light turns on.

5) Infrared sensors are also used in thermal imaging. The detected infrared is turned into an electrical signal, which is displayed on a screen as a picture. The image shows which parts of something are hotter and colder — it is used e.g. to find hot pipes or where a building is losing heat.

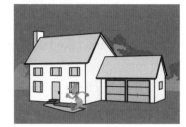

Different colours represent different amounts of IR radiation being detected. Here, the redder the colour, the more infrared radiation is being detected.

...Or Increase it

1) Absorbing IR radiation causes objects to get hotter. Food can be cooked using IR radiation — the temperature of the food increases when it absorbs IR radiation. An electric grill uses this — it has a heating element that heats up and emits IR radiation when a current runs through it.

2) Electric heaters heat a room in the same way. Electric heaters contain a long piece of wire that heats up when a current flows through it. This wire then transfers lots of energy by radiation, mostly as infrared radiation. This energy is transferred to the internal energy stores of the objects and the air in the room, causing their temperature to increase.

3) IR radiation can be dangerous. Absorbing too much of it causes skin burns.

Infrared Can Be Used in Communications

1) Information can be encoded in pulses of infrared radiation, and transferred between an emitter and a receiver. The distances must be fairly small and the receiver must be in the line of sight of the emitter.

2) This is how TV remote controls work — a little bulb at the end of the remote emits infrared radiation, which is received by the TV.

3) Files can be sent wirelessly between mobile phones or laptops over short distances in this way.

4) Infrared pulses can also be used to carry data longer distances at high speed through glass cables called optical fibres.

> Short-wavelength infrared waves and visible light pass through glass, which makes them ideal for transmitting data through the glass cores of optical fibres (see p.77). Optical fibres are used to carry cable TV signals and high-speed broadband, because short-wavelength infrared waves and visible light can quickly transmit large amounts of data.

Photography Uses Visible Light

1) Visible light is the light that we can see. We use it for illuminating things so that we can see them.

2) Photographic film reacts to light to form an image. This is how traditional cameras create photographs.

3) Digital cameras contain image sensors, which detect visible light and generate an electrical signal. This signal is then converted into an image that can be stored digitally or printed.

More Uses of Electromagnetic Waves

Here are just a few more uses of EM waves — time to turn to the high frequency end of the spectrum.

Ultraviolet is Used in Security Marking and Sterilisation

1) Security pens can be used to mark property (e.g. laptops). Under UV light the ink will glow, but it's invisible otherwise, helping to identify stolen property.

2) Bank notes also have markings that only become visible under ultraviolet light. This means fake bank notes, which don't have the correct markings, can be detected.

3) Ultraviolet radiation also kills bacteria and viruses, so can be used to sterilise water. It kills bacteria in the water, making it safe to drink.

4) Too much exposure to ultraviolet radiation is harmful to people. It damages surface skin cells and eyes, which can lead to skin cancer and eye conditions.

X-rays Let Us See Inside Things

1) X-rays can be used to view the internal structure of objects and materials, including our bodies.

2) They affect photographic film in the same way as light, meaning you can take X-ray photographs. But X-ray images are usually formed electronically these days.

3) Radiographers in hospitals take X-ray images to help doctors diagnose broken bones — X-rays are transmitted by flesh but are absorbed by denser material like bones or metal.

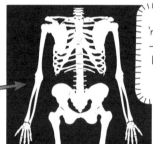

This is a 'negative' image — the brighter bits are where fewer X-rays get through.

4) To produce an X-ray image, X-ray radiation is directed through the object or body onto a detector. Material which absorbs more X-rays produce a 'shadow' on the image.

5) X-rays are also used in airport security scanners to detect hidden objects in baggage.

6) Care has to be taken when using X-rays though. X-rays can be harmful to people because they are a form of ionising radiation (p.134). This means they carry enough energy to knock electrons out of atoms. This can cause gene mutation, cell destruction, and cancer when it happens in the human body.

7) So people using X-rays regularly (like radiographers) will take safety measures such as wearing lead aprons and standing behind a lead screen or leaving the room to keep their exposure to a minimum.

Gamma Rays Can be Used in Medicine and in Sterilisation

1) Gamma rays can be used in medical tracers — this is where a gamma-ray source is injected into the patient, and its progress is followed around the body.

2) This can help doctors to diagnose medical issues, such as cancer. Gamma radiation is well suited to this because it can pass out though the body to be detected.

3) Gamma rays can also be used to treat people with cancer. This is called radiotherapy. High doses of gamma rays will kill all living cells they hit (they're ionising, just like X-rays, which can also be used for this). This means they kill cancer cells that they're directed towards.

4) Gamma rays can also be used to sterilise medical equipment and food. They kill microbes, and as they are able to pass through most objects, they can reach parts that would otherwise be difficult to sterilise.

5) Like X-rays, gamma rays are a form of ionising radiation, so they can cause gene mutation, cell destruction, and cancer if they ionise atoms in the human body.

Analogue and Digital Signals

On the last few pages you've seen how electromagnetic waves can be used to communicate across the planet. Well, there are two types of signal that you need to know about — analogue and digital.

Signals can be **Analogue** or **Digital**

1) Analogue signals can have any value within a range — they show continuous variation.

2) Digital signals can only take certain values.

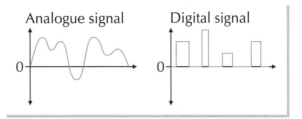

There are **Advantages** to **Digital** Transmissions

1) Digital signals can be sent over a greater range than analogue signals without loss of quality.

2) When you transmit an electronic signal it picks up noise (interference) from electrical disturbances or other signals. The further signals travel, the more noise they pick up and the weaker they get. Signals can be amplified, but the noise is amplified too.

3) The receiver needs to reconstruct the original signal from the noisy signal. The process of removing the noise is called regeneration. Regeneration is much more accurate with digital signals than with analogue signals because the number of values a digital signal can take is limited.

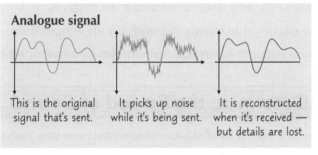

Analogue signal

This is the original signal that's sent.

It picks up noise while it's being sent.

It is reconstructed when it's received — but details are lost.

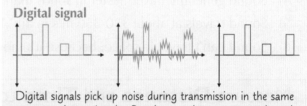

Digital signal

Digital signals pick up noise during transmission in the same way as analogue signals. But they can be reconstructed much more accurately because they only include certain values.

4) Digital signals also transmit data at a faster rate than analogue signals. With radio, this means that a greater number of programmes can be transmitted, with higher-quality sound.

5) Another advantage is that computers can easily process digital signals, as computers are digital devices too.

Sound can be Transmitted as **Analogue** or **Digital** Signals

1) The amplitude and frequency of sound waves vary continuously. This continual variation can be transmitted using analogue signals. FM and AM radio are transmitted in this way.

2) It's possible to turn an analogue signal into a digital signal — this is called digitising the signal.

3) To digitise a signal, you take the value of the signal at regular time intervals, then find the nearest digital value.

4) The digital signal you end up with won't be exactly the same as the analogue signal, but it's quite close.

5) DAB (Digital Audio Broadcast) radio is transmitted using digital signals.

Find the value of the analogue signal at regular intervals...

...then convert the analogue values to the nearest digital value.

Digital values

Time

Analogue signal   Digital signal

Sound Waves

You hear sounds when vibrations reach your eardrums. Read on to find out how sound waves work...

Sound Travels as a Wave

1) Sound waves are caused by vibrating objects. The vibrations are passed through the surrounding medium (material) as a series of high density areas (where particles are bunched up) and low density areas (where particles are spread out). Sound is a type of longitudinal wave — page 69.

2) The areas of high density are called compressions, and the areas of low density are called rarefactions.

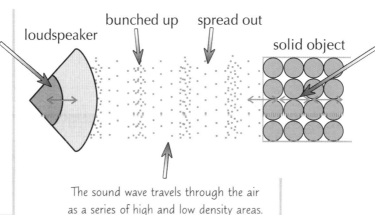

A paper diaphragm in a speaker vibrates back and forth, which causes the surrounding air to vibrate, creating areas where the particles are bunched up (high density), and areas where they are spread out (low density). A sound wave is created.

loudspeaker   bunched up   spread out

solid object

The sound wave travels through the air as a series of high and low density areas.

When the sound wave hits a solid object, the air particles hitting the object (the pressure — p.50) cause particles in the solid to move back and forth (vibrate). These particles hit the next particles in line and so on — passing the sound wave through the object as a series of vibrations.

3) Since sound waves are made up of vibrating particles, sound waves have to travel through a medium, whether that be a solid, liquid, or gas.

4) Sound generally travels faster in solids than in liquids, and faster in liquids than in gases.

5) Sound travels at about 330-350 m/s in air. The exact value mostly depends on air temperature.

6) Sound can't travel in space, because it's mostly a vacuum (there are no particles to move or vibrate).

Measure Distance and Time to Determine the Speed of Sound

Like any speed, the speed of a sound wave can be calculated by distance divided by time (see page 1). Sound travels rather fast, so to get accurate results you should use a data logger and microphones.

1) Set up two microphones several metres apart, and place a source of sound so that the source and both microphones are all along the same line. The source of sound could be a speaker or a person making a 'clap' noise.

2) Measure the distance between the microphones.

3) Set up the data logger so that it records the time a sound reaches each microphone.

4) Calculate the difference between these times. This gives the time taken for the sound to travel the measured distance between the microphones.

5) Use the formula speed = distance ÷ time to find the speed of the sound waves passing through the air.

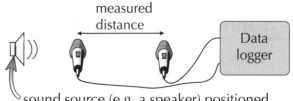

measured distance

Data logger

sound source (e.g. a speaker) positioned along a line with the two microphones

Reduce errors when determining the speed of sound...

PRACTICAL TIP

The method above uses a data logger to avoid human error in timing the sound. Sound travels 5 m in around 0.1 seconds — impossible to measure using a stop watch. If you are going to do the experiment with a stopwatch, you need to use a really, really big distance (hundreds of metres).

More on Sound Waves

All sounds have pitch and volume, and they're linked to the sound's wave properties...

The **Characteristics** of a Sound Depend on its **Wave Properties**

1) Two key properties of sound are volume (loudness) and pitch. These properties of sound are directly related to its wave properties — see page 68 for a refresher on wave properties.

2) You can use a microphone and an oscilloscope to display sound waves as a trace, so you can easily examine their wave properties. The microphone converts the sound waves to electrical signals. An oscilloscope is a device which can display the microphone signal as a trace on a screen.

Loudness Increases with **Amplitude**

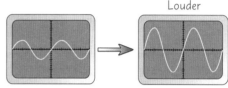
Louder

1) The greater the amplitude, the more energy it transfers.

2) For sound waves, this means it'll be louder.

3) Louder sound waves will have a trace with a larger amplitude on an oscilloscope.

The **Higher** the **Frequency**, the Higher the **Pitch**

1) Frequency is the number of complete vibrations each second, and it's measured in hertz (Hz) — 1 Hz is equal to 1 vibration per second.

2) If the source of sound vibrates with a high frequency the sound is high-pitched, e.g. a squeaking mouse.

3) If the source of sound vibrates with a low frequency the sound is low-pitched, e.g. a mooing cow.

4) You can compare the frequency of waves on an oscilloscope. If the waves are being compared on the same scale, the more complete cycles displayed on the screen, the higher the frequency.

Other common units are kHz (1000 Hz) and MHz (1 000 000 Hz).

The horizontal axis on an oscilloscope display is time, so more wave cycles on the screen means more in a given time, and so a higher frequency.

Original Sound

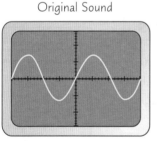

Higher pitched

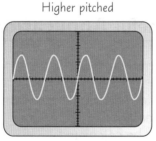

Lower pitched

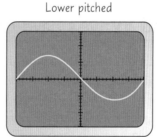

Higher pitched and louder

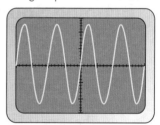

Echoes Happen when Sound Waves **Reflect**

Reflected sound waves, the echo

HONK!

Sound waves from horn

1) Sound waves are reflected by hard flat surfaces.

2) This is very noticeable in an empty room. A big empty room sounds completely different once you've put carpet, curtains and a bit of furniture in it. That's because these things absorb the sound quickly and stop it echoing around the room.

3) Echoes are just reflected sound waves.

4) You hear a delay between the original sound and the echo because the echoed sound waves have to travel further, and so take longer to reach your ears.

Frequency is measured in hertz (Hz)...

Remember, on a trace of a sound wave, the more wave cycles there are in a given time, the higher the frequency and the higher the pitch. The taller the wave, the greater the amplitude and the louder the sound.

Using Sound Waves

There are lots of uses of sound waves — the most obvious of which is us hearing sounds...

We **Hear Sound** when Sound Waves Reach Our **Ears**

1) Sound waves travel into someone's ear and reach their eardrum, which leads to them hearing a sound.

2) Humans can hear sound waves with frequencies in the range of 20 Hz – 20 kHz.

3) Sound waves that are too high-frequency for us to hear have a special name — ultrasound.

 KEY TERM — Ultrasound waves are sound waves with a frequency greater than 20 kHz (20 000 Hz).

Ultrasound has **Medical** and **Industrial** Uses

1) Ultrasound waves can pass through the body, but whenever they reach a boundary between two different media (like fluid in the womb and the skin of a foetus) some of the wave is reflected back and detected.

2) The exact timing and distribution of these echoes are processed by a computer to produce a video image of structures inside the body (e.g. a foetus).

3) Ultrasound can also be used to test materials in a non-destructive way. E.g. to find flaws in wood or metal.

4) Ultrasound waves entering a material will usually be reflected by the far side of the material. But if there is a flaw such as a crack inside the object, the wave will be reflected sooner.

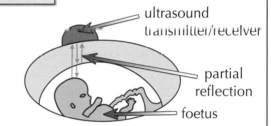

ultrasound transmitter/receiver
partial reflection
foetus

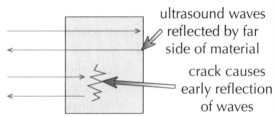

ultrasound waves reflected by far side of material
crack causes early reflection of waves

Echoing Sound Waves have Useful **Applications**

1) You can use the time it takes for a sound wave to be emitted, reflected, and return to a detector to measure how far away a boundary is.

2) This is how sonar or 'echo sounding' by ships and submarines works. A pulse of sound waves is directed at the sea-floor. The depth of the sea beneath the vessel can be calculated using the time it takes to detect the reflected pulse.

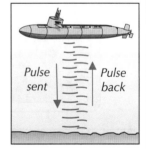

Pulse sent   Pulse back

EXAMPLE: A pulse of sound waves takes 4.5 seconds to travel from a submarine to the sea bed and back again. The speed of sound in seawater is 1520 m/s. How far away is the submarine from the sea bed?

1) Rearrange the equation for speed from page 1 and substitute in the values.

2) You were given the time it took for the wave to travel to and from the sea bed, so the distance to the sea bed is half of the total distance.

speed = total distance ÷ total time
total distance = speed × total time
= 1520 × 4.5 = 6840 m

distance to seabed = 6840 ÷ 2 = 3420 m

 MATHS TIP — ## Make sure you can use $s = vt$ to work out distances...

You should be familiar with the equation linking distance, speed and time from page 1 and be comfortable using it with waves. Remember, with echoes, the sound wave travels to the boundary and back, so you'll need to account for this in calculations.

Supplement

Warm-Up & Exam Questions

There's quite a few different sorts of waves — and you never know which ones might come up in the exams... So check which you're still a bit hazy on with these questions.

Exam Questions

1   The images below show the traces of different sound waves over 30 s.
     Which of the sound waves shown below has the lowest pitch?

☐ A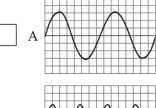

☐ C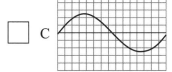

☐ B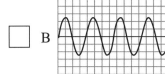

☐ D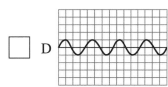

[Total 1 mark]

2   X-rays are used by truck scanners at country border control points
     to form an image of the inside of the truck.

   (a)   Explain how an image of the objects inside the truck is formed.

[3]

   (b)   While the truck is scanned, the driver and any passengers are asked to step outside
         the vehicle for their own safety. Suggest why this happens.

[1]

   (c)   Describe one medical use for X-rays.

[1]

[Total 5 marks]

3   Chandra owns a smart TV which responds to voice commands in addition to infrared signals from a
     remote control. She speaks 'off' to tell the TV to turn off, and presses the 'off' button on the remote
     control at the same time.

     Will the sound of her voice or the signal from the controller reach the television first?
     Explain your answer.

[Total 2 marks]

Revision Summary

And that's the end of Section 4 — now it's time to see how much you've learnt.
- Try these questions and tick off each one when you get it right.
- When you've done all the questions under a heading and are completely happy with it, tick it off.

The Basics of Waves (p.68-69) ☐

1) True or false? Waves only transfer energy, not matter.
2) What is the amplitude, wavelength and frequency of a wave?
3) Describe the difference between transverse and longitudinal waves.
4) Give one example each of a transverse and a longitudinal wave.
5) What needs to be multiplied by the wavelength of a wave to get its wave speed?

Waves at Boundaries (p.71-78) ☐

6) What is the 'normal' in a ray diagram?
7) A light ray is reflected from a plane mirror at an angle of reflection of 25°.
   What was the angle of incidence?
8) What is a wavefront?
9) Draw a diagram showing a light ray crossing, at an angle, into a medium in which it slows down.
10) Describe an experiment you could do to investigate the refraction of light through a block.
11) What is the meaning of the term 'refractive index'?
12) What happens when a light ray hits a boundary at an angle of incidence
    that is greater than the critical angle?
13) What is the equation that relates the critical angle at a material-air boundary
    to the refractive index of the material?
14) What is diffraction?
15) Describe how you could demonstrate diffraction using water waves in a ripple tank.

Lenses and Dispersion (p.81-85) ☐

16) What is the principal axis of a lens?
17) Give the three rules for refraction in a thin converging lens.
18) What is a virtual image?
19) What type of lens is used to correct long-sightedness?
20) Describe how a thin converging lens can be used as a magnifying glass.
21) What is meant by the dispersion of light?
22) What is monochromatic light?

Electromagnetic Waves and Sound Waves (p.87-94) ☐

23) True or false? All electromagnetic waves are transverse.
24) True or false? Microwaves can damage human body tissue.
25) Which type of electromagnetic radiation is used in most satellite communication?
26) What type of orbits are used by satellites for direct broadcast satellite television?
27) Give one use of infrared radiation.
28) Give two advantages of transmitting sound as a digital signal rather than as an analogue signal.
29) Give a range for the approximate speed of sound in air.
30) True or false? The higher the frequency of a sound, the lower the pitch.
31) What is the frequency range of human hearing?
32) Describe how ultrasound can be used to find flaws in a building material.

Static Electricity

Static electricity builds up on insulating materials. This is due to the transfer of electrons.

Like Charges Repel, Unlike Charges Attract

1) There are positive and negative electric charges.

2) Electrically charged objects exert a force on one another.

3) Two things with opposite types of electric charge are attracted to each other, while two things with the same type of electric charge will repel each other.

4) These forces get weaker the further apart the things are.

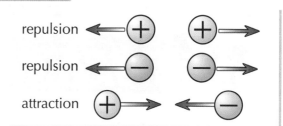

5) Electric charge can be measured. Charge is measured in coulombs (C). 1 coulomb is equivalent to the size of the total charge on a certain number of electrons (about 6.24×10^{18} electrons).

Add or Remove Electrons to Charge Objects

1) When certain insulating materials are rubbed together, negatively charged electrons will be scraped off one and dumped on the other. This is due to friction between the objects.

2) As the materials are insulators (see next page), these electrons are not free to move — this build-up of charge is static electricity.

3) The materials become electrically charged, with a positive static charge on the one that has lost electrons and an equal negative static charge on the other.

4) Which way the electrons are transferred depends on the two materials involved.

5) But whether an object has a positive or negative charge, it's only the negative electrons that have moved.

6) The classic examples are polythene and acetate rods being rubbed with a cloth duster.

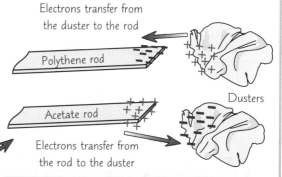

Electrons transfer from the duster to the rod

Polythene rod

Dusters

Acetate rod

Electrons transfer from the rod to the duster

Two Simple Experiments to Show Electrostatic Charges

When you rub your hair with a balloon, electrons are transferred from your hair to the balloon. The balloon and your hair are then oppositely charged, so they attract each other.

1) Another way to see the forces between charged objects is to suspend a rod with a known charge from a piece of string (so it is free to move).

2) Placing an object with the same type of charge nearby will repel the rod — the rod will move away from the object.

3) An oppositely-charged object will attract the rod, causing it to move towards the object.

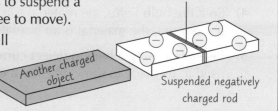

Another charged object

Suspended negatively charged rod

Only electrons move — never positive charges...

The material that the electrons have been transferred to will end up with a negative static charge, and the material the electrons have been transferred from will end up with a positive static charge.

Insulators and Conductors

On the previous page you saw how insulating objects can be charged by being rubbed together, causing the transfer of electrons. Well, if you're wondering what insulators are, you're about to find out.

Conductors Conduct Charge — Insulators Don't

 Electrical conductors conduct charge easily — a current (e.g. electrons) can flow through them. They're usually metals, e.g. copper and silver.

 Electrical insulators don't conduct charge very well — so a current can't flow. Examples include plastic and rubber.

Current in Metals is the Flow of Free Electrons

Not all electrical conductors are metals — but they must contain charged particles (e.g. electrons) that are free to move throughout the material.

1) Atoms contain a nucleus made from positive protons and neutral neutrons, with negatively charged electrons orbiting the nucleus (p.133).

2) The atoms in metals are bonded in such a way that metals are made up of a lattice (a grid) of positive ions surrounded by free electrons.

3) These electrons are free to move through the whole metal. Electric current in metals is the flow of these free electrons.

4) In insulators the atoms hold onto their electrons tightly, so a current can't flow.

positive ion

free electron

Electrical Conductors can Complete an Electrical Circuit

1) A simple way to test whether a material is a conductor or an insulator is to use a circuit, such as the one shown on the right.

2) The material being tested has a crocodile clip attached to each end.

3) For the bulb to light, there must be a current flowing through it. A current only flows in a complete circuit — if the material being tested is a conductor, then a current can flow through it and it forms a complete circuit. However if it is an insulator, a current can't pass through so the circuit is incomplete.

4) So if the bulb lights, the material is a conductor. If it doesn't, the material is an insulator.

5) Instead of using a bulb to detect current, an ammeter (p.104) could be used in its place to show whether a current is flowing.

ACE BATTERIES

Material being tested

Electrons flow freely in conductors...

Make sure you understand the point about free electrons in metals — it's key to being able to explain the difference between conductors and insulators. You don't need to know why metals bond like they do, but it's important to know that they're a lattice of positive ions, with free electrons that can create a current.

Electric Fields

You saw on the last two pages that electrical charges exert a force on each other.
These forces can be explained in terms of electric fields...

Electric **Charges** Create an **Electric Field**

An electric field is created around any electrically charged object.

 An electric field is an area where a force acts on an electric charge.

The direction of an electric field at any point is the
direction of the force on a positive charge at that point.
As like charges repel, electric fields point away from positive and towards negative.

You can Show Electric Fields around Objects using **Field Lines**

Remember these three key points about field lines:

1) Electric field lines go from positive to negative.
2) They're always at a right angle to the surface of the charged object.
3) The closer together the lines are, the stronger the field is — you can see that the further from a charge you go, the further apart the lines are and so the weaker the field is.

There are **Three Types** of Field Patterns You Must **Learn**

Field Around A Point Charge

A point charge is just charge
concentrated at a single point.

+q   −q

Field Around A Charged Conducting Sphere

This is similar to the electric field
around a point charge.

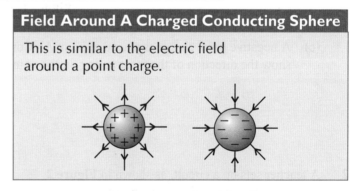

Field Between Two Oppositely Charged Parallel Plates

The electric field between two oppositely
charged parallel plates is uniform.

Electric field lines always go from positive to negative...

Electric fields may seem a bit weird at first — but the good news is they're very similar to magnetic fields (which are over on page 117), so if you understand one of them, you can understand them both.

Supplement

Warm-Up & Exam Questions

Have you been paying close attention to the last few pages? Only one way to tell really — have a go at these delightful warm-up and exam questions. If you get any wrong, go back and read it all again.

Warm-Up Questions

1) Do opposite electric charges attract or repel each other?
2) Describe an experiment to determine whether a charged object has a positive or negative charge.
3) Give an example of a material that is an electrical conductor.
4) What is an electric field?
5) What type of objects have electric fields?
6) Sketch the electric field between two parallel plates with opposite charges.

Exam Questions

1   A student rubbed a plastic sphere with a cloth, and the sphere became negatively charged.

    (a)   State the type of electric charge on the cloth.

[1]

    (b)   Describe the movement of charge which caused the sphere to become charged.

[1]

An image of the charged sphere is shown in **Figure 1**.

A

Figure 1

    (c)   A negative point charge is placed at point A. Copy the diagram and draw an arrow to show the direction of the force acting on the point charge due to the charged sphere.

[1]

[Total 3 marks]

2   A teacher sets up a circuit, as shown in **Figure 2**. She attaches a piece of aluminium foil between the crocodile clips. She then removes the foil and attaches a rubber band between the clips.

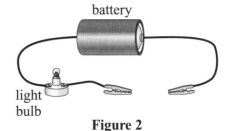

battery

Figure 2

light bulb

    (a)   Describe what the teacher would observe while following these steps.

[2]

    (b)   Explain these observations by referring to the particle structure of both the aluminium foil and the rubber band.

[2]

[Total 4 marks]

Circuits and Current

Electricity's a pretty important topic in physics. First up, some symbols and definitions to learn...

Learn these **Circuit Diagram Symbols**

1) You need to be able to understand circuit diagrams and draw them using the correct symbols.
2) Make sure all the wires in your circuit are straight lines and that the circuit is closed, i.e. you can follow a wire from one end of the power supply, through any components, to the other end of the supply (ignoring any switches).

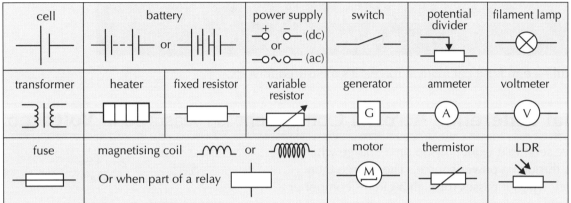
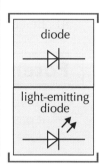

Supplement

Current is related to the flow of **Electric Charge**

1) Electric current is a measure of electric charge flowing around a circuit. It is measured in amperes, A.
2) In metals, current is due to a flow of free electrons (p.98) — they're negatively charged particles.
3) Current will only flow around a complete (closed) circuit.
4) There also needs to be a source of energy to push the charge (electrons) round the circuit. See the next page for more.

Conventional Current is **Opposite** to **Electron Direction**

Supplement

1) Free electrons in a circuit flow from the negative terminal of the power supply (e.g. a battery) to the positive terminal.
2) However, scientists originally thought charge flowed from positive to negative, so that was how they defined current.
3) When the theory changed, they termed the old idea of current 'conventional current'.
4) A lot of the science on electricity was developed based on conventional current. So when we talk about the direction of current in this book, we mean conventional current.

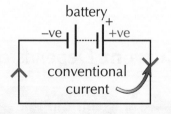

Supplement

Make sure you can draw all the circuit symbols...

In the exams, you might be asked to draw a circuit featuring any of the symbols above. The best way to learn them is to close the book and see how many of them you can draw from memory. Then check which you missed or got wrong, shut the book again, and see if you can get them all.

E.m.f., Potential Difference and Current

Some important definitions are coming up. And if you're taking the Extended course, some equations too.

E.m.f. is the **Energy Supplied** by a **Power Source**

1) Charge won't flow around a circuit unless the circuit is a complete loop and there is a source of energy to drive the charge around the circuit.

2) This source of energy may be a cell or a battery.

3) The amount of energy it supplies to each unit of charge is called its electromotive force (e.m.f.).

 KEY TERM The electromotive force, or e.m.f., is a measure of the electrical work done moving each unit of charge around a circuit.

4) Be careful — e.m.f. isn't actually a force. It's measured in volts.

Potential Difference Across a Component is Measured in **Volts** too

1) So you've seen that work is done on a charge when it passes through a power source. The charge then does work when it passes through a circuit component.

Remember — work done is the same as energy transferred (p.31).

 KEY TERM Potential difference, or p.d., is the amount of work done by each unit of charge as it passes through a circuit component.

2) You can measure the p.d. between any two points in a circuit — this is just the total work done by the charge as it moves between those two points.

3) The potential difference across the source can be considered to have an equal value to the e.m.f..

4) This means the formulas for p.d. and e.m.f. are the same:

p.d. (V) — $V = \dfrac{W}{Q}$ — work done (J) — charge (C)   e.m.f. (V) — $E = \dfrac{W}{Q}$ — work done (J) — charge (C)

EXAMPLE: **3600 J of energy is supplied to 300 C of charge as it passes through a battery. Calculate the e.m.f. of the battery.**

$$E = \frac{W}{Q} = 3600 \div 300 = 12 \text{ V}$$

Current Depends on how Fast **Charge** Flows

 KEY TERM Current is the amount of charge that passes a point in a circuit each second.

You can calculate current using this equation:

$$\text{Current (amperes, A)} = \frac{\text{Charge (coulombs, C)}}{\text{Time (seconds, s)}} \qquad I = \frac{Q}{t}$$

EXAMPLE: **A battery charger passes a current of 2.0 A through a cell over a period of 2.5 hours. How much charge is transferred to the cell?**

Rearrange the equation $I = \frac{Q}{t}$: $\quad Q = It = 2.0 \times (2.5 \times 60 \times 60) = 18\ 000$ C

The time is given in hours, so multiply it by 60 to convert it to minutes, then by 60 again to convert it to seconds.

Supplement

Resistance

Prepare yourself to meet one of the most important equations in electronics. It's all about resistance, current and potential difference... Now if that doesn't tempt you to read this page, I don't know what will.

Resistance Opposes Current

 KEY TERM Resistance is anything in the circuit which slows the flow of charge down.

1) Resistance is measured in ohms, Ω.

2) The larger the resistance of a conductor, the smaller the current flowing through the conductor (for a given potential difference across the conductor).

3) Resistance, potential difference and current are linked by a very useful formula:

$$\text{Resistance } (\Omega) = \frac{\text{Potential difference (V)}}{\text{Current (A)}} \qquad R = \frac{V}{I}$$

The Resistance of a **Wire** is Related to its **Length** and **Width**

A wire's resistance depends on its material and also on its length and cross-sectional area:

1) The longer the wire, the more difficult it is for current to flow, so the greater the resistance.

2) The greater the cross-sectional area, the easier it is for electrons to pass along it, so the smaller the resistance.

Supplement

A wire's resistance is directly proportional to its length. So if the length doubles, the resistance doubles too. If the length halves, the resistance halves too.

A wire's resistance is inversely proportional to its cross-sectional area. So if cross-sectional area doubles, resistance halves. If cross-sectional area halves, resistance doubles.

Supplement

Resistance can Change According to Environmental Factors

Light-Dependent Resistors (LDRs)

1) A light-dependent resistor or LDR is a resistor whose resistance depends on the intensity of light.

2) As light gets brighter, the resistance falls. In darkness, the resistance is highest.

3) They're useful for things like automatic night lights.

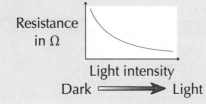

Resistance in Ω

Light intensity

Dark ⟹ Light

Thermistors

1) A thermistor is a temperature dependent resistor.

2) As it gets hotter, the resistance drops. As it gets colder, the resistance goes up.

3) Thermistors make useful temperature detectors, e.g. car engine sensors and electronic thermostats.

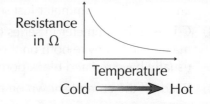

Resistance in Ω

Temperature

Cold ⟹ Hot

 EXAM TIP ## Make sure you always show your working...

... when substituting numbers into formulas. Writing out each step means you're less likely to make mistakes and you can still get some marks if your final answer's wrong but your working's correct.

Determining Resistance

Time for something a bit more practical. Here's how you can find the resistance of a circuit component.

You Can Measure **Potential Difference** and **Current**

1) On the previous page you met the formula for calculating resistance: $R = \frac{V}{I}$.

2) So to determine the resistance of a circuit component you need to measure the potential difference across the component (with a voltmeter) and the current through it (with an ammeter) using a circuit like this one:

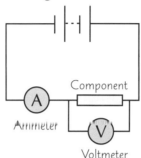

Component

(A) Ammeter

(V) Voltmeter

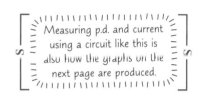

Measuring p.d. and current using a circuit like this is also how the graphs on the next page are produced.

3) Once you've measured the potential difference and current, you can substitute them into $R = \frac{V}{I}$ to work out the resistance.

There are different types of voltmeter and ammeter, but whatever types you have, you need to make sure you know how to use them correctly...

Voltmeters Measure **Potential Difference**

1) If you're using an analogue voltmeter, choose one with an appropriate range. For example, if you expect a component to have a p.d. of a few millivolts then you can't make an accurate measurement using a voltmeter with 1 V increments.

2) If you're using a digital voltmeter, you'll most likely be able to switch between different settings to find an appropriate range.

3) Connect the voltmeter in parallel (p.111) across the component you want to test.

4) The voltmeter wires are usually red (positive) and black (negative). These go into the matching red and black coloured ports on the voltmeter.

5) Then simply read the potential difference from the scale (or from the screen if it's digital).

Ammeters Measure **Current**

1) Just like with voltmeters, you could use either an analogue or digital ammeter.

2) For an analogue ammeter, you'll need to choose the ammeter with the most appropriate range, and for a digital ammeter just select the most appropriate setting.

3) Connect the ammeter in series (p.110) with the component you want to test, making sure they're both on the same branch of the circuit (p.111). Again, they usually have red and black ports to show you where to connect your wires.

4) Read off the current shown on the scale or by the screen.

PRACTICAL TIP

Don't get your wires in a tangle when you're using circuits...

Make sure you wire voltmeters and ammeters into your circuit correctly. Just remember, the red wires should go into the red ports and the black wires should go into the black ports.

Current-Voltage Graphs

Now you've seen how to use ammeters and voltmeters on the previous page, it's time to put that to good use.

Three Very Important Current-Voltage Graphs

1) You can use the method on the previous page to measure the current through and potential difference across a component, and then plot a current-voltage graph for the component.

2) A current-voltage graph shows how the current (*I*) flowing through a component changes as the potential difference (*V*) across it is increased.

You might also see these graphs referred to as 'current-voltage characteristics'.

Resistor of Constant Resistance

1) As its name suggests, a resistor of constant resistance has a resistance that doesn't change when current changes.

2) At a constant temperature, the current through the resistor is directly proportional to the potential difference across it.

3) So resistors with a constant resistance have a current-voltage graph that's a straight line through the origin (0, 0).

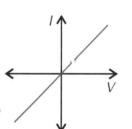

Filament Lamp

1) The resistance of a filament lamp increases as current increases.

2) As the current increases, the temperature of the filament increases. This makes the ions in the metal vibrate more vigorously.

3) The electrons are more likely to collide with the vigorously vibrating ions and are slowed down, so resistance increases.

4) Less current can flow per unit potential difference, so a filament lamp has a curved current-voltage graph.

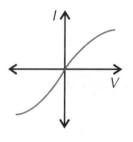

Diode

1) Diodes only let current through in one direction.

2) They have a very high resistance in the reverse direction.

3) So the current-voltage graph for a diode shows that the current is zero when the p.d. is negative (due to the very high resistance) and when the p.d. is positive, there is a current. The current increases as the p.d. increases.

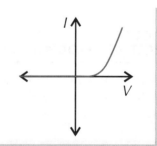

One type of diode is an LED (light-emitting diode). LEDs emit light when a current flows through them in the positive direction.

The direction of the triangle in a diode circuit symbol shows the direction of the current allowed through.

You may be asked to sketch a current-voltage graph...

So practise sketching them. Use a ruler to draw the axes and any other straight lines, and get used to drawing the curves smoothly in one go. It'll make your graphs look a lot neater.

Supplement

Energy and Power in Circuits

You can think about electrical circuits in terms of energy transfer —
the circuit transfers energy from the power source to the electrical components.

Energy is Transferred from a Power Source

1) You know from page 102 that a power source (e.g. an electrical cell, battery or mains supply) does work to move charge around a circuit, and that charge does work when it passes through a circuit component.

2) Overall, this means that energy is transferred electrically from the power source's energy store to the energy stores of the circuit components.

3) The energy in the components' energy stores is then transferred to the internal energy store of the surroundings, usually by heating.

> In this circuit, energy in the battery's chemical energy store is transferred electrically to the bulb's internal energy store. Energy is then transferred to the internal energy store of the surroundings by heating and by light.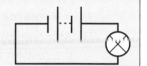

> In this circuit, energy is transferred electrically from the mains supply to the motor's kinetic energy store. Energy is then transferred to the internal energy store of the surroundings by heating and by sound.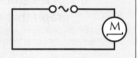

Electrical Power is the Rate at which a Device Transfers Energy

1) A device with a high power transfers a lot of energy in a short time.

2) Power is measured in watts (W). The formula for electrical power is:

> **Electrical Power (W) = Current (A) × Potential Difference (V)** $P = IV$

 **EXAMPLE:** A device has a potential difference of 12 V across it and a power of 60 W. Find the current through it.

Rearrange the equation above to get current, I, on one side. Then substitute in the values.

$P = IV \rightarrow I = P \div V = 60 \div 12 = 5$ A

Electrical Appliances Transfer Energy Electrically

1) The energy transferred by an appliance depends on the power of the appliance and how long it is on for (measured in seconds, s): energy transferred = power × time (see p.32).

2) Join that with the formula for electrical power above, and you get this formula for energy transferred:

> **Energy transferred = Current × Potential Difference × Time** $E = IVt$

 **EXAMPLE:** The motor in an electric toothbrush is attached to a 3.0 V battery. If a current of 0.80 A flows through the motor for 3.0 minutes, calculate the energy transferred by the motor.

First convert the time from minutes to seconds. $t = 3.0 \times 60 = 180$ s
Then substitute the values into the formula. $E = I \times V \times t = 0.80 \times 3.0 \times 180 = 432$ J

Cost of Electricity

Before you can work out how much it costs to use an electrical appliance, you need to know how to calculate the amount of energy transferred by the appliance. And for that, you need a new unit for energy transferred...

Kilowatt-hours is a Unit of Energy

1) Electricity companies measure the amount of energy transferred to customers in kilowatt-hours (kWh).

 KEY TERM A kilowatt-hour is the amount of energy that is transferred by a 1 kW device running for one hour.

A kilowatt is 1000 watts.

2) If you know the power of a device in kW and the length of time it runs for in hours, you can use this equation to calculate the energy transferred by the device in kWh:

Energy transferred (kWh) = Power (kW) × Time (h)

 **EXAMPLE:**

A student uses a 1600 W hairdryer for 12 minutes. Calculate the energy transferred in kWh.

1) Convert the power into kW and the time into hours.

Power = 1600 ÷ 1000 = 1.6 kW
Time = 12 ÷ 60 = 0.2 hours

2) Substitute the converted values into the equation.

Energy transferred = power × time = 1.6 × 0.2 = 0.32 kWh

Calculate the Cost of Using Appliances with Price per kWh

Electricity companies charge for electricity by the kWh.

Use this formula to work out the cost of using an electrical appliance for a certain length of time:

Cost (p) = Energy transferred (kWh) × Price per kWh (p per kWh)

This price could be in any currency, not just pence (in pounds sterling).

 **EXAMPLE:**

An electricity company charges 16.3p per kWh. A man vacuums his house with a 900 W vacuum cleaner which is switched on for 36 minutes. Calculate the cost of using the vacuum cleaner for this length of time to the nearest penny.

1) Convert the power into kW and the time into hours.

Power = 900 ÷ 1000 = 0.9 kW
Time = 36 ÷ 60 = 0.6 hours

2) Substitute the values into the equation for energy transferred.

Energy transferred = power × time = 0.9 × 0.6 = 0.54 kWh

3) Substitute this value and the price per kWh into the equation for the cost.

Cost = energy transferred × price per kWh
= 0.54 × 16.3 = 8.802p = 9p to the nearest penny

 EXAM TIP

Double check your units...

The energy transferred equation on the previous page requires time in seconds. However, for the equation above, you'll need time to be in hours. So before you use any of these energy equations, make sure that time is in the correct units for the equation that you're using.

Warm-Up & Exam Questions

Phew — circuits aren't the easiest things in the world, are they? Make sure you've understood the last few pages by trying these questions. If you get stuck, just go back and re-read the relevant page.

Warm-Up Questions

1) True or false? Current in metals is the flow of positive ions.
2) Which direction does conventional current flow in?
3) True or false? Increasing the length of a wire increases its resistance.
4) How should a voltmeter be connected in a circuit to measure the p.d. across a component?
5) State the equation that links electrical power, current and potential difference.

Exam Questions

1   What unit is electromotive force measured in?

☐ **A** newtons   ☐ **B** volts   ☐ **C** joules   ☐ **D** amps

[Total 1 mark]

2   **Figure 1** shows a circuit diagram.
     When the switch is closed, the ammeter reads 0.30 A and the voltmeter reads 1.5 V.

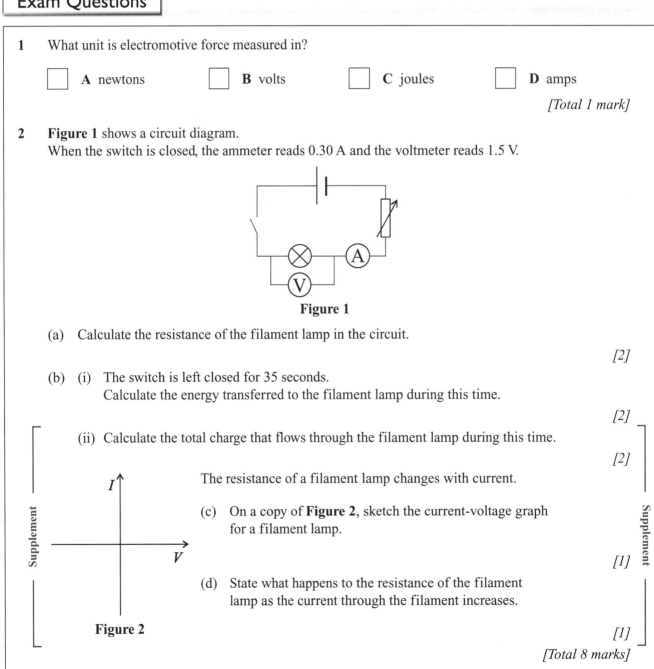

Figure 1

(a)   Calculate the resistance of the filament lamp in the circuit.

[2]

(b)   (i)   The switch is left closed for 35 seconds.
            Calculate the energy transferred to the filament lamp during this time.

[2]

      (ii) Calculate the total charge that flows through the filament lamp during this time.

[2]

            The resistance of a filament lamp changes with current.

(c)   On a copy of **Figure 2**, sketch the current-voltage graph
      for a filament lamp.

[1]

(d)   State what happens to the resistance of the filament
      lamp as the current through the filament increases.

Figure 2

[1]

[Total 8 marks]

Exam Questions

3   Last week, a teacher used his 3.0 kW kettle for a total of 90 minutes.

    (a)   How much energy, in kWh, did the teacher's kettle transfer last week?

[2]

    (b)   Electricity costs the teacher 15.9p per kWh. Calculate the cost of the electricity used by the teacher's kettle last week to the nearest penny (p).

[2]

[Total 4 marks]

4   A student carried out an experiment using a test circuit where she varied the current through a diode and monitored what happened to the potential difference across the diode. **Figure 3** shows a graph of her results.

    (a)   Explain why the graph in **Figure 3** shows zero current when the p.d. is negative.

[1]

    (b)   Calculate the resistance of the diode at the point marked A.

[2]

[Total 3 marks]

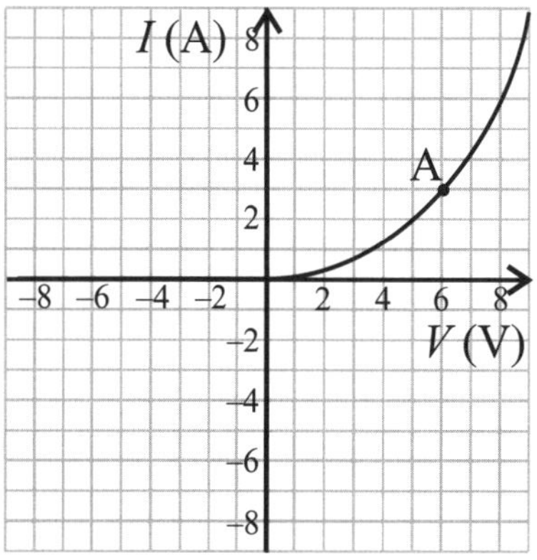

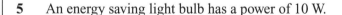

Figure 3

5   An energy saving light bulb has a power of 10 W.

    (a)   The light bulb has a potential difference across it of 120 V.
         Calculate the current through it.

[2]

    (b)   The light bulb is left on for three hours.
         Calculate the amount of energy transferred by the light bulb during this time.
         Give your answer in joules.

[3]

    (c)   Calculate the amount of charge transferred through the light bulb during the three hour period.

[2]

    (d)   The light bulb is connected to the mains supply.
         Describe the energy transfers that take place while the light bulb is switched on.
         Include references to the mains supply, the light bulb and the surroundings.

[2]

[Total 9 marks]

Supplement

Series Circuits

You'll need to make sure you know the rules for current and p.d. in series circuits.

Series Circuits — **All** or **Nothing**

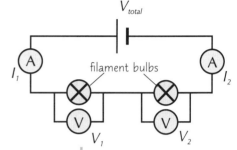

1) In series circuits, the different components are connected in a line, end to end, between the positive and negative ends of the power supply (except for voltmeters, which are always connected in parallel, but they don't count as part of the circuit).

2) For a series circuit:

> The current is the same everywhere. $I_1 = I_2$ etc. The size of the current depends on the total e.m.f. and the total resistance of the circuit ($I = V \div R$).

> The total resistance of the circuit increases as you add resistors.
> The total resistance of two components in a series circuit is just the sum of their resistances.

For the circuit diagram shown, calculate the total resistance.

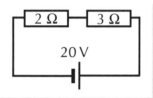

The resistors are in series, so add their resistances to find the total. $R_{total} = 2 + 3 = 5 \ \Omega$

Source E.M.F.s **Add Up**

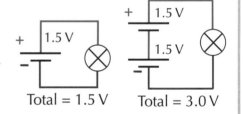

1) There is a bigger e.m.f. when more energy sources (such as cells) are in series, provided the cells are all connected the same way.

2) The e.m.f.s of cells connected in series are just added together — for example when two cells with an e.m.f. of 1.5 V are connected in series, they supply a total e.m.f. of 3 V.

The Source E.M.F. is **Shared**

Supplement

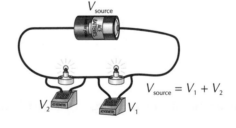

1) In series circuits, the e.m.f. of the supply is shared between the various components. So the potential differences round a series circuit always add up to the source e.m.f.:

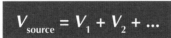

$$V_{source} = V_1 + V_2 + \ldots$$

See p.113 for how to work out the potential difference across each component.

See p.113 for how to work out the potential difference across each component.

2) Another way of looking at this is that the potential difference across all of the components is equal to the p.d.s of each component added together.

Supplement

Series circuits aren't used very much in the real world...

Since series circuits put all components on the same loop of wire, and the current is the same through each component, if one component breaks, it'll break the circuit, and all other components will stop working too. Parallel circuits are much more useful and can avoid this problem — as you're about to find out...

Parallel Circuits

Parallel circuits are a little bit trickier to understand than series circuits, but they're much more useful.

Parallel Circuits — Everything is Independent

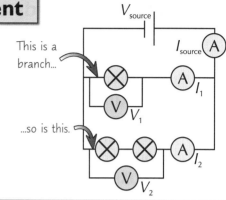

1) Parallel circuits are made up of multiple branches that have one or more components on them. Each branch is separately connected to the positive and negative ends of the supply.

This is a branch...

2) The advantages of parallel circuits are that you can switch things on and off separately, and if one part breaks, the other parts still work. This is why many things are connected this way, for example lamps in lighting circuits.

...so is this.

Three Important Facts About Parallel Circuits

1) The current from the source is larger than the current in each branch. So in the circuit above I_{source} is greater than I_1 and also greater than I_2.

2) The combined resistance of two resistors in parallel is lower than the individual resistance of either resistor. So in the circuit on the right, the combined resistance of the two resistors is less than 2 Ω.

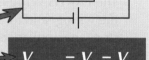

3) In parallel circuits all branches get the full source e.m.f., so the p.d. is the same across all branches. In the circuit above:

$$V_{source} = V_1 = V_2$$

Current is Shared Between Branches

1) In parallel circuits the current from the source is equal to the total of all the currents through the separate branches:

$$I_{source} = I_1 + I_2 + ...$$

2) In a parallel circuit, there are junctions where the current either splits or rejoins. The total current going into a junction has to equal the total current leaving it.

3) How current splits at a junction depends on the resistance of each branch. A greater proportion of the current goes down the branch with the lower resistance. For example:

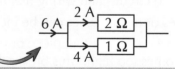

Combined Resistance can be Calculated with a Formula

This formula can be used to calculate the combined resistance of two resistors in parallel:

$$\frac{1}{R_{total}} = \frac{1}{R_1} + \frac{1}{R_2}$$

EXAMPLE:

For the circuit diagram shown, calculate the combined resistance of the two resistors.

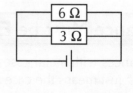

Substitute the resistances of the parallel resistors into the equation.

$$\frac{1}{R_{total}} = \frac{1}{R_1} + \frac{1}{R_2} = \frac{1}{3} + \frac{1}{6} = \frac{1}{2}$$

$$R_{total} = \frac{2}{1} = 2\ \Omega$$

Learn the difference between series and parallel circuits...

REVISION TIP

Make a table of rules for series and parallel circuits. Remember, current is the same through all components in series, but the p.d. across each can differ. For components in parallel it's the other way round — the p.d. across each branch is the same, but the current through each can differ.

Electrical Safety

Electricity can be dangerous, yet we use it every day — so it's important that we use it safely.

Learn these **Hazards** of **Electricity**

Electricity is hazardous. Avoiding the following makes it far less dangerous.

1) **DAMAGED WIRE INSULATION** — This can lead to the live wire being exposed. Touching the live wire leads to a current flowing through you, which could cause a deadly electric shock.

2) **OVERHEATING OF CABLES** — The larger the current, the thicker the cable you need to carry it. If you use wire that's too thin it can overheat and cause a fire.

3) **DAMP CONDITIONS** — Impure water conducts electricity, so wet or damp conditions can cause a current to flow outside wires, leading to a nasty electric shock.

4) **OVERLOADING** — Plugging too many appliances into one plug socket by using, for example, an extension lead with multiple sockets, can mean excess current flows which could cause a fire.

A **Mains** Circuit Consists of **Three Wires**

The wire that provides the alternating p.d. can also be called the line wire.

The **EARTH WIRE** is for protecting the wiring, and for safety — it stops the appliance casing from becoming live. It doesn't usually carry a current — only when there's a fault (see below). It's at 0 V.

(UK plug)

A **LIVE WIRE** provides the alternating potential difference (at about 230 V in the UK) from the mains supply. As the live wire provides the source of electricity, switches are connected to the live wire so the circuit can be switched off, making the appliance no longer live.

The **NEUTRAL WIRE** completes the circuit — when the appliance is operating normally, current flows through the live and neutral wires. It is around 0 V.

For more on alternating p.d., see p. 127.

A **Fuse** or **Trip Switch** Protects a Circuit

1) A fault in an electric appliance can cause a sudden increase in current. This is dangerous as it can lead to circuits and wiring melting or causing a fire. Faulty appliances can also cause deadly shocks.

2) Fuses or trip switches can be included in circuits to prevent these hazards.

3) A fuse contains a thin piece of wire that melts if the current through the fuse becomes too high. This breaks the circuit and stops a current from flowing.

4) The rating of the fuse determines how much current can flow before the fuse melts.

   - Fuses should be rated as near as possible to, but just higher than, the normal operating current.
   - For example, if you're choosing between fuses rated at 3 A, 5 A and 13 A for an appliance with an operating current of 4.3 A, then you should choose the 5 A fuse.

5) Trip switches are slightly different — they just open when the current is too large. Their setting is also chosen to be just higher than the normal operating current.

An Appliance Must be **Earthed** or **Double-Insulated** for **Safety**

1) All appliances with metal cases must be "earthed" to reduce the danger of electric shock. "Earthing" just means the case must be attached to the earth wire.

2) An earthed conductor can never become live. If a fault develops in which a live wire touches the metal case, a big current flows through the earth wire because it has a very low resistance.

3) This surge in current 'blows' (melts) the fuse (or turns off the trip switch), cutting off the live supply and making it impossible to get an electric shock from the case. It also stops circuits and wires melting.

4) When an appliance is double-insulated, it doesn't need to have an earth wire — this is because double-insulated appliances have a plastic casing (rather than metal) that can't become live. These appliances still have fuses, to protect their circuit and cabling from being damaged by a large current.

Potential Dividers

Series circuits might not make the best lighting circuits. But they do have their uses, as you're about to see...

Use a **Potential Divider** to get a **Fraction** of a **Source Voltage**

1) If the current through an electrical conductor remains constant, then the potential difference across it must increase if its resistance increases. It's on this principle that a potential divider works.

2) At its simplest, a potential divider is a circuit with an energy source and a couple of resistors in series.

3) The potential difference across the energy source (e.g. a battery) is split between the resistors in the ratio of their resistances. For example:

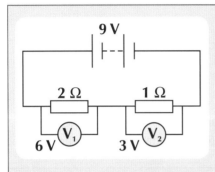

The 9 V p.d. across the source is shared between the resistors. The bigger the resistance the bigger its share of the p.d..

The total resistance of the two resistors is $2 + 1 = 3\ \Omega$.

The 2 Ω resistor has $\frac{2}{3}$ of the source p.d. across it.

$\frac{2}{3}$ of 9 V = **6 V**

The 1 Ω resistor has $\frac{1}{3}$ of the source p.d. across it.

$\frac{1}{3}$ of 9 V = **3 V**

4) There's an equation which links the two resistances, R_1 and R_2, with the potential differences across each of them.

$$\frac{R_1}{R_2} = \frac{V_1}{V_2}$$ — p.d. across R_1, p.d. across R_2

Use a **Variable Resistor** to Vary the **Potential Difference** Supplied

1) A potential divider can supply any potential difference between zero and the p.d. across the energy source. You just have to choose the correct resistors to split the p.d. in the way you want.

2) However, if you use a variable resistor you can easily change the potential difference supplied.

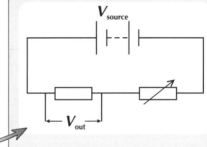

When the variable resistor is set to zero, the p.d. supplied, V_{out}, is equal to the p.d. across the source, V_{source}.

As you increase the resistance of the variable resistor, V_{out} gets smaller.

EXAMPLE:

A circuit consists of a 12 V power source, a fixed resistor of 3 Ω and a variable resistor, as shown below. The p.d. across the fixed resistor needs to be 7.5 V. What resistance should the variable resistor be set to?

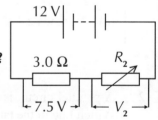

1) First calculate V_2. $V_{source} = V_1 + V_2 \Rightarrow V_2 = V_{source} - V_1$

$= 12 - 7.5 = 4.5$ V

2) Rearrange the equation above and substitute the values to find R_2. $\frac{R_1}{R_2} = \frac{V_1}{V_2} \Rightarrow R_2 = R_1 \div \frac{V_1}{V_2} = 3.0 \div (7.5 \div 4.5) = 1.8\ \Omega$

A **Variable Potential Divider** is A Special Circuit Component

1) A variable potential divider (sometimes called a potentiometer) has a single variable resistor replacing the two resistors of the potential divider, but it uses the same idea.

2) You move a slider or turn a knob to adjust the relative sizes of R_1 and R_2 in the diagram. That way you can vary V_{out} from 0 V up to the source potential difference, V_{source}.

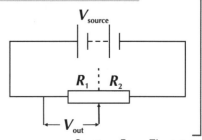

Supplement

Warm-Up & Exam Questions

Time to see if you've been paying close attention to the last four pages — have a go at these marvellous warm-up and exam questions. If you get any wrong, look back for a quick recap.

Warm-Up Questions

1) True or false? Current is the same everywhere in a series circuit.

2) Two cells are connected in series in a circuit.
   Describe how you calculate the combined e.m.f. of the cells.

3) Which has the higher total resistance: two resistors connected in series, or the same two resistors connected in parallel?

4) True or false? In a parallel circuit, the current from the source is less than the current in any branch of the circuit.

5) True or false? The total current entering a junction is equal to the total current leaving the junction.

6) Two fixed resistors are connected in series with a battery. One is a 10 Ω resistor and the other is a 2 Ω resistor. Which resistor will have the greater potential difference across it?

Exam Questions

1   **Figure 1** shows a series circuit.

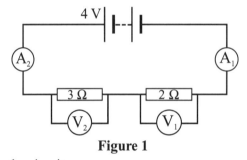

Figure 1

(a) Calculate the total resistance in the circuit.

[1]

(b) The reading on A_1 is 0.8 A. Give the reading on A_2. Explain your answer.

[2]

(c) V_2 reads 2.4 V. Calculate the reading on V_1.

[1]

[Total 4 marks]

2   A parallel circuit is connected as shown in **Figure 2**.
    Which line in the table describes the current from the source
    and the combined resistance of the two resistors?

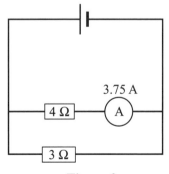

Figure 2

		Current from the source	Combined resistance
☐	**A**	Less than 3.75 A	Less than 3 Ω
☐	**B**	Less than 3.75 A	Greater than 4 Ω
☐	**C**	Greater than 3.75 A	Less than 3 Ω
☐	**D**	Greater than 3.75 A	Greater than 4 Ω

[Total 1 mark]

Exam Questions

3   A kettle is connected to the mains electricity supply.

The kettle develops a fault so that a live wire is in contact with the kettle's metal casing.

(a)   The kettle's metal casing is earthed.
Explain the benefit of earthing in this situation.

[2]

(b)   Some appliances are not earthed.
Describe what safety feature an appliance must have if it is not earthed.

[1]

(c)   When using the kettle, the user has to be wary of the hazards of damp conditions.
Explain why damp conditions could pose a danger to a person using the kettle.

[2]

[Total 5 marks]

4   A dishwasher uses 1800 W of power. It is connected to the 230 V mains electricity supply.

(a)   The dishwasher can be fitted with a 5 A or 8 A fuse.
Explain which fuse would be the best choice.

[3]

(b)   Give an alternative to using a fuse to isolate a faulty appliance.

[1]

[Total 4 marks]

Supplement

5   **Figure 3** shows a circuit with a fixed resistor and a variable resistor connected in series. The variable resistor is set to 200 Ω and the potential difference across it is 6 V. The fixed resistor has a resistance of 100 Ω.

Calculate the potential difference across the fixed resistor.

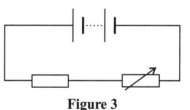

Figure 3

[Total 2 marks]

6   **Figure 4** shows a circuit in which two resistors are connected in parallel with a 12 V power source.

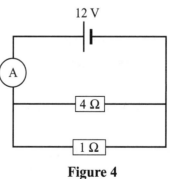

12 V

A

4 Ω

1 Ω

Figure 4

Calculate the reading on the ammeter shown in the circuit.

[Total 3 marks]

Supplement

Revision Summary

You've made it through Section 5 — now for some questions to test you on the whole section.
- Try these questions and tick off each one when you get it right.
- When you've done all the questions under a heading and are completely happy with it, tick it off.

Static Electricity and Fields (p.97-99) ☐

1) True or false? Two positive charges attract each other. ☐
2) How does the rubbing of materials cause static electricity to build up? ☐
3) Outline the difference between electrical conductors and electrical insulators. ☐
4) How can you test if a material is an electrical conductor or insulator? ☐
5) In which direction do the arrows on electric field lines point? ☐
6) Describe the electric field pattern around a negative point charge. ☐

Circuits, Current, Resistance, Energy and Power (p.101-107) ☐

7) Draw the circuit symbols for: a cell, a lamp, a fuse and an LDR. ☐
8) Name the particle that flows to produce an electric current in a metal. ☐
9) What is meant by e.m.f.? ☐
10) Define current and state an equation that links current, charge and time. State the units for each. ☐
11) What is meant by resistance in a circuit? ☐
12) What is the equation that links potential difference, current and resistance? ☐
13) Which has the greatest resistance: a short, fat piece of copper wire or a long, thin piece? ☐
14) How does the resistance of an LDR vary with light intensity? ☐
15) What happens to the resistance of a thermistor as it gets colder? ☐
16) Name a device used to measure current in a circuit and describe how to use it. ☐
17) Describe the current-voltage graph of a resistor of constant resistance. ☐
18) What equation links the energy transferred by a device, the current through it,
   the potential difference across it and the time it is switched on for? ☐
19) What is meant by a kilowatt-hour? ☐
20) How do you calculate the cost of using an appliance if you know the energy transferred
   by the appliance and the price of electricity per kWh? ☐

Series and Parallel Circuits and Safety (p.110-112) ☐

21) Explain what is meant by the terms 'series circuit' and 'parallel circuit'. ☐
22) True or false? The potential difference across each branch in a parallel circuit is different. ☐
23) State four hazards related to electricity. ☐
24) How does a fuse protect a circuit? ☐
25) The operating current of a device is 11.5 A. Should you use a 5 A or a 13 A fuse? ☐
26) True or false? A double-insulated appliance must have a fuse. ☐

Potential Dividers (p.113) ☐

27) True or false? A potential divider can supply a potential difference
   that is greater than the potential difference supplied by the source. ☐
28) Describe how a variable resistor and a fixed resistor can be used to
   make a potential divider that supplies a range of potential differences. ☐

Magnetism

I think magnetism is an attractive subject, but don't get repelled by the exam — revise.

Magnets Produce Magnetic Fields

1) All magnets have two poles — north (N) and south (S).

2) If two poles of a magnet are put near each other, they will exert a force on each other.
Two poles that are the same (like poles) experience a force of repulsion away from each other.
Two unlike (opposite) poles experience a force of attraction towards each other.

3) All magnets produce a magnetic field.

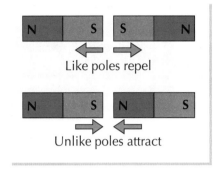
Like poles repel

Unlike poles attract

 KEY TERM A magnetic field is a region where a magnetic pole experiences a force acting on it.

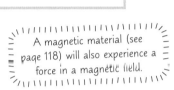 A magnetic material (see page 118) will also experience a force in a magnetic field.

4) You can show a magnetic field by drawing magnetic field lines.
The field lines of a bar magnet look like this:

5) The magnetic field (and its lines) always goes from the north pole to the south pole.

6) The direction of a magnetic field line at any point shows the direction of the force that would act on a north pole of a magnet placed at that point.

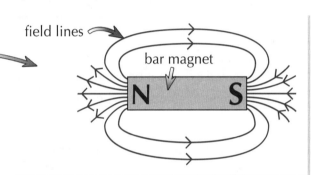
field lines

bar magnet

N   S

Magnetic Field Lines Also Show the Strength of the Field

1) The spacing of magnetic field lines tells you the relative strength of a magnetic field.

2) The magnetic field of a magnet is strongest near its poles.
At these points the field lines are closest together.

3) Magnetic field strength decreases with distance from a magnet. This is shown by field lines becoming increasingly spread out the further from a magnet you get.

4) Magnetic forces are caused by interactions between magnetic fields.

Attraction
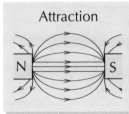
The force of attraction experienced by two unlike poles is caused by the two fields connecting.

Repulsion
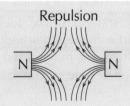
The force of repulsion experienced by two like poles near to each other is due to the two opposing fields diverging because they are unable to overlap.

Supplement

EXAM TIP ## A bar magnet's magnetic field lines go from north to south...

If you're asked to draw the field lines around a bar magnet, always draw a few above and below the magnet — and don't forget to draw the arrows on each field line to show the direction.

Induced Magnetism

Magnetic fields don't just affect magnets — they affect magnetic materials too.

Magnetic Materials are Attracted to Magnets

A magnetic material (e.g. iron, steel, nickel or cobalt) experiences a force in a magnetic field. The force between a magnet and a magnetic material is always attractive.

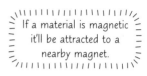
If a material is magnetic it'll be attracted to a nearby magnet.

Non-magnetic materials (e.g. plastic, rubber, glass and wood) don't experience a force in a magnetic field.

Magnetic Materials become Induced Magnets in Magnetic Fields

1) Permanent magnets (e.g. bar magnets) produce their own magnetic field all the time.

2) If you put any magnetic material into a magnetic field, it is magnetised and it becomes an induced magnet.

3) Induced magnets have their own poles and magnetic field.

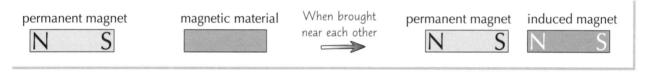

4) The south pole of the permanent magnet will always induce a north pole in the part of the magnetic material closest to it. And likewise, a north pole of a permanent magnet will induce a south pole. This explains why the force between a magnet and a magnetic material is always attractive.

5) Induced magnets only produce a magnetic field while they're in another magnetic field. When you take away the magnetic field, induced magnets will eventually lose their magnetism (they go back to being unmagnetised).

6) How easily an induced magnet gains and loses its magnetism depends on the material.

- Some magnetic materials can gain and lose their magnetism quickly — e.g. soft iron. These are called temporary magnets.
- Other magnetic materials, like steel, take longer to become magnetised and will keep their induced magnetism for longer. These materials can be magnetised so they keep their magnetism for a long period of time, and so become permanent magnets.

This is why soft iron is used in electromagnets (p.121) and transformers (p.128), rather than steel.

A magnetic field can magnetise a magnetic material...

There are lots of very similar terms on this page — magnet, magnetised, magnetic material, etc. Learn what each term means and when to use it, and then test yourself to make sure you know it.

Electromagnetism

Permanent and induced magnets aren't the only things that produce magnetic fields.
When an electric current flows it produces a magnetic field too.

A **Moving Charge** Creates a Magnetic Field

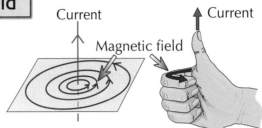

1) When a current flows through a conductor, a magnetic field is created around the conductor.

2) The magnetic field around a straight wire is made up of concentric circles perpendicular to the wire, with the wire in the centre.

3) The direction of the field is given by the right-hand thumb rule.

The Right-Hand Thumb Rule

Using your right hand, point your thumb in the direction of current and curl your fingers. The direction of your fingers is the direction of the field.

Supplement

- The closer you get to the current-carrying wire, the stronger the magnetic field is. This means that closer to the current-carrying wire, the magnetic field lines are closer together.
- Increasing the size (magnitude) of the current makes the magnetic field stronger.
- Changing the direction of the current changes the direction of the magnetic field — use the right-hand thumb rule to work out which way it goes.

Supplement

A **Solenoid** is a Coil of Wire

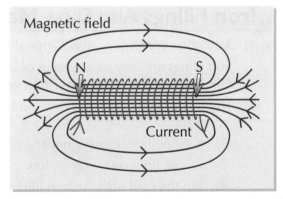

1) If you wrap a current-carrying wire into a coil, it is called a solenoid.

2) Inside a solenoid, the magnetic field lines around each loop of wire line up with each other. This results in lots of straight field lines pointing in the same direction.

3) Outside the solenoid, the magnetic field is just like the one round a bar magnet (p.117). This means one end of the solenoid has a north pole and the other end has a south pole.

Supplement

- Because the field lines around each loop of the solenoid line up, the magnetic field inside the solenoid is strong and uniform (the field lines are close together and parallel).
- Outside the solenoid, the magnetic field is strongest near the poles and decreases as you get further away from the solenoid, shown by the spacing of the field lines increasing.
- As with increasing the size of the current in a wire, increasing the current through a solenoid increases the magnetic field strength. Reversing the direction of the current causes the magnetic field direction to change — so the north and south pole switch positions.

Supplement

Just point your right thumb in the direction of the current...

...and your fingers show the direction of the field produced. Remember, use your right thumb not your left. If you're doing the Extended course you'll use your left hand on page 123, so it shouldn't feel left out...

Plotting Magnetic Fields

Although we can't see magnetic fields, there are ways to reveal what they look like — read on and find out...

Compasses Show the Direction of Magnetic Fields

Inside a compass is a tiny bar magnet (the needle). The north pole of this magnet is attracted to the south pole of any other magnet it is near. So the compass needle points in the direction of the magnetic field it is in.

You can do the experiment below to identify the pattern and direction of magnetic field lines around a bar magnet.

1) Put the magnet on a piece of card and draw round it.

2) Place the compass on the card near the magnet. The needle will point in the direction of the field line at this position.

3) Mark the direction of the compass needle by drawing two dots — one at each end of the needle.

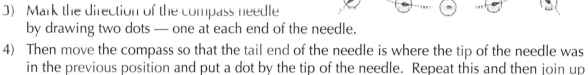

4) Then move the compass so that the tail end of the needle is where the tip of the needle was in the previous position and put a dot by the tip of the needle. Repeat this and then join up the marks you've made — you'll end up with a drawing of one field line around the magnet.

5) Repeat this method at different points around the magnet to get several field lines.

6) Make sure you draw arrows from north to south on your field lines.

You could also use multiple compasses at the same time, but you shouldn't put the compasses too close to each other. Compasses also produce magnetic fields — you need to make sure each compass is measuring the field of the magnet, not the compasses nearby.

Iron Filings Also Show Magnetic Fields

1) As well as compasses, iron filings align themselves with magnetic fields.

2) Iron filings are very small pieces of iron. Because iron is a magnetic material (see page 118), iron filings become very small magnets when placed in a magnetic field, so they act like compass needles.

3) This means you could also use iron filings to see magnetic field patterns.

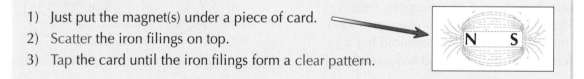

1) Just put the magnet(s) under a piece of card.
2) Scatter the iron filings on top.
3) Tap the card until the iron filings form a clear pattern.

Use the Same Methods for Wires and Solenoids

You can plot the magnetic field of a wire or solenoid in the same way as you can for a bar magnet. You'll just need to position a piece of card in the following way before you use a compass or iron filings:

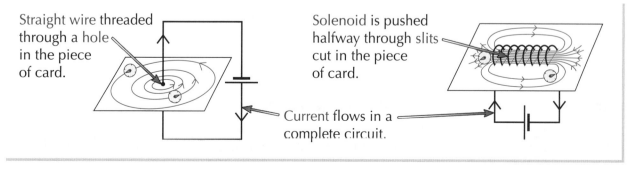

Straight wire threaded through a hole in the piece of card.

Solenoid is pushed halfway through slits cut in the piece of card.

Current flows in a complete circuit.

Electromagnets

Electric currents can create magnetic fields (see page 117). This means magnets that can be switched on and off can be made — these are electromagnets.

Electromagnets Are Made Using **Solenoids**

1) On p.119 you saw how a magnetic field is produced when a current flows through a solenoid.
2) When a block of soft iron is placed in the centre of the coil, the magnetic field strength of the solenoid is increased.
3) This happens because the soft iron is easily magnetised by the solenoid and becomes an induced magnet when the current flows. This adds to the overall magnetic effect.
4) If you switch off the current, the magnetic field disappears, because the soft iron is easily demagnetised.
5) This arrangement is an electromagnet.

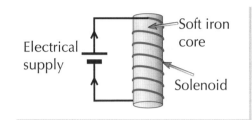

 An electromagnet is a solenoid with a soft iron core.

Electromagnets Have **Useful** Properties

One advantage of electromagnets is that you can switch them on and off quickly. They can also be made a lot stronger than permanent magnets, and you can vary their strength by changing the current.

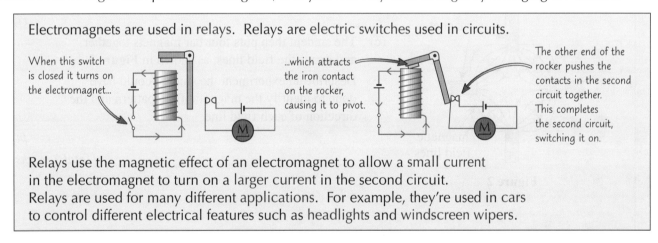

Electromagnets are used in relays. Relays are electric switches used in circuits.

When this switch is closed it turns on the electromagnet...

...which attracts the iron contact on the rocker, causing it to pivot.

The other end of the rocker pushes the contacts in the second circuit together. This completes the second circuit, switching it on.

Relays use the magnetic effect of an electromagnet to allow a small current in the electromagnet to turn on a larger current in the second circuit.
Relays are used for many different applications. For example, they're used in cars to control different electrical features such as headlights and windscreen wipers.

Permanent Magnets and **Electromagnets** are Used **Differently**

1) Permanent magnets always produce a magnetic field, so they don't need a current to work.
2) They have many uses, for example, they are used in generating electricity (p.127), and in encoding information in the magnetic strip of a credit card.
3) Whether a permanent magnet or an electromagnet is used depends on the situation. E.g. permanent magnets are used in fridge magnets — it isn't practical for them to have a current supply, and you don't need to be able to change the strength of the magnetic field or switch it off.

Electromagnets have lots of different uses...

Electromagnets pop up in lots of different places — e.g. they're used in electric bells, car ignition circuits and some security doors. They have the very handy ability to be switched on and off and to change strength.

Warm-Up & Exam Questions

It's time for another page of questions to check how much knowledge you've retained. See if you can do the warm-up questions without breaking into a sweat, then move on to the exam questions.

Warm-Up Questions

1) Define the term 'magnetic field'.
2) Draw a diagram to show the magnetic field around a single bar magnet.
3) Describe the pattern of the magnetic field around a straight current-carrying wire.
4) True or false? Reversing the direction of the current through a solenoid causes its magnetic poles to swap over.
5) Briefly explain how a relay makes use of an electromagnet.

Exam Questions

1   A student arranges two magnets as shown in **Figure 1**.

Figure 1

   (a)   State whether there will be a force of attraction, repulsion, or no force between the two magnets. Explain your answer.

[2]

   (b)   A magnetic south pole placed at a point in a magnetic field experiences a force. State the direction of this force relative to the direction of the magnetic field lines.

[1]

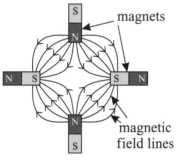

   (c)   The student then puts four bar magnets together and draws the field lines, as shown in **Figure 2**.

   Describe an experiment the student could have done to identify the magnetic field pattern and the direction of each field line.

[4]

[Total 7 marks]

Figure 2

2   An electromagnet is used by a crane to lift, move and drop iron and steel.

   (a)   The electromagnet contains a solenoid. State what is meant by a solenoid.

[1]

   (b)   Describe the shape of the magnetic field produced inside a solenoid.

[2]

   (c)   When a current is passed through the electromagnet, an iron bar on the ground nearby is attracted to it. When the current is stopped, the bar drops back to the ground. Explain why this happens.

[3]

   (d)   The crane's electromagnet contains a soft iron core. Explain why putting a steel core in the electromagnet would cause the crane to not work properly.

[2]

[Total 8 marks]

Force on a Current-Carrying Conductor

Passing an electric current through a wire produces a magnetic field around the wire (p.119).
If you put that wire into a magnetic field, the two fields interact and a force is exerted on the wire.

A **Current** in a **Magnetic Field** Experiences a **Force**

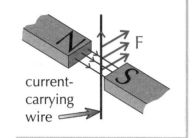

1) When a current-carrying wire (or any other conductor) is put in a magnetic field, the wire experiences a force. This can cause the wire to move and is called the motor effect.

2) To experience the full force, the wire has to be at 90° to the magnetic field. If the wire runs parallel to the magnetic field, it won't experience any force at all. At angles in between, it will experience some force.

current-carrying wire

3) The force always acts at right angles to the magnetic field of the magnets and the direction of the current in the wire.

> Reversing the direction of the current reverses the direction of the force.
> Reversing the direction of the magnetic field also causes the direction of the force to reverse.

Fleming's **Left-Hand Rule** tells you **Which Way** the Force Acts

Supplement

You can find the direction of the force with Fleming's left-hand rule.

thuMb
Motion

1) Using your left hand, point your **F**irst finger in the direction of the **F**ield.

First finger
Field

2) Point your se**C**ond finger in the direction of the **C**urrent.

3) Your thu**M**b will then point in the direction of the force (**M**otion).

seCond finger
Current

> Your fingers need to be at 90° to each other, like in this diagram.

Fleming's left-hand rule shows that if either the current or the magnetic field is reversed, then the direction of the force will also be reversed. This rule can be used to find the direction of the force in all sorts of things — like motors, as shown on page 125.

EXAMPLE:

On the diagram on the right, show the direction of the force acting on the wire.

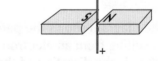

1) Draw in a current arrow (use conventional current, i.e. positive to negative)

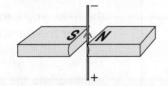

2) Use Fleming's left-hand rule.

seCond finger
Current

First finger
Field

thuMb
Motion

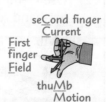

3) Draw in the direction of the force (motion).

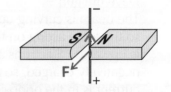

Supplement

Loudspeakers Work Because of the **Motor Effect**

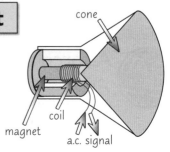

cone

1) The a.c. electrical signals (p.127) from an amplifier are fed to a coil of wire in the speaker, which is wrapped around the base of a cone.

2) The alternating current produces a changing magnetic field around the coil. Because the coil is surrounded by a permanent magnet, it experiences a changing force that causes it to move back and forth.

coil

magnet

a.c. signal

3) These movements make the cone vibrate and this creates sounds.

Force on a Current-Carrying Conductor

You can't see magnetic fields, but you can see the effects of forces they exert on current-carrying conductors.

You Can Show the **Direction** of the **Force** with an **Experiment**

A good way of showing the direction of the force acting on a current-carrying conductor in a magnetic field is to use a horseshoe magnet and a freely moving bar.

1) A set of rails are put inside a horseshoe magnet and a bar is placed on the rails. The rails and the bar are conductors and form a complete circuit.

2) When a current flows through this circuit, a force is produced that causes the bar to roll along the rails.

3) The magnitude (strength) of the force increases with the strength of the magnetic field.

4) The force also increases with the amount of current passing through the conductor.

5) Reversing the direction of either the current **or** the field causes the bar to roll in the opposite direction.

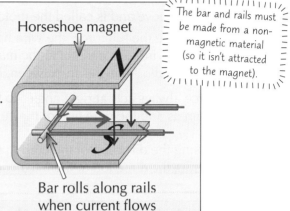

Horseshoe magnet

The bar and rails must be made from a non-magnetic material (so it isn't attracted to the magnet).

Bar rolls along rails when current flows

A **Force** Also Acts on a **Beam** of **Charged Particles** in a **Field**

1) A current is basically a flow of charged particles (p.102). So a charged particle passing through a magnetic field experiences a force just like a current-carrying conductor in a magnetic field does.

2) This means that you can also use Fleming's left hand rule for a beam of particles moving in a magnetic field. The tricky part is knowing in which direction to point your second finger.

3) Conventional current flows from positive to negative (see p.101). So for a beam of positively charged particles, current is in the same direction as their movement, so point your second finger in the direction that they're initially moving. For a beam of negatively charged particles, current is in the opposite direction to their movement, so point your second finger in the opposite direction to their initial movement.

EXAMPLE:

The diagram shows the path of a beam of electrons travelling from an electron gun into a magnetic field. What is the direction of the magnetic field?

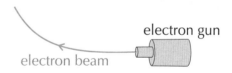

electron gun

electron beam

1) <u>As the electrons leave the gun:</u>
The beam is curving upwards so the force acting on them is upwards. Electrons are negatively charged, so the current is in the opposite direction to their movement.

2) Use Fleming's left-hand rule.

thu<u>M</u>b <u>M</u>otion

<u>F</u>irst finger <u>F</u>ield

se<u>C</u>ond finger <u>C</u>urrent

3) Now you know the direction of the field, you can answer the question.

The magnetic field is pointing into the page.

A force always acts on a current...

... which is a flow of charged particles. And if the current is flowing through something that can move (like a wire or a bar) the force will make it move. If you're doing the Extended course, don't be scared to use the left-hand rule in the exam. You might look a bit silly, but it makes getting those marks so much easier. So learn what each finger and thumb direction represents.

Electric Motors

Electric motors use the motor effect (see pages 123-124) to get them moving (and to keep them moving).

A Current-Carrying **Coil** of Wire **Rotates** in a Magnetic Field

A current-carrying conductor in a magnetic field experiences a force (p.123). If you twist a current-carrying wire into a coil and put it into a magnetic field, the forces cause a turning effect.

The turning effect on the coil is increased by:
1) Increasing the current in the coil
2) Increasing the number of turns on the coil
3) Increasing the strength of the magnetic field

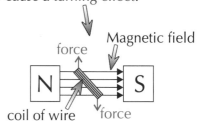

A **D.C. Motor** Uses This Effect

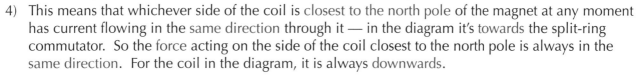
Direct current (d.c.) is current that only flows in one direction (p.127)

1) A d.c. motor is made from a coil of wire in a magnetic field. When a direct current (d.c.) is turned on in the coil, forces act on the two side arms of the coil.

2) Because one force acts upwards and one force acts downwards, the coil rotates on its axis.

3) The split-ring commutator is attached to the coil and rotates with it. The split-ring commutator stays connected with the d.c. circuit through a pair of conductive brushes. Because the coil is turning, it swaps which sides of the commutator are touching which brushes every half turn, which swaps the direction of the current through the coil every half-turn.

4) This means that whichever side of the coil is closest to the north pole of the magnet at any moment has current flowing in the same direction through it — in the diagram it's towards the split-ring commutator. So the force acting on the side of the coil closest to the north pole is always in the same direction. For the coil in the diagram, it is always downwards.

5) The force on the side of the coil closest to the south pole is always in the opposite direction, so the motor keeps rotating in the same direction.

6) The direction of the motor can be reversed either by reversing the direction of the current through the coil or swapping the magnetic poles over.

7) You can use Fleming's left-hand rule to work out which way the coil will turn:

EXAMPLE:

Is the coil turning clockwise or anticlockwise?

1) Draw in current arrows (positive to negative).

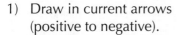

2) Use Fleming's left-hand rule on one branch (below shows it used on the right-hand branch).

seCond finger Current
First finger Field
thuMb Motion

3) Draw in direction of force (motion) and answer the question.

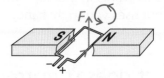

The coil is turning anticlockwise.

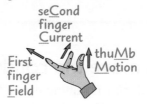

Supplement

Electromagnetic Induction

Electromagnetic induction — sounds scary, but read this page carefully and it shouldn't be too complicated.

A **Changing** Magnetic Field Induces an **E.m.f.** in a **Conductor**

> Electromagnetic induction is the creation of an e.m.f. (and a current if there's a complete circuit) in a conductor which is experiencing a change in a magnetic field or which is moving relative to a magnetic field.

1) There are two different situations in which electromagnetic induction happens.

2) The first is if an electrical conductor and a magnetic field move relative to each other:

Voltmeter

- You can induce an e.m.f. in a straight wire by placing it next to a magnet and then moving either the wire or the magnet — the wire 'cuts through' the magnetic field lines.
- Alternatively, you can push a magnet into a coil of wire.
- Connecting a voltmeter across the ends of the wire or the coil allows you to see the magnitude and direction of the induced e.m.f..
- If you reverse the movement of the conductor or magnet — e.g. pull the magnet out of the coil — the direction of the e.m.f. will be reversed. Likewise if the polarity of the magnet is reversed (by turning the magnet around), then the direction of the e.m.f. will be reversed too.

3) The second situation is when the magnetic field through an electrical conductor changes (gets bigger or smaller or reverses). This is what happens in a transformer (p.128).

4) You can increase the magnitude (size) of the induced e.m.f. by:
- Increasing the STRENGTH of the magnetic field.
- Increase the SPEED of movement of the conductor (or magnet), or the SPEED at which the magnetic field is changing.
- Using a coil of wire that has MORE TURNS PER UNIT LENGTH.

> You can also say that a potential difference or voltage is induced, instead of e.m.f. (since they're the same thing — see p.102).

Supplement

An Induced E.m.f. **Opposes** the Change that Made It

1) A change in magnetic field can induce a current in a wire. But, as you saw on page 119, when a current flows through a wire, a magnetic field is created around the wire. (That's a second magnetic field — different to the one whose field lines were being cut in the first place.)

2) The direction of the magnetic field created by an induced current is always such that it acts against the change that made it (whether that's the movement of a wire or a change in the field it's in). Basically, it's trying to return things to the way they were.

> If a current flows in the diagram above, then as the magnet is being pushed into the coil, the right-hand end of the coil becomes a south pole so that it repels the magnet (and so opposes the change).

3) For the magnetic field to be in this direction, the induced current must be in a certain direction, and so must the induced e.m.f. that created it.

4) If the conductor isn't part of a complete circuit, a current won't be induced. However, the e.m.f. that is induced is in the direction that would create a current with an opposing field.

You can work out the direction of the induced current in a wire moving through a magnetic field by using Fleming's right-hand rule. This works in the same way as Fleming's left-hand rule (p.123) but uses your right hand.

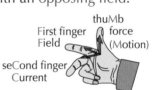
thuMb force (Motion)
First finger Field
seCond finger Current

Supplement

It doesn't matter if you move the conductor or the magnet...

The important thing is that the conductor is cutting through the field lines. Also important are the factors that cause the direction or size of the induced e.m.f. and current to change, so learn them.

Generators

Power stations use a.c. generators to produce electricity — it's just a matter of turning a coil in a magnetic field.

Current Can Be **Alternating** or **Direct**

Alternating current (a.c.) is a current that constantly changes direction.

Direct current (d.c.) is a current that always flows in the same direction.

1) Alternating current flows back and forth around a circuit — it reverses its direction many times each second. It is produced by an alternating potential difference in which the positive and negative keep switching.

The mains electricity supply in most countries is a.c..

2) Direct current is created by a direct potential difference. Cells and batteries supply d.c..

A.C. Generators — Just Turn the **Coil** and There's a Current

A generator is a coil in a magnetic field. It requires a force to be applied to turn the coil, which induces a current. (This is different to a motor (p.125), which uses a flow of current to generate forces which produce a turning effect.)

In some generators, a magnet is rotated inside a coil instead

Here's how it works:

1) An applied force causes a coil to rotate about an axis.

2) As the coil spins, it cuts through the magnetic field lines. This induces a potential difference (e.m.f.) between the ends of the coil. As the coil is part of a circuit, a current flows.

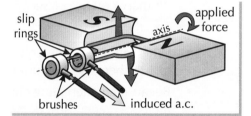

3) Slip rings and brushes are used so that the contacts don't swap every half turn of the coil (like they do in a motor).

4) A slip ring is attached to each end of the coil and rotates with it. Each slip ring is in continuous contact with a brush, which doesn't rotate with the coil and is connected to the rest of the circuit.

5) The slip rings and brushes mean that the current changes direction every half turn, so it is a.c..

The **Voltage Output** of A.C. Varies with **Time**

The voltage output (or e.m.f) against time for an a.c. generator is shown below. The position of the coil that corresponds to each point marked on the graph is also shown.

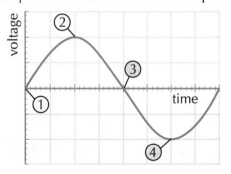
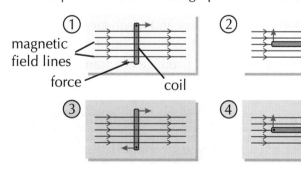

- The voltage output is greatest when the coil is parallel to the field lines because it is cutting through the field lines at the fastest rate. The greatest voltage output is at points 2 and 4.

- Point 2 is a positive maximum and point 4 a negative maximum. Between these points the coil has rotated through 180°, so the side that was cutting upwards through the field lines is now cutting downwards through them.

- The voltage output is zero when the coil is perpendicular to the field lines (at points 1 and 3). This is because the coil is not cutting through field lines at this position — it's moving along them.

Transformers

Transformers only work with an alternating current. Try using a d.c. battery and you'll get nowhere.

Transformers Change the Voltage of Alternating Currents

1) Transformers are used to change the size of the voltage of an alternating electricity supply.
2) They consist of two coils wound around a core made from soft iron.
3) An input voltage is applied across a primary coil. This produces an output voltage across a secondary coil.

> There is no electrical connection between the primary and secondary coils.

4) If the second coil is part of a complete circuit, this causes a current to be induced.
5) There are two types of transformer, step-up and step-down:

Step-up transformers increase the voltage. They have more turns on the secondary coil than the primary coil.

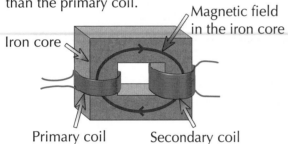

Step-down transformers decrease the voltage. They have more turns on the primary coil than the secondary coil.

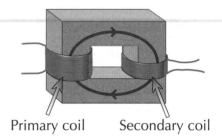

Supplement

- When an alternating voltage is applied across the primary coil, it creates an electromagnet (p.121) because the current that flows in the coil induces a magnetic field in the iron core.
- Because an alternating current is used and the core is made from soft iron, the core magnetises, demagnetises and remagnetises in the opposite direction quickly (p.118), so the magnetic field is constantly changing.
- The secondary coil is also wrapped around the core, so the changing magnetic field is in the secondary coil as well, which induces an alternating voltage in the secondary coil.
- The input has to be an alternating current because the magnetic field has to be changing in order to induce a voltage in the secondary coil (p.126).

Supplement

The Transformer Equation — Use it Either Way Up

1) The ratio between the primary and secondary voltages is the same as the ratio between the number of turns on the primary and secondary coils.
2) You can calculate the output voltage of a transformer from the input voltage and the number of turns on each coil.

$$\frac{\text{input (primary) voltage}}{\text{output (secondary) voltage}} = \frac{\text{number of turns on primary coil}}{\text{number of turns on secondary coil}} \qquad \frac{V_p}{V_s} = \frac{N_p}{N_s}$$

3) This equation can be used either way up — so $\frac{V_s}{V_p} = \frac{N_s}{N_p}$ works just as well.

Step-up transformers increase the voltage...

If you're struggling to remember the difference between step-up and step-down transformers, think about what's changing from the primary coil (input) to the secondary coil (output). If the number of turns is increasing, the voltage will also increase across the transformer — both things have been 'stepped up' (increased), so it's a step-up transformer.

Transmitting Electricity

Transformers are used to change the voltage of electricity produced in power stations.

Electricity is Transmitted at a High Voltage

1) Electricity needs to be transmitted from power stations to consumers (people using the electricity) all around a country. It is usually transmitted in power cables supported by pylons.

2) The huge amounts of power are transmitted at a very high voltage.

3) To get the electricity to this voltage, step-up transformers are used between power stations and the transmission cables.

4) The voltage is then decreased to safe, usable levels once the electricity has reached consumers. For this, step-down transformers are used.

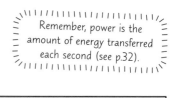
Remember, power is the amount of energy transferred each second (see p.32).

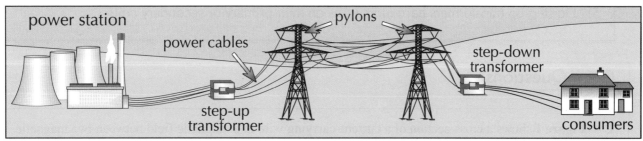

5) As the voltage is stepped up, the power remains at the same high level but the current decreases because $P = IV$ (see p.106).

6) Transmitting electricity with a low current reduces the power losses in the cables, making high voltage transmission the most efficient and cheap way of transferring electricity.

7) This equation linking power loss from a wire (P), current (I) and resistance (R) shows that the higher the current in a wire is, the greater the power loss from the wire will be. This is because high currents would cause the wires to heat up, resulting in lots of energy being lost to the surroundings as thermal energy. $P = I^2R$

There Are Almost No Power Losses in Transformers

1) Transformers are almost 100% efficient. This means you can assume that the input power is equal to the output power.

2) Power is given by $P = IV$ (see p.106) So input power = output power can also be written as:

primary voltage   secondary current

primary current 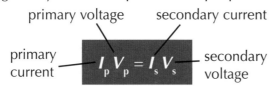 secondary voltage

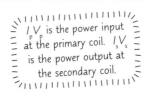
I_pV_p is the power input at the primary coil. I_sV_s is the power output at the secondary coil.

 A transformer has a potential difference of 15 V and a current of 10 A in its secondary coil. The current in the transformer's primary coil is 25 A. Assuming the transformer is 100% efficient, calculate the potential difference across the transformer's primary coil.

1) Substitute the values into the $I_pV_p = I_sV_s$.
$I_pV_p = I_sV_s$
$25 \times V_p = 10 \times 15$

2) Then rearrange for V_p.
$V_p = (10 \times 15) \div 25 = 6$ V

Electricity transmission — it's a powerful thing...

Electricity is transmitted at a high voltage to reduce energy losses by heating. The high voltage is achieved using a step-up transformer. However, such high voltages are very dangerous, so the voltage is decreased again (using a step-down transformer) before the electricity gets to the consumers.

Warm-Up & Exam Questions

There were lots of new ideas in that section, including one or two new equations. Have a go at these questions so you can really see what you've learned and what you might need to go over again.

Warm-Up Questions

1) In Fleming's left-hand rule, what's represented by the first finger, the second finger and the thumb?

2) Briefly describe an experiment to show that a force acts on a current-carrying conductor in a magnetic field.

3) What is meant by electromagnetic induction?

4) True or false? An a.c. generator uses a split-ring commutator.

5) Do step-up transformers have more turns on their primary or secondary coil?

Exam Questions

1   **Figure 1** shows a cross-section of a current-carrying wire in a magnetic field between two magnetic poles, X and Y. The circle represents the wire carrying current out of the page, towards you. The force acting on the wire is shown by an arrow.

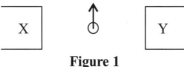

Figure 1

(a) For each of X and Y, state whether it is a north or south pole.

[1]

(b) Describe what would happen to the force acting on the current-carrying wire if the direction of the current was reversed.

[1]

(c) The wire is twisted into a coil as shown in **Figure 2**. As a current is passed through the coil, the coil rotates around an axis. State **two** ways the turning effect could be increased.

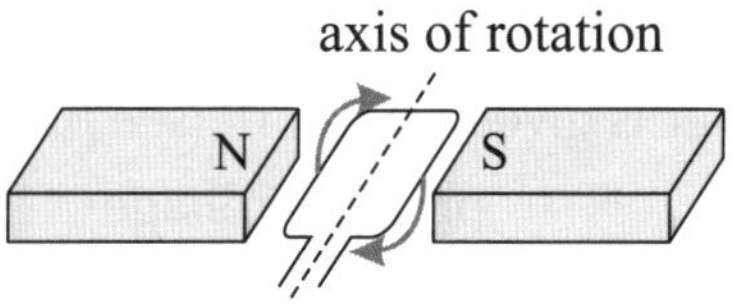

Figure 2

[2]

[Total 4 marks]

2   A beam of positive ions is fired into a magnetic field, as shown in **Figure 3**. The magnetic field lines are shown pointing out of the page. In which direction will a force act on the beam of particles as it enters the magnetic field?

⊙   ⊙   ⊙   ⊙

→
beam of
particles

⊙   ⊙   ⊙   ⊙

⊙   ⊙   ⊙   ⊙   magnetic field lines

Figure 3

[Total 1 mark]

Exam Questions

3   **Figure 4** shows a coil of wire connected to a voltmeter.
A student moves a bar magnet into the coil as shown.
The pointer on the voltmeter moves to the left.

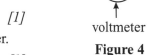

Figure 4

   (a)   Explain why the pointer moves.

[1]

   (b)   Suggest how the student could get the voltmeter's
pointer to move to the right.

[1]

   (c)   State how he could get a larger reading on the voltmeter.

[1]

   (d)   State what reading the voltmeter will show if the student holds the magnet still inside the coil.

[1]

[Total 4 marks]

4   Transformers are used in electricity distribution to change the voltage of the power supply.

   (a)   Describe how step-up and step-down transformers are used in the transmission
of electricity from power stations to consumers.

[2]

   (b)   Explain why transmitting electricity is more efficient when it is transmitted at a higher voltage.
Include equations to support your answer.

[3]

A student is testing a transformer. She connects a power source which applies a potential difference
of 12 V across the primary coil. The potential difference across the secondary coil is 4.0 V.

   (c)   The primary coil has 15 turns. Determine how many turns there must be on the secondary coil.

[2]

   (d)   A current of 2.5 A flows through the primary coil. Calculate the current in the secondary coil.

[2]

[Total 9 marks]

5   A student is investigating a simple a.c. generator.
In the a.c. generator, there is a loop of wire in a
magnetic field that is rotated about an axis,
as shown in **Figure 5**.

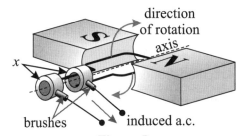

Figure 5

   (a)   (i)   Name the components of the
a.c. generator labelled with an *x*.

[1]

       (ii)   Explain the purpose of the components labelled *x*.

[1]

   (b)   **Figure 6** shows voltage output against time for the generator.
State what position the coil is in at 10 ms. Explain your reasoning.

[3]

[Total 5 marks]

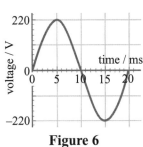

Figure 6

Revision Summary

Congratulations — you've battled to the end of Section 6. Now see how much you've really learnt.
- Try these questions and tick off each one when you get it right.
- When you've done all the questions for a topic and are completely happy with it, tick off the topic.

Magnetism, Induced Magnetism and Electromagnetism (p.117-121) ☐

1) In which direction do magnetic field lines point? ☐
2) How does the spacing between magnetic field lines relate to the strength of the magnetic field? ☐
3) What is the difference between a magnetic material and a non-magnetic material? ☐
4) True or false? The force between a magnet and a magnetic material is always repulsive. ☐
5) Describe how temporary magnets and permanent magnets are different. ☐
6) Which rule can be used to find the direction of the magnetic field around a current-carrying wire? ☐
7) Draw the magnetic field around a solenoid. ☐
8) Describe an experiment you could do to determine the shape
   of the magnetic field around a straight current-carrying wire. ☐
9) What is an electromagnet? ☐
10) Give one example of a use for electromagnets and one example of a use for permanent magnets. ☐

Forces on Current-Carrying Conductors and Motors (p.123-125) ☐

11) A current-carrying wire in a magnetic field experiences a force.
    What happens to the direction of this force if the direction of the magnetic field is reversed? ☐
12) When using Fleming's left hand rule for a beam of negatively charged particles
    entering a magnetic field, in which direction should you point your second finger? ☐
13) Explain how a basic d.c. motor works. ☐
14) Which rule is used to determine the direction of rotation of the coil in a d.c. motor? ☐

Electromagnetic Induction and Generators (p.126-127) ☐

15) Briefly describe how an e.m.f. can be induced using a coil of wire and a magnet. ☐
16) Give three factors you could change to increase the size of an induced e.m.f.. ☐
17) True or false? Induced currents create magnetic fields that oppose the change that made them. ☐
18) What is Fleming's right-hand rule used for? ☐
19) What is the difference between a.c. and d.c.? ☐
20) Sketch a labelled diagram of an a.c. generator and briefly explain how it works. ☐
21) What is the position of the coil in a rotating coil generator when the maximum e.m.f. is induced? ☐

Transformers (p.128-129) ☐

22) Describe how a basic transformer is constructed. ☐
23) What is the core of a transformer made from? ☐
24) True or false? Step-down transformers have more
    turns on their primary coil than on their secondary coil. ☐
25) A transformer has an input potential difference of 100 V and
    an output potential difference of 20 V. What kind of transformer is it? ☐
26) State whether electricity is transmitted across countries at high or low voltage. Explain why. ☐
27) Write down the equation that relates the input and output currents and voltages of transformers.
    What assumption is made when using this equation? ☐

The Atomic Model

Atoms are made up of a positive nucleus, negative electrons and a lot of empty space.

The **Nuclear Model** of the **Atom**

It is called 'nuclear' as it contains a nucleus.

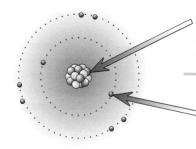

The nucleus is tiny but it makes up most of the mass of the atom. It contains protons and neutrons. Protons are positively charged and neutrons are neutral. This gives the nucleus an overall positive charge.

The rest of the atom is mostly empty space. Negative electrons orbit the nucleus at set distances.

Each type of particle has a different charge:

Particle	Actual Charge (C)	Relative Charge
Proton	1.6×10^{-19}	+1
Neutron	0	0
Electron	-1.6×10^{-19}	−1

The actual charge on each atom is measured in coulombs (C). Relative charge doesn't have a unit.

There are always the same number of protons and electrons in an atom. Protons and electrons have equal but opposite charges, so overall the atom is neutral.

Alpha Scattering Provides **Evidence** for the **Nuclear Model**

When a beam of alpha particles (see p.135) is fired at a thin sheet of metal foil:

- Most of the alpha particles go straight through the sheet. They are undeflected.

- A tiny amount of alpha particles are scattered by the sheet — a few are even deflected back the way they came.

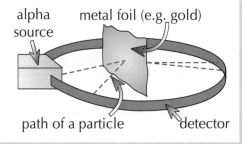

These results show that the metal atoms in the foil are mostly empty space, with a tiny region where positive charge and most of the mass is concentrated (the nucleus):

1) Alpha particles are positively charged, so the few that rebound from the foil must be repelled by another positive charge.

2) The observation that most alpha particles carry straight on shows that the metal atoms must be mostly empty space. The majority of alpha particles don't travel close enough to the positive charge to be repelled by it — it must be concentrated in a small part of the atom.

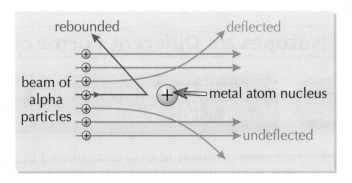

3) Most of the mass must be in the nucleus, since the alpha particles, which have a relatively high mass and momentum, are deflected by the stationary nucleus.

Only a tiny amount of alpha particles are actually scattered...

Before this alpha scattering experiment, the atom was believed to be a sphere of positive charge with tiny negative electrons stuck in it. This experiment showed that this model was wrong. The nuclear model of the atom matched the evidence, so it was adopted instead. That's how science works.

Atoms and Isotopes

Isotopes of the same element have different numbers of neutrons.

Atoms of the Same Element have the Same Number of Protons

1) An element is a substance whose atoms all have the same number of protons (but they can have different numbers of neutrons — see below).

The PROTON NUMBER (or atomic number) is the number of protons in an atom's nucleus.

So the number of neutrons is the nucleon number minus the proton number.

The NUCLEON NUMBER (or mass number) is the number of protons + the number of neutrons in an atom's nucleus.

A NUCLIDE is an atom with a particular number of protons and neutrons.

2) The number of protons and neutrons in a nuclide can be shown using nuclide notation:

A is the nucleon number → $^{A}_{Z}X$ ← *X — the element symbol*
Z is the proton number

Example: Nucleon number → $^{16}_{8}O$ ← Element (oxygen atom)
Proton number →

- This oxygen nuclide has a proton number of 8 ($Z = 8$). ← *All oxygen nuclides have 8 protons.*
- It has a nucleon number of 16 ($A = 16$). Since it has 8 protons, it must have $16 - 8 = 8$ neutrons.

You Can Find Relative Mass and Charge on a Nucleus

1) The relative mass of a nucleus depends on how many protons and neutrons it contains.

2) The mass of a proton and a neutron is pretty much the same, so the relative mass of a nucleus is just equal to the nucleon number (or mass number).

3) The relative charge of a nucleus only depends on the number of protons — neutrons are neutral.

4) The relative charge of a proton is +1, so the relative charge on a nucleus is equal to the proton number.

Isotopes are Different Forms of the Same Element

Isotopes of an element are atoms with the same number of protons (same proton number) but a different number of neutrons (different nucleon number).

1) For example, carbon-12 ($^{12}_{6}C$) and carbon-13 ($^{13}_{6}C$) are isotopes because they both have the same proton number but a different nucleon number (carbon-13 has one more neutron).

2) An element can have more than one isotope, but there are usually only one or two stable ones.

3) Unstable isotopes are isotopes that tend to decay into other elements and give out ionising radiation as they try to become more stable. These isotopes are radioactive (see next page).

4) Ionising radiation is radiation that can remove electrons from atoms that it hits, turning them into ions.

Ions are atoms (or molecules) that have lost or gained electrons, giving them an overall charge. Positive ions have lost electrons and negative ions have gained electrons.

Radioactive Emissions

There are three types of radioactive emission you need to know about — alpha, beta and gamma.

Alpha, Beta and Gamma Emissions are all Very Different

KEY TERM — Radioactive decay is the process in which unstable nuclei change to become more stable by emitting ionising radiation.

1) Radioactive substances emit one or more types of ionising radiation from their nucleus — the ones you need to know are alpha, beta and gamma radiation.

Alpha, beta and gamma radiation are also called radioactive emissions.

2) An alpha particle (α) consists of two neutrons and two protons (the same as a helium nucleus). It has a relative charge of +2 and a large mass compared to beta particles and gamma rays.

3) A beta particle (β) is a fast-moving electron. It has a relative charge of –1 and virtually no mass.

4) Gamma rays (γ) are waves of electromagnetic radiation (p.87). They have a relative charge of 0 and no mass.

These are sometimes written like this: α-particles, β-particles and γ-rays.

Each Emission has a Different Relative Penetrating and Ionising Power

1) The stronger the penetrating power, the further the emission can travel into a material before being absorbed.

2) The stronger the ionising power, the more likely the emission is to remove electrons from atoms it collides with.

Emission	Penetrating Power	Ionising Power
Alpha	Poor	Strong
Beta	Moderate	Moderate
Gamma	Strong	Weak

Supplement

3) The ionising power depends on the energy of the emission and its electric charge.

- The more energy in the kinetic energy store of an emission, the more energy it can transfer to the kinetic energy store of the atom it collides with. This makes it more likely to ionise that atom.

- The more electric charge an emission has, the more strongly it will repel or attract the electrons in the atom. This means it's more likely to 'rip out' electrons from the atom.

4) Alpha particles are more ionising than beta particles. Although alpha particles are slow, they have much more mass than beta particles and so have much more energy in their kinetic energy store. They also have more charge (+2, compared to –1).

5) Gamma rays are least ionising — they have no mass and no charge, so they tend to pass through atoms (rather than collide with them).

Lead Absorbs All Types of Radioactive Emissions

1) Alpha particles only travel a few cm in air and are absorbed by a sheet of paper.

2) Beta particles travel a few metres in air and are absorbed by thin aluminium (around 5 mm thick).

3) Gamma rays travel a long distance through air and are only absorbed by thick sheets of lead or metres of concrete.

Alpha would also be absorbed by aluminium and lead. Beta would also be absorbed by lead.

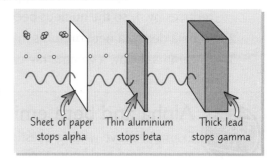

Sheet of paper stops alpha   Thin aluminium stops beta   Thick lead stops gamma

Radioactive Decay Equations

Radioactive decay can affect the composition of a nucleus.

An **Alpha** or **Beta Decay** Will **Produce** a **New Element**

1) When a nucleus emits either an alpha or beta particle, it changes from one element to another.
2) This is because the number of protons in the nucleus changes (see below).
3) When gamma decay occurs in a nucleus, there is no change to the number of protons, so the type of element doesn't change.

Alpha Decay — Number of **Protons** and **Neutrons Decreases**

1) Alpha particles are made up of two protons and two neutrons. So when a nucleus emits an alpha particle, its proton number decreases by 2 and its nucleon number decreases by 4.
2) Nuclear equations are a way of showing radioactive decay by using nuclide notation (see p.134). They're written in the form: atom before decay → atom(s) after decay + emission(s).
3) There is one golden rule to remember: the proton and nucleon numbers must be equal on both sides.
4) In nuclear equations, an alpha particle can be written as $^4_2\alpha$ or $^4_2$He (a helium nucleus).

Here's an example of an alpha decay equation:

$$^{238}_{92}U \rightarrow {}^{234}_{90}Th + {}^4_2\alpha$$

Check the nucleon and proton numbers:
$238 \rightarrow 234 + 4$
$92 \rightarrow 90 + 2$

Beta Decay — Number of Protons **Increases by One**

1) When a nucleus emits a beta particle, a neutron in the nucleus turns into a proton.
2) This means the number of protons in the nucleus (the proton number) increases by 1.
3) Because the nucleus has lost a neutron and gained a proton, the nucleon number doesn't change.
4) In nuclear equations, a beta particle can be written as $^0_{-1}\beta$ or $^0_{-1}$e (an electron).

Here's an example of a beta decay equation:

$$^{14}_6C \rightarrow {}^{14}_7N + {}^0_{-1}\beta$$

$14 \rightarrow 14 + 0$
$6 \rightarrow 7 + (-1)$

Gamma decay doesn't change the proton number or nucleon number. In nuclear equations, gamma rays are written as $^0_0\gamma$.

Nuclei Decay to become **More Stable**

Isotopes can be unstable if they have too much energy, have too many neutrons in the nucleus, or are too heavy overall. Decaying makes the nucleus more stable:

1) During alpha decay, the total number of nucleons reduces by 4, so the nucleus becomes less heavy overall.
2) In beta decay, a neutron turns into a proton. This reduces the excess number of neutrons.
3) In gamma decay, a gamma ray carries away excess energy.

Alpha and beta emissions change the element...

Examiners love writing questions comparing alpha, beta and gamma emissions, so make sure you are prepared and know their properties in relation to one another, and also what stops each type.

Supplement

Detecting and Deflecting Radioactive Emissions

You can't see radioactive emissions, but you can detect them in other ways...

Geiger-Muller Detectors Detect Radioactive Particles

1) Radioactive emissions can cause photographic film or plates to darken. This is how they were first discovered and detected over 100 years ago.

2) Nowadays, we often use a Geiger-Muller detector and counter (or Geiger counter) to detect and count radioactive emissions. A Geiger-Muller detector is a tube filled with a gas which is ionised when radioactive emissions enter it. This causes there to be a small electrical pulse, which is counted electronically.

There are different types of detectors but a Geiger-Muller detector is very common.

Alpha and Beta Particles are Deflected in Electric Fields

1) Charged particles in an electric field experience a force (see p.99).

2) Alpha and beta particles are charged, so as they pass through an electric field they experience a force and are deflected.

Note: deflection only happens when the particles DON'T travel parallel to the field.

3) An electric field can be set up between two flat oppositely charged plates.

4) Beta particles are negatively charged, so will be deflected towards the positively charged plate.

5) Alpha particles are positively charged, so will be deflected towards the negatively charged plate.

6) Alpha particles are deflected less than beta particles due to their greater mass.

7) Gamma rays are uncharged, so they are not deflected in electric fields.

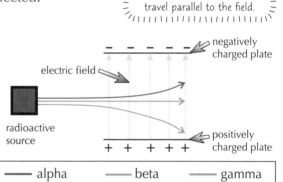

Alpha and Beta Particles are also Deflected in Magnetic Fields

1) Alpha and beta particles are also deflected in magnetic fields (as long as they are not travelling parallel to the field).

2) Again, this is because alpha and beta particles are charged, and as they move they are effectively an electric current.

It's the same effect as that which causes a force to act on a current-carrying conductor in a magnetic field — see page 123.

3) Gamma rays carry no charge, so they are not deflected in magnetic fields.

4) Alpha and beta particles are deflected in opposite directions as they have opposite charges.

5) You can use Fleming's left-hand rule (see p.123) to find the direction of an alpha particle's deflection. This is because the movement of the positively charged alpha particles matches the direction of conventional current (p.101).

Gamma emissions are not deflected in electric or magnetic fields...

... because gamma rays carry no charge. Alpha and beta particles are oppositely charged — this means they will be deflected in opposite directions by a uniform magnetic or electric field.

Fission and Fusion

Splitting up atoms and joining them together can release lots of useful energy.

Nuclear **Fission** — **Splitting** a **Large**, **Unstable** Nucleus

Nuclear fission is a type of nuclear reaction that is used to release energy from large and unstable atoms (e.g. uranium or plutonium) by splitting them into smaller atoms.

1) Fission rarely just happens. Usually, the nucleus has to absorb a neutron before it will split.

2) When the heavy atom splits it forms two new lighter elements that are roughly the same size, and releases gamma rays. Two or three neutrons are also released.

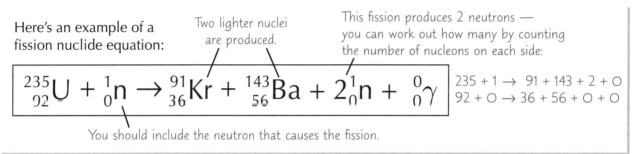

Here's an example of a fission nuclide equation:

Two lighter nuclei are produced.

This fission produces 2 neutrons — you can work out how many by counting the number of nucleons on each side:

$$^{235}_{92}U + ^{1}_{0}n \rightarrow ^{91}_{36}Kr + ^{143}_{56}Ba + 2^{1}_{0}n + ^{0}_{0}\gamma$$

$$235 + 1 \rightarrow 91 + 143 + 2 + 0$$
$$92 + 0 \rightarrow 36 + 56 + 0 + 0$$

You should include the neutron that causes the fission.

3) The total mass is lower after a fission reaction than before it, because some of the mass is converted into energy (don't panic, you don't need to know how).

4) This energy is released in the fission — some of it is transferred to the kinetic energy stores of the products (the lighter nuclei and the neutrons), and some is carried away by the gamma rays.

5) The energy released can be used to heat water, making steam to turn turbines and generators (p.39).

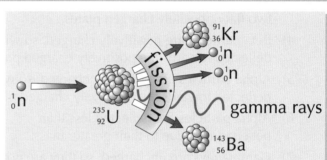

Nuclear **Fusion** — **Joining Small Nuclei**

1) Nuclear fusion is the opposite of nuclear fission.

2) In nuclear fusion, two light nuclei collide at high speed and join (fuse) to create a larger, heavier nucleus. For example, hydrogen nuclei can fuse to produce a helium nucleus.

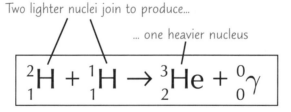

Here's an example of a fusion nuclide equation:

Two lighter nuclei join to produce...

... one heavier nucleus

As always, the nucleon and proton numbers must be the same before and after:

$$^{2}_{1}H + ^{1}_{1}H \rightarrow ^{3}_{2}He + ^{0}_{0}\gamma$$

$$2 + 1 \rightarrow 3 + 0$$
$$1 + 1 \rightarrow 2 + 0$$

3) The combined mass of the two lighter nuclei is greater than the mass of the new heavier nucleus. Some of the mass of the lighter nuclei is converted to energy. This energy is then released as radiation and in the kinetic energy stores of the products.

4) Fusion releases a lot of energy (more than fission for a given mass of fuel).

5) Nuclear fusion could be an extremely useful source of energy, but so far scientists haven't found a way of using fusion to generate energy for us to use (p.40).

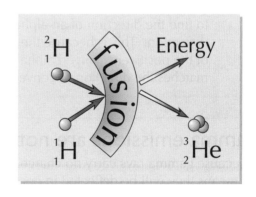

Supplement

Warm-Up & Exam Questions

Time to test your knowledge of atoms, isotopes, radioactive emissions and more.

Warm-Up Questions

1) Describe the nuclear model of the atom.
2) When alpha particles are fired at a thin metal foil, most of them pass straight through it. What does this tell you about the atom?
3) What is the proton number of this nuclide: $^{50}_{22}$Ti ?
4) Which are the most penetrating — alpha particles or beta particles?
5) Why are alpha particles more ionising than beta particles?
6) State which type(s) of radioactive emissions are stopped by:
   a) paper,   b) thin aluminium   c) thick lead
7) State the two types of radioactive decay that cause a nucleus to change from one element to another.
8) Describe the deflections of alpha, beta and gamma emissions as they pass through a uniform electric field at a 90° angle to the direction of the field.
9) Define nuclear fission and nuclear fusion.
10) Why do fission and fusion both release energy?

Exam Questions

1   **Table 1** contains information about three nuclides.

(a)   The nucleus of each nuclide consists of two types of particles. Name these particles and give their relative charge.
   [2]

	Nucleon number	Proton number
Nuclide A	32	16
Nuclide B	33	16
Nuclide C	32	15

Table 1

(b)   What is the 'nucleon number' of a nuclide?
   [1]

(c)   Which two of the nuclides in **Table 1** are isotopes of the same element? Explain your answer.
   [2]

   [Total 5 marks]

2   During radioactive decay, a phosphorous nuclide emits an electron and changes into a sulfur nuclide.

(a)   Define 'radioactive decay'.
   [1]

(b)   State the type of radioactive decay the phosphorous nuclide undergoes.
   [1]

(c)   Complete the nuclear equation, shown in **Figure 1**, which shows phosphorus (P) decaying into sulfur (S) by emitting an electron (e).

$$^{32}_{15}\text{P} \rightarrow \underset{\cdots}{\overset{\cdots}{\text{S}}} + \underset{\cdots}{\overset{\cdots}{\text{e}}}$$

Figure 1
   [2]

   [Total 4 marks]

Half-Life

Some radioactive sources decay much quicker than others. The rate they decay is measured using half-life.

Radioactive Emission is a Totally Random Process

1) When radioactive substances decay, they give out emissions from the nuclei of their atoms.

2) Radioactive decay is entirely random and spontaneous. So you can't predict exactly which nucleus in a sample will decay next, or when any one of them will. The emissions are also random in direction.

3) Radioactive emissions can be measured with a Geiger-Muller tube and counter (see p.137). This records the count rate — the number of radioactive emissions reaching it per unit time (e.g. counts per minute or counts per second).

Half-Life is the Time Taken for the Number of Nuclei to Halve

1) Over time, the number of radioactive nuclei in a radioactive sample will decrease as they gradually decay. This means the number of radioactive decays per unit time (and the detected count rate) will decrease.

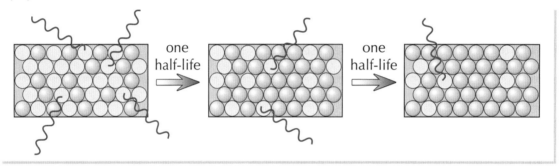

2) The idea of half-life is used to measure how quickly the count rate of a substance falls.

KEY TERM

Half-life is the time taken for the number of nuclei of a radioactive isotope in a sample to halve.

After 1 half life, the number of nuclei of a particular isotope in a sample has halved. This means that the mass of that isotope in the sample has halved also.

3) Half-life can also be described as the time taken for the count rate of a radioactive substance to halve.

4) Half-life can be used to make predictions about radioactive sources, even though their decays are random.

The half-life of a radioactive sample is 3 hours. The sample initially contains 9.6×10^{15} atoms of a radioactive nuclide. How many atoms of the radioactive nuclide will remain after 6 hours?

1) Find the number of half-lives that will have passed after 6 hours:

6 hours ÷ 3 hours = 2 half-lives

2) Now, find the number of atoms after two half-lives have passed:

After one half-life: $9.6 \times 10^{15} \div 2 = 4.8 \times 10^{15}$

After two half-lives: $4.8 \times 10^{15} \div 2 = 2.4 \times 10^{15}$

You might be asked to give the percentage of the original substance remaining after a certain length of time. After one half-life, 50% will remain, and after two half-lives, 25% will remain.

Different substances have different half-lives...

... some have half-lives less than a second, others have half-lives of millions of years. A short half-life means the count rate falls quickly, because the nuclei are very unstable and rapidly decay. A long half-life means the opposite — it will take a long time for the count rate to decrease.

Half-Life Calculations

You might be given data for a half-life calculation in a table or a graph...

You can Find the **Half-Life** of a Sample using a **Graph**

1) A graph of the number of radioactive nuclei in a sample against time, or the count rate against time, is always shaped like the one below.

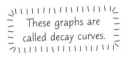
If you're doing the Extended course, you might need to correct graphs for background radiation before finding the half-life (p.142).

2) The half-life is found from the graph by finding the time interval on the bottom axis corresponding to a halving of the number of nuclei or count rate on the vertical axis.

The count rate of a sample of a radioactive material, X, is shown on the decay curve below. Calculate the half-life of material X.

These graphs are called decay curves.

1) Read the initial count rate off the decay curve (the count rate when time = 0).

2) Find half of the initial count rate:

   80 ÷ 2 = 40 counts/hour

3) Find this value on the y-axis and read along horizontally to the curve.

4) Then read down from the curve at this point to find the half-life.

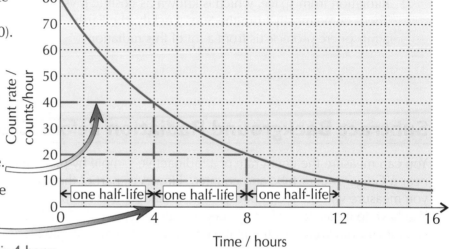

The half-life of material X is **4 hours**.

You can Calculate the **Mass** of a **Radioactive Isotope** Remaining

A sample contains 600 g of a radioactive isotope. The count rate of the isotope is measured each minute over a five minute period and recorded in the table below.

Time (mins)	0	1	2	3	4	5
Count rate (counts/minute)	3000	2121	1500	1061	750	531

Calculate the mass of the radioactive isotope in the sample after 6 minutes.

1) Find the half-life of the isotope — the time taken for the count rate to reach half of its initial value.

   3000 ÷ 2 = 1500 counts per minute
   Half-life = 2 minutes

2) Find the number of half-lives in 6 minutes:

   6 minutes ÷ 2 minutes = 3 half-lives

3) Calculate the mass of the isotope after 3 half-lives:

   After 1 half-life: 600 g ÷ 2 = 300 g
   After 2 half-lives: 300 g ÷ 2 = 150 g
   After 3 half-lives: 150 g ÷ 2 = 75 g

You can determine half-lives from graphs...

You need to know how to work out half-lives from decay curves. Memorise these three steps:
1) Read off the initial count rate or number of nuclei from the y-axis, 2) Work out half of this number, 3) Read off the time from the x-axis for this value — this is one half-life.

Background Radiation

You are constantly exposed to background radiation. It's unavoidable.

Background Radiation Comes From Many Sources

Background radiation is the low-level radiation that's around us all the time.
Background radiation is low-risk and it varies from place to place. It mostly comes from:

1) Radioactivity of naturally occurring unstable isotopes which are all around us:
   - In the air — radon gas is a radioactive gas that comes up from the ground.
   - In food and drink.
   - In building materials and in the rocks under our feet.

2) Radiation from space, which is known as cosmic rays. These come mostly from the Sun. Luckily, the Earth's atmosphere protects us from a lot of this radiation.

Radiation also comes from human activity, e.g. fallout from nuclear explosions or nuclear waste. But this only represents a tiny proportion of the total background radiation.

Subtract Background Radiation Before Calculating Half-Life

You can measure the count rate of a radioactive sample by placing it near a Geiger-Muller tube and counter. However, part of the count rate you measure will be due to background radiation, and not the sample. You have to measure the background radiation separately and then subtract it from your data to get the count rate from the sample alone.

To measure the background radiation, record the count rate when there is no radioactive sample present.

EXAMPLE:

Poorvi measures the count rate of a radioactive sample over 12 minutes. Her data is shown by the red curve on the graph below.

She did not correct her measurements for the background radiation, which has a count rate of 20 counts/minute.

Plot a corrected curve on the graph and calculate the half-life of the sample.

1) Plot points of count rate – background radiation on the original graph at places where values can be easily plotted:

   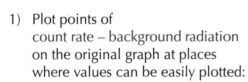

   e.g. 80 – 20 = 60
   50 – 20 = 30

2) Draw a new decay curve through your plotted points (the blue curve on the graph).

   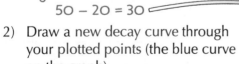

3) Use the method from p.141 to find the half-life.

   The half-life of the sample is 2 minutes.

If you don't subtract background radiation, you get a half-life of about 3 minutes which is wrong.

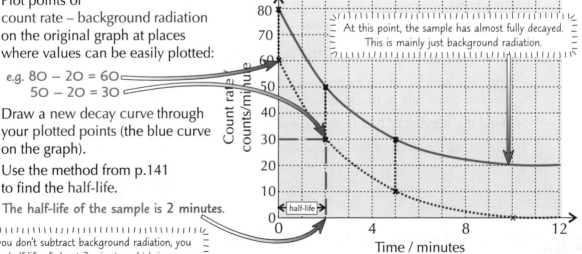

At this point, the sample has almost fully decayed. This is mainly just background radiation.

Supplement

Uses of Radioactive Emissions

Radioactive emissions are used for different things depending on their properties, including half-life.

Alpha Emitters are used in Smoke Detectors

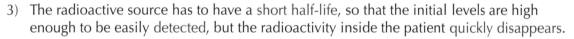

There are loads of different uses, these are just a few examples.

1) Alpha particles ionise air particles in the smoke detector, causing a current to flow.
2) If smoke enters the detector, it attaches to the ionised air particles and makes them uncharged — this causes the current to fall and an alarm goes off.
3) Alpha particles are used as they ionise air particles more easily than beta and gamma emissions.
4) The source's half-life should be long to avoid needing to replace it in the lifetime of the detector.

Gamma Rays can be Used to Diagnose and Treat Cancer

A medical tracer is a radioactive substance that is put into a patient's body. The path of this substance is tracked by a detector outside of the body. Doctors use this method to diagnose cancers and other problems (p.90).

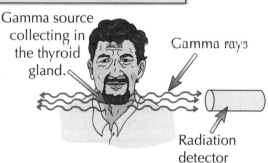

Gamma source collecting in the thyroid gland.

Gamma rays

Radiation detector

1) A gamma source is often used, because gamma rays pass out of the body easily (and so can be detected).
2) They are also only weakly ionising, so they don't cause much damage to the patient's cells (see p.144).
3) The radioactive source has to have a short half-life, so that the initial levels are high enough to be easily detected, but the radioactivity inside the patient quickly disappears.

Gamma rays can also be used to treat cancer — this is known as radiotherapy. Radiotherapy kills the cancer cells and stops them dividing — it involves using a high dose of gamma rays, carefully directed to kill the cells in the tumour while keeping the dose to the rest of the body as low as possible.

Food and Equipment can be Sterilised Using Gamma Rays

1) A high dose of gamma rays can be used to sterilise food (p.90) to keep it fresh for longer, by killing the bacteria on it.
2) Medical equipment can also be sterilised using gamma rays.
3) Using gamma rays for sterilisation is good because, unlike boiling, it doesn't involve high temperatures. So fresh fruit or plastic instruments can be sterilised without being damaged.

unsterilised · gamma source · sterilised

4) The radioactive source used for this needs to be a very strong emitter of gamma rays with a reasonably long half-life (at least several months) so that it doesn't need replacing too often.

Thickness Gauges use Beta Emitters

1) Beta radiation is used to help control thickness, for example when making paper.
2) Radiation is directed through the paper being made, with a detector on the other side, connected to a control unit. When the detected radiation level changes, it means the paper

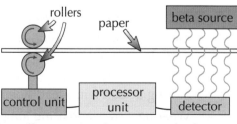

rollers
paper
beta source
control unit
processor unit
detector

is coming out too thick or too thin, so the control unit adjusts the rollers to give the correct thickness.
3) It needs to be a beta source, because then the paper will partly block the radiation (see page 135). Gamma radiation would all go through the paper, and alpha would all be blocked by it. In either case, the reading won't change at all as the thickness changes.
4) The half-life should be long, so that the count rate stays fairly constant (making it easier to control thickness with) and so that the source doesn't need replacing too often.

Supplement

Safety and Radiation

Ionising radiation can be damaging to all living things. There are ways to handle and store it safely though.

Radiation **Damages** Living Cells

1) Radiation can enter living cells and ionise (see p.134) atoms and molecules within them. This can lead to tissue damage (such as burns on human skin).

2) Lower doses tend to cause minor damage without killing the cells. This can create mutant cells that don't work correctly. Long term exposure to low doses of radiation increases the risk of creating mutant cells which divide uncontrollably. This is cancer.

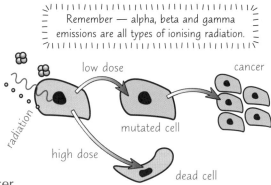

Remember — alpha, beta and gamma emissions are all types of ionising radiation.

3) Higher doses tend to kill cells completely. If a lot of cells are exposed at once it causes radiation sickness (involving vomiting, tiredness and hair loss) and could be fatal.

Exposure and **Risk of Contamination** need to be **Minimised**

1) It's important that radioactive materials are used and stored safely. Minimising your exposure to emissions and your risk of contamination makes dealing with radioactive substances safer.

2) Contamination is when radioactive atoms get onto or into objects (e.g. if you touch a radioactive material without wearing gloves, your hands would be contaminated). These contaminating atoms might then decay, releasing emissions which could cause you harm.

Precautions should be taken during **Handling** and **Storage**

When handling radioactive sources:

- Use gloves.
- Minimise your exposure time.
- Maintain your distance from the material. Use tongs (or tweezers) to increase your distance from the material.

Some industrial workers wear protective suits to reduce the risk of their bodies becoming contaminated.

When storing radioactive sources, keep them in a lead-lined box.

Safety Precautions Reduce your **Radiation Dose**

The more radiation you are exposed to, the more damage it will do. Safety precautions reduce your dose.

1) Reducing your exposure time as much as possible reduces the total dose you get — the less time you spend with the material, the less time you are exposed to its emissions.

2) Increasing the distance between you and the source (by using tongs and keeping your distance) means that more radiation will be absorbed by the air before it reaches you. Remember, alpha particles can only travel a few cm in air, and beta particles only a few metres (p.135).

3) Thick lead absorbs all types of radiation, so it can be used as shielding. Storing a source in a lead-lined box reduces exposure.

4) Wearing gloves and using tongs means you aren't physically touching the material. This reduces the risk of contamination by radioactive particles, which could decay and cause exposure.

Supplement

All you need is gloves, tongs and a lovely lead-lined box...

A question might ask for examples of safety precautions to be followed when using radioactive materials. If you answer with some of the bullet points above, you should get those marks easily.

Warm-Up & Exam Questions

Have a go at the practice questions below to see if you're radiating radiation knowledge.

Warm-Up Questions

1) True or false? You can predict exactly which nucleus in a sample will decay next.
2) What is meant by the half-life of a radioactive substance?
3) A sample has an initial count rate of 2000 counts/hour.
   What will its count rate be after one half-life?
4) List three main sources of background radiation.
5) State one use of beta decay. Explain why beta decay is suitable for this use.
6) What effect can a low dose of radiation have on cells?
7) Give two safety precautions that should be taken
   when working with radioactive sources in a laboratory.

Exam Questions

1   A multicellular living organism receives a high dose of ionising radiation.

   (a) Given that the living organism has a similar resistance to ionising radiation as humans,
       suggest one effect that the ionising radiation could have on the organism's cells.

       [1]

   (b) Suggest how the effect described in (a) could affect the health of the living organism.

       [1]

   (c) Describe a way in which the effect of ionising radiation on cells described in (a) can be useful.

       [1]

       [Total 3 marks]

2   A student is investigating the half-life of a sample of a
    radioactive isotope. Before starting the experiment,
    the Geiger-Muller tube and counter are placed
    far away from any obvious radioactive sources.
    The count rate measured each minute is recorded in **Table 1**.

Time (mins)	1	2	3	4	5
Count rate (counts/min)	22	23	18	19	23

    Table 1

   (a) State the reason why radiation is detected.

       [1]

   (b) Explain why the count rate recorded was not constant.

       [1]

   (c) Calculate an average value for the count rates in **Table 1**.

       [2]

   (d) How should the student use the average count rate calculated in c) when investigating
       the half-life of the radioactive isotope? Explain your answer.

       [2]

   (e) State **two** items that the student could use to handle the sample safely during his investigation.

       [2]

   (f) The initial mass of the isotope the student uses is 860 mg. The half-life of the isotope is 2 weeks.
       What mass of the isotope will remain after 4 weeks?

       [2]

       [Total 10 marks]

Exam Questions

3 A radioactive substance emits gamma rays and has a half-life of 80 days.

    (a) Explain why this substance would not be used:

        (i) as a medical tracer to diagnose cancer.

[2]

        (ii) in a thickness gauge for paper.

[2]

    (b) Give a possible use of this substance.

[1]

[Total 5 marks]

4 The initial number of radioactive atoms in a sample of a radioactive isotope is 8.8×10^{14}. Six hours later, the number of radioactive atoms has fallen to 1.1×10^{14}. Calculate the half-life of the sample.

[Total 3 marks]

5 A sample consists of a radioactive isotope with a 50 minute half-life. The initial count rate of radiation detected from the sample is 120 counts/min.

    (a) On a copy of the axes in **Figure 1**, plot a graph to show how the count rate will change over the first 160 minutes.

[2]

    (b) Determine how much time it will take for the mass of the radioactive isotope in the sample to fall to 25% of its initial mass.

[2]

[Total 4 marks]

Figure 1 (Count rate / counts/min vs Time / mins)

6 A sample of radioactive gas is being investigated. The count rate recorded is shown in **Table 2**.

Time (mins)	0	1	2	3	4	5
Count rate (counts/min)	210	173	143	120	101	87

Table 2

Before the count rate of the gas was measured, the count rate of background radiation was measured as 30 counts/minute. Background radiation has **not** been subtracted from the data in **Table 2**.

Calculate the half-life of the radioactive gas.

[Total 3 marks]

Revision Summary

Well, that's the end of Section 7 — now put yourself to the test and see how much you really know.

- Try these questions and tick off each one when you get it right.
- When you've done all the questions under a heading, and are completely happy with it, tick it off.

The Atomic Model and Isotopes (p.133-134) ☐

1) Draw a sketch to show the currently accepted model of the atom. ☑
2) True or false? The nucleus has an overall positive charge. ☑
3) Describe an experiment that provides evidence for the nuclear model of the atom. ☑
4) What is the difference between nucleon number and proton number? ☑
5) True or false? Isotopes of the same element have different numbers of neutrons. ☑

Radioactive Emissions, Nuclear Equations and Fission and Fusion (p.135-138) ☐

6) True or false? Radioactive decay is the process in which stable nuclei become more stable by emitting ionising radiation. ☑
7) Describe the particles emitted during alpha and beta decay. What are their relative charges? ☑
8) Out of alpha, beta and gamma emissions:
   a) which are the most ionising?   b) which are the most penetrating? ☑
9) Explain why gamma emissions are less ionising than beta emissions. ☑
10) A radioactive emission is not absorbed by 10 mm of paper or 10 mm of aluminium. Which emission must it be? ☑
11) True or false? A nucleus changes from one element to a different element when it emits a beta particle. ☑
12) What must be equal on both sides of a nuclear equation? ☑
13) How could you represent an alpha particle in nuclear equations? ☑
14) Describe how alpha and beta emissions are deflected in a magnetic field. ☑
15) Give one similarity of, and one difference between, nuclear fission and nuclear fusion. ☑

Half-Life and Uses of Radiation (p.140-143) ☐

16) How does the mass of a radioactive nuclide in a sample after one half-life compare to its initial value? ☑
17) Explain how you would find the half-life of a source, given a graph of its count rate over time. ☑
18) What is meant by background radiation? ☑
19) True or false? Background radiation is extremely dangerous. ☑
20) What must be done to count rate data measured from radioactive samples before half-life is calculated? ☑
21) State one use of alpha emitters. Explain why an alpha emitter is suitable for this use rather than a beta or gamma emitter. ☑

Safety and Radiation (p.144) ☐

22) Describe the different ways that ionising radiation can damage living cells. ☑
23) Describe how radioactive materials should be handled to minimise the risk of harm due to exposure to ionising radiation. ☑
24) True or false? All radioactive materials should be stored in a wooden box. ☑

Section 8 — Space Physics

Days, Months and Seasons

How we measure time has a lot to do with how the Earth and the Moon move through space...

The **Rotation** of The **Earth** causes **Day** and **Night**

1) The Earth does one complete rotation in about 24 hours. That's what a day actually is — one complete rotation of the Earth about its axis.

2) This rotation of the Earth is what makes it look like the Sun moves across the sky during the day.

3) As the Earth rotates, any place on its surface (like England, say) will sometimes face the Sun (day time) and other times face away into dark space (night time).

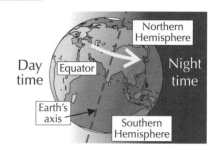

The **Moon** Orbits the Earth in **28 days**

1) The Moon orbits (p.150) the Earth. It takes approximately 1 month (about 28 days) to complete one orbit around the Earth.

2) The Moon doesn't glow itself — it only reflects light from the Sun. Only the half facing the Sun is lit up, leaving the other half in shadow.

3) As the Moon orbits the Earth, we see different amounts of the Moon's dark and lit-up surfaces. These are called 'phases'.

4) You see a 'full moon' when the whole of the lit-up surface is facing the Earth, and a 'new moon' when the dark half faces us. One cycle of the phases takes about 28 days (one orbit).

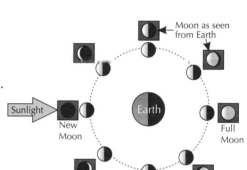

The **Seasons** are **Caused** by the **Earth's Tilt**

1) The Earth takes about 365 days to orbit once around the Sun. That's one year.

2) Each year has four seasons. The seasons are caused by the tilt of the Earth's axis.

3) When it's summer in the northern hemisphere, it's winter in the southern hemisphere — and vice versa.

A year is 365¼ days to be exact — the extra ¼ day is sorted out every leap year.

For the **Northern** Hemisphere:

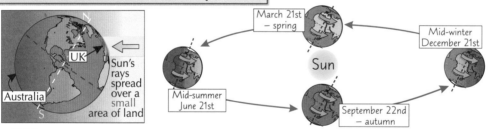
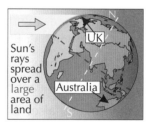

Summer (northern hemisphere)

1) During this time of year everything above the equator is tilted towards the Sun.

2) The northern half of the Earth spends more time in sunlight than it does in darkness, i.e. days are longer than nights. Longer days mean more hours of sunshine — so the land heats up...

3) Not only that, but the Sun's rays cover a small area of land. This means that the heat is focused on a small area. So it gets warm and this area experiences summer.

Winter (northern hemisphere)

1) At this time of year the northern hemisphere is tilted away from the Sun.

2) The north now spends less time in sunlight so days are shorter than nights.

3) Also, the Sun's rays cover a larger area of land so the heat is more spread out. So it gets colder and this area experiences winter.

Galaxies and the Solar System

Our whole solar system is just part of a huge galaxy. And there are billions upon billions of galaxies...

We are Part of the **Milky Way Galaxy**

You are here.

1) The Universe is a large collection of billions of galaxies. A galaxy is a collection of billions of stars.

2) Our Sun is just one of many billions of stars which form the Milky Way galaxy. Our Sun is about halfway along one of the spiral arms of the Milky Way.

3) The other stars in the Milky Way are much, much further away from the Earth than the Sun is. That's why other stars look like tiny dots in the sky whereas the Sun looks so big and bright.

4) The force which keeps the stars together in a galaxy is gravity, of course. And like most things in the Universe, galaxies rotate.

5) Galaxies themselves are often millions of times further apart than the stars are within a galaxy.

6) So the Universe is mostly empty space and is really, really big.

Our Solar System has **One** Star — The **Sun**

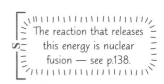
The reaction that releases this energy is nuclear fusion — see p.138.

1) The Sun is a medium-sized star. It is made up of mostly hydrogen and helium.

2) Reactions inside the Sun release energy which is radiated as electromagnetic radiation. The Sun emits most of its energy as infrared radiation, ultraviolet radiation and, of course, visible light.

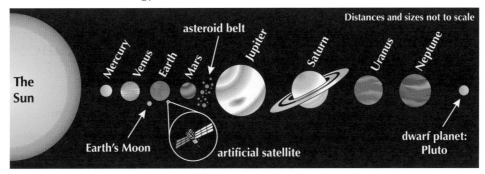

Distances and sizes not to scale

The Sun · Mercury · Venus · Earth · Mars · asteroid belt · Jupiter · Saturn · Uranus · Neptune · dwarf planet: Pluto · Earth's Moon · artificial satellite

Our solar system is all the stuff that orbits the Sun. This includes things like:

1) Planets — these are large objects that orbit a star. The eight planets in our solar system are, in order (from the Sun outwards): Mercury, Venus, Earth, Mars, Jupiter, Saturn, Uranus and Neptune.

2) Moons — these orbit planets with almost circular orbits. They're a type of natural satellite (i.e. they're not man-made).

3) Artificial satellites (ones humans have built) — these usually orbit the Earth in fairly circular orbits.

A satellite is an object that orbits a second, more massive object.

4) Comets — lumps of ice and dust that orbit the Sun. Their orbits are usually highly elliptical (a very stretched out circle) — some travel from near to the Sun to the outskirts of our solar system and back again.

5) Minor planets — a minor planet is any object that orbits the Sun that isn't a planet or a comet. The two main types you'll encounter are:
Dwarf planets — like Pluto. These are planet-like objects that aren't big enough to be planets.
Asteroids — lumps of rock and metal that orbit the Sun. They're usually found in the asteroid belt.

REVISION TIP

There are a lot of different objects in our solar system...

You can use a mnemonic to help you remember the order of the planets — for example: 'Many Voles Eat Mushroom Jam Silently Under Newspaper'. Why not make up your own?

Gravity and Orbits

The structure of the Solar System is determined by orbits — the paths that objects take as they move around each other in space. I bet you can't wait to find out more. Well, read on...

Gravity Provides the Force That Creates Orbits

1) The Moon moves in an almost circular orbit around the Earth.

2) If an object is travelling in a circle it is constantly changing direction, which means there must be a force acting on it.

3) The force causing this acts towards the centre of the circle.

4) This force would cause the object to just fall towards whatever it was orbiting, but as the object is already moving, it just causes it to change its direction.

5) The force that makes this happen is provided by the gravitational force (gravity). Satellites are kept in their orbits around planets by the gravitational attraction of the planet.

6) The gravitational attraction of the Sun keeps the planets and comets in their orbits around it in a similar way. These objects tend to move in elliptical orbits, rather than circular ones (see page 151).

Objects travelling in a circle are also constantly accelerating — see page 11.

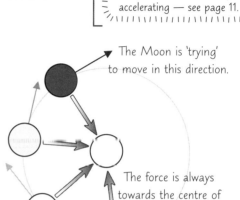

The Moon is 'trying' to move in this direction.

The force is always towards the centre of the circle.

The Force due to Gravity Depends on Mass and Distance

1) Gravitational field strength depends on the mass of the body creating the gravitational field. The larger the mass of the body, the stronger its gravitational field. On page 5 you saw how this can affect the weight of an object.

2) For two planets of similar size (e.g, the Earth and Venus), the larger the mass of the planet, the stronger the gravitational field strength at its surface. The Earth has a greater mass than Venus, so the Earth's gravitational field is stronger on its surface than Venus' gravitational field is on Venus' surface.

3) The Sun contains most of the mass in the solar system. The Sun's mass is so large that it has the strongest gravitational field in the solar system. This is why all the planets orbit the Sun, even though they are closer to other objects with strong gravitational fields.

4) Gravitational field strength also varies with distance. The further away from a star or planet you get, the weaker the gravitational force is.

5) So the further you are from the Sun, the weaker its gravitational field. And although you don't need to know why, this also means that the further a planet is from the Sun, the lower its orbital speed (see the next page). So Mercury travels fastest as it orbits the Sun, Neptune travels slowest.

Gravity and Orbits

Most Objects Orbit the Sun in **Elliptical Orbits**

1) The orbits of planets, minor planets and comets are elliptical, rather than circular.

2) This means that the Sun isn't at the centre of their orbits  — it will be closer to one end of their orbit than the other.

3) In an elliptical orbit, the orbiting object will travel faster the closer it is to the Sun.

4) This is because as an object moves closer to the Sun, the energy in its gravitational potential energy store decreases (p.27).

5) Since energy must be conserved, the energy lost from its gravitational potential energy store has to be transferred to another store.

6) Just like with a falling object on Earth, the energy is transferred to the object's kinetic energy store, and it gets faster.

7) As it moves away from the Sun again, energy is transferred away from its kinetic energy store back to its gravitational potential energy store, and it slows down.

8) Elliptical orbits are not all the same shape. Some planets have almost circular orbits while comets have very elliptical orbits. The Sun is located very near one end of a comet's orbit and very near the centre of an approximately circular orbit.

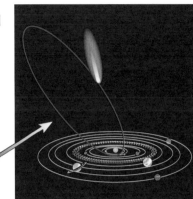

You can Calculate **Orbital Speeds**

1) You can calculate the average speed of an orbit using the equation:

$$\text{average orbital speed} = \frac{2 \times \pi \times \text{average radius of orbit}}{\text{orbital period}} \qquad v = \frac{2\pi r}{T}$$

2) The orbital period is the time it takes for the object to complete one full orbit.

3) The average radius of the orbit is the average distance from the centre of the object being orbited to the centre of the object orbiting it.

 **EXAMPLE:** **Calculate the average orbital speed of the Earth in m/s. The average distance between the Earth and the Sun is 1.5 × 10¹¹ m. Assume that 1 year = 365 days.**

1) Find the orbital period, T, in seconds.

$T = 365 \times 24 \times 60 \times 60 = 31\ 536\ 000$ s

2) Then substitute the values into the equation.

$\text{average orbital speed} = \dfrac{2 \times \pi \times 1.5... \times 10^{11}}{31\ 536\ 000} = 2.9885... \times 10^4$ m/s

$= 30\ 000$ m/s (to 2 s.f.)

Pay close attention to the units of values you're given...

The values you get given in the question may not be in units you want for the equation, especially for very large values like the radius of a star or an object's orbit. Make sure you convert them to the right units first.

Supplement

Supplement

The Formation of the Solar System

The Solar System started off as one big cloud of dust and gas floating in space. Then gravity got involved...

Gravity Acted on Dust and Gas to Form the Solar System

Our best idea for how the solar system formed is the accretion model. The accretion model states:

1) The Solar System originated from a big rotating cloud of interstellar gas and dust. This cloud included many elements that had come from supernovae (see page 154).

Interstellar means 'in between stars'.

2) Over a long period of time, the force of gravity brought everything in the cloud closer together.

3) As the matter collapsed towards the centre of the rotating cloud, the density of the cloud increased, particularly at the centre.

4) Areas of higher density had a greater gravitational pull, so they got denser and denser.

5) The force of gravity compressed the matter, increasing the temperature and pressure, so the denser regions also got hotter and hotter.

6) The region at the very centre of the cloud became so dense and hot that it eventually formed a star (p.154) — the Sun.

7) The rest of the cloud formed itself into an accretion disc — a disc of dust and gas that orbits around an object (usually a star) at its centre.

8) The temperature was very high close to the Sun and got lower as you got further from it. Lighter elements were vaporised by the high temperatures closer to the Sun, so the accretion disc was made up of heavier elements closer to the Sun and lighter elements further out.

9) Areas of high density in the disc eventually also got denser and hotter. Eventually the matter was compressed enough to form planets.

10) The heavier substances close to the Sun formed the terrestrial planets — Mercury, Venus, Earth and Mars (see p.149). These planets are comparatively small, and mostly made of rocky substances.

11) Lighter substances, such as gases, gathered together further away from the Sun. These formed the gaseous giant planets — Jupiter, Saturn, Uranus and Neptune. These are much larger than the terrestrial planets.

There are Trends in the Properties of the Planets

In general, the greater the average orbital radius (orbital distance)...

- ...the greater the orbital period (orbital duration), as the planet travels slower (its orbital speed is lower, p.151) and it has to move through a larger distance to complete its orbit.

- ....the lower the density of the planets. The inner four planets are all rocky and have roughly the same density. The outer four planets have much lower densities than the inner four planets, as they're made of gas. The gas giants all have similar densities to each other though.

- ...the lower the surface temperature of the planets. This is because the further out planets absorb less energy from the Sun, since the energy emitted by the Sun gets more spread out over greater distances.

The exception to this is Venus — it has a higher temperature than Mercury because it has so much carbon dioxide (CO_2) in its atmosphere.

There's no trend in the gravitational field strength of the planets at their surface (surface gravity). As you saw on page 150, surface gravity depends on the mass of the planet — for similarly-sized planets, the higher the mass of the planet, the stronger the gravitational field on its surface.

In the exam, you could be given some data that shows these trends and be asked to interpret or analyse it.

Supplement

Warm-Up & Exam Questions

Space contains some pretty cool stuff, but that doesn't mean you can escape a few practice questions...

Warm-Up Questions

1) Approximately how long does it take for the Earth to complete one full rotation on its axis?
2) Name the eight planets in our Solar System, in the order of nearest to furthest from the Sun.
3) Name three types of object in our Solar System, other than the Sun and the eight planets.
4) What is the force responsible for keeping planets in orbit?
5) Describe the trend in the orbital speeds of the planets as you get closer to the Sun.

Exam Questions

1 Which of the following statements is **false**?

   A   One cycle of the phases of the Moon is equivalent to one orbit of Earth around the Sun.

   B   The Moon takes about 28 days to complete one orbit of the Earth.

   C   The Moon is visible from Earth because it reflects light from the Sun.

   D   As the Moon orbits the Earth, we see different amounts of its dark and light sides.

[Total 1 mark]

2 The accretion model is an explanation for how the Solar System formed.

(a) The accretion model involves the formation of an accretion disc.
State what an accretion disc is made up of.

[1]

(b) Describe how the accretion model explains why the inner planets of the Solar System
are rocky and the outer planets are gaseous.

[3]
[Total 4 marks]

3 The table shows the properties of three objects, A, B and C, that orbit the Sun.

Object	Orbital period (days)	Density (g/cm³)	Average surface temperature (K)
A	10 759	0.69	134
B	88	5.43	440
C	687	3.93	210

(a) Object C has an average orbital radius of 2.28×10^{11} m.
Calculate the average orbital speed of object C in m/s.

[3]

(b) One of the objects in the table is a gaseous planet, and the other two are rocky planets.
The gaseous planet is further from the Sun than the rocky planets. State which object
is the gaseous planet, and give one piece of evidence for this from the table.

[2]
[Total 5 marks]

Supplement

Stellar Evolution

Stars go through some <u>dramatic transformations</u> during their life cycle.

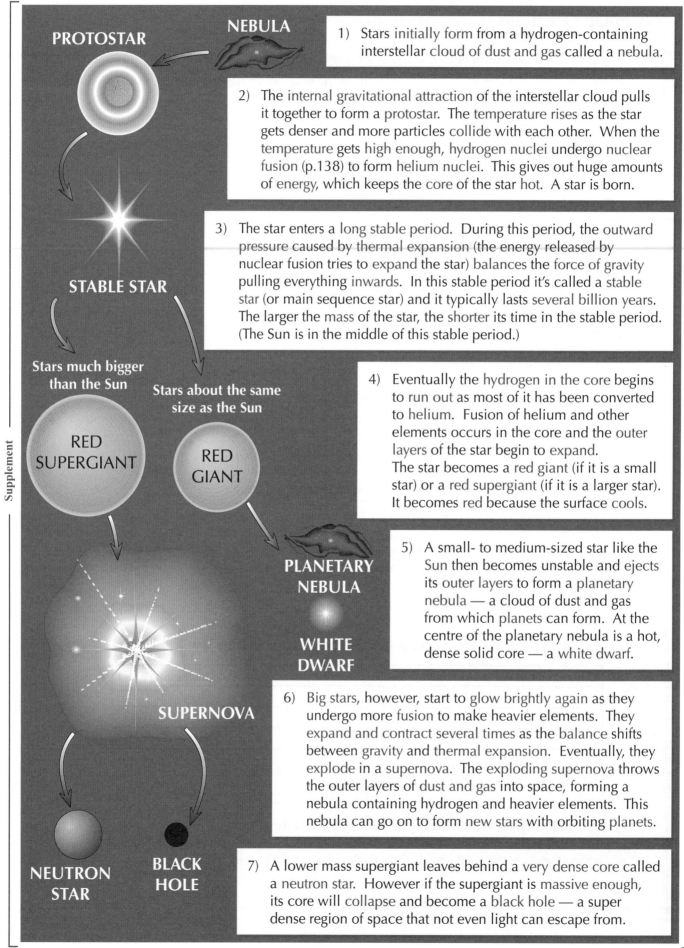

PROTOSTAR **NEBULA**

1) Stars initially form from a hydrogen-containing interstellar cloud of dust and gas called a nebula.

2) The internal gravitational attraction of the interstellar cloud pulls it together to form a protostar. The temperature rises as the star gets denser and more particles collide with each other. When the temperature gets high enough, hydrogen nuclei undergo nuclear fusion (p.138) to form helium nuclei. This gives out huge amounts of energy, which keeps the core of the star hot. A star is born.

STABLE STAR

3) The star enters a long stable period. During this period, the outward pressure caused by thermal expansion (the energy released by nuclear fusion tries to expand the star) balances the force of gravity pulling everything inwards. In this stable period it's called a stable star (or main sequence star) and it typically lasts several billion years. The larger the mass of the star, the shorter its time in the stable period. (The Sun is in the middle of this stable period.)

Stars much bigger than the Sun

Stars about the same size as the Sun

RED SUPERGIANT **RED GIANT**

4) Eventually the hydrogen in the core begins to run out as most of it has been converted to helium. Fusion of helium and other elements occurs in the core and the outer layers of the star begin to expand. The star becomes a red giant (if it is a small star) or a red supergiant (if it is a larger star). It becomes red because the surface cools.

PLANETARY NEBULA

WHITE DWARF

5) A small- to medium-sized star like the Sun then becomes unstable and ejects its outer layers to form a planetary nebula — a cloud of dust and gas from which planets can form. At the centre of the planetary nebula is a hot, dense solid core — a white dwarf.

SUPERNOVA

6) Big stars, however, start to glow brightly again as they undergo more fusion to make heavier elements. They expand and contract several times as the balance shifts between gravity and thermal expansion. Eventually, they explode in a supernova. The exploding supernova throws the outer layers of dust and gas into space, forming a nebula containing hydrogen and heavier elements. This nebula can go on to form new stars with orbiting planets.

NEUTRON STAR **BLACK HOLE**

7) A lower mass supergiant leaves behind a very dense core called a neutron star. However if the supergiant is massive enough, its core will collapse and become a black hole — a super dense region of space that not even light can escape from.

Astronomical Distances and Redshift

Space is big. Very big. So big, that we need a new unit of distance to easily measure it...

Distances in Space are Huge

1) Objects in space are very far apart. They're so far apart that it can even take light a long time to travel between them.

Light travels very fast in space — at a speed of 3.0×10^8 m/s.

EXAMPLE: **The distance between the Sun and the Earth is about 1.5×10^{11} m. Light travels through space at a speed of 3.0×10^8 m/s. Calculate the time it takes for light from the Sun to reach the Earth in minutes and seconds.**

1) Rearrange the speed equation to give the time taken.

2) Then substitute in the values.

3) Finally, convert the time from seconds to minutes.

$$\text{time taken} = \frac{\text{total distance}}{\text{speed}}$$
$$= \frac{1.5 \times 10^{11}}{3.0 \times 10^8} = 500 \text{ s}$$
$$\text{time in minutes} = 500 \div 60$$
$$= 8.33... \text{ mins} = \textbf{8 minutes and 20 seconds}$$

2) Due to the size of distances in space, our usual units for measuring distance (m, km) give very large numbers that are difficult to work with. Instead, we use different units to measure distances in space.

3) One unit makes use of how long it takes light to travel between points in space — the light-year.

KEY TERM A light-year is the distance that is travelled by light moving through space in one year.

1 light-year = 9.5×10^{15} m

4) One light-year is a huge distance and the Milky Way is about 100 000 light-years in diameter. That just goes to show how enormous galaxies are, and how big the Universe must be.

Redshift Occurs When a Light Source is Moving Away

1) Waves are affected by the motion of the wave source. If a wave source is moving towards an observer, the frequency of the wave they observe will be higher and the wavelength will be shorter than the original wave emitted by the source.

2) If a wave source is moving away from an observer, the frequency of the wave they observe will be lower and the wavelength will be longer than the original wave emitted by the source.

3) This is because the wave's speed is constant — if the source is moving, it 'catches up' to the waves in front of it. This causes the wavefronts to bunch up in front of the moving source and spread out behind it, which means the observed frequency and wavelength changes.

KEY TERM Redshift is an increase in the observed wavelength of the electromagnetic radiation emitted from stars and galaxies that are receding (moving away) from an observer on Earth.

It's known as redshift because for visible light, the wavelength shifts towards the red end of the spectrum.

4) Astronomers on Earth observing the light emitted from distant galaxies observe that it has a longer wavelength (lower frequency) compared to the same light emitted on Earth. The light is redshifted. The galaxies must be moving away from the Earth.

5) The faster a light source is moving away, the greater the change in wavelength due to redshift.

6) Astronomers can measure the change in wavelength of starlight from a galaxy by comparing it to a known wavelength of light from a stationary source. Using this, they can calculate the speed, v, at which a galaxy is moving away from the Earth.

Light from distant galaxies has been redshifted...

Remember, red light has the lowest frequency and longest wavelength of visible light. So when visible light has been shifted towards the red end of the spectrum, the light has an increased wavelength and decreased frequency compared to the light originally emitted by the source.

The Big Bang

'How did it all begin?' is a tricky question. The most widely-accepted theory now is the Big Bang Theory.

Redshift Suggests the Universe is Expanding

1) Measurements of redshift suggest that all the distant galaxies are moving away from us very quickly — and it's the same result whichever direction you look in.

2) More distant galaxies have greater redshifts than nearer ones — they show a bigger observed increase in wavelength.

3) This means that more distant galaxies are moving away faster than nearer ones.

4) The inescapable conclusion appears to be that the whole Universe (space itself) is expanding.

- Imagine a balloon covered with pompoms.
- As you blow into the balloon, it stretches. The pompoms move further away from each other.
- Every point on the balloon 'sees' the same thing — all of the pompoms are moving away from it. The furthest pompoms are moving away faster than the closest pompoms.
- The balloon represents the Universe and each pompom is a galaxy. As time goes on, space stretches and expands, moving the galaxies away from each other.
- This is a simple model (balloons only stretch so far) but it shows how the expansion of space makes it look like galaxies are moving away from us.

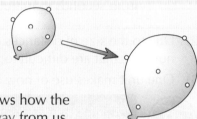

This Evidence Suggests the Universe Started with a Bang

The galaxies are moving away from each other at great speed — suggesting something must have got them going from a single starting point. That 'something' was probably a big explosion — the Big Bang.

The Big Bang Theory states that:
- Initially, all the matter in the Universe occupied a single point.
- This tiny space was very dense and very hot.
- This single point then 'exploded' — the Big Bang.
- Space started expanding, and the expansion is still going on.

There's Microwave Radiation from All Directions

1) Scientists can detect microwave radiation that has a specific, low frequency coming from all directions and all parts of the Universe.

2) It's known as the cosmic microwave background radiation (CMBR).

3) This can be explained by the Big Bang Theory. According to the Big Bang Theory, the CMBR is the leftover radiation from the initial explosion — it was formed shortly after the Universe itself.

4) The CMBR was originally higher energy electromagnetic radiation with a shorter wavelength. As the Universe expanded, this background radiation has been expanded. Its wavelength has increased, causing it to reach the microwave region of the electromagnetic spectrum today.

We can't say for sure if the Big Bang Theory is correct...

...it's just the best theory that we have at the moment. There's a lot of evidence that supports it, but if new evidence comes along it might need adapting. Theories often need to be changed, especially when it comes to things we can't directly observe, like the origins of the Universe.

The Age of the Universe

How old the Universe is might seem like something we couldn't possibly figure out. But it turns out, with a bit of clever analysis, scientists can make a pretty good guess...

You Can Use **Supernovae** to Find **Distances** to Galaxies

1) The distances to most other galaxies in space are too big to measure directly.

2) However, the distance to a far off galaxy can often be found using a supernova within that galaxy.

3) A certain type of supernovae all have a known brightness — we know how much energy they release as visible light.

4) How bright an object appears to an observer changes the further the observer is from the object. In fact, the observed brightness of an object is inversely proportional to the distance-squared.

5) To find the distance, d, to a galaxy, astronomers measure how bright one of these supernovae occurring in that galaxy appears on Earth.

6) Since they know how bright the supernova should be up-close, they can use this brightness data to determine how far away the supernova is, and so how far away the galaxy is.

The **Speed** of a Galaxy Depends on its **Distance** from Earth

1) The light from galaxies is redshifted, because all the galaxies are moving away from each other (as you saw on p.156).

2) Scientists are able to plot a graph of the speed at which galaxies are moving away from the Earth (calculated from the redshift) and the distance of the galaxies from Earth (found using supernovae).

3) This shows that the speed and the distance are proportional — i.e. the speed that galaxies move away from us is greater the further they are away from us (p.156).

 KEY TERM The Hubble constant is the ratio of the speed that a galaxy is receding (moving away) from Earth to its distance from Earth.

4) It is possible to calculate the Hubble constant, H_0, from this graph.

$$\text{Hubble constant} = \frac{\text{speed of galaxy (m/s)}}{\text{distance of galaxy from Earth (m)}} \qquad H_0 = \frac{v}{d}$$

5) A current estimate for the Hubble constant is 2.2×10^{-18} per second. You should get roughly this value of H_0 for most galaxies.

The **Hubble Constant** is Linked to the **Age** of the **Universe**

1) You know from page 1 that average speed = total distance ÷ time taken.

2) The Big Bang Theory supposes that all matter in the Universe was originally concentrated in one place — so the distance of a galaxy from Earth is the total distance it has travelled since the Big Bang.

3) If we assume that the galaxies have been travelling at a constant speed since the Big Bang, we can use this to estimate the time since the Big Bang, and so the age of the Universe.

4) Rearranging the equation for speed: time taken = total distance ÷ average speed, so:

$$\text{age of the Universe (s)} = \frac{d}{v} = \frac{1}{H_0}$$

5) This estimates that the age of the Universe is about 14.4 billion years.

6) This agrees with other observations — we have not observed anything older than this estimate — so this provides evidence that all matter in the Universe did originate from a single point, and that the Big Bang Theory is correct.

Supplement

Supplement

Warm-Up & Exam Questions

You're so close to the end of the section. Time for just a few more questions before you can take a break, and reward yourself for making it this far. So get going with these questions...

Warm-Up Questions

1) True or false? All stars go through the same set of stages in their life cycle.
2) What is the definition of the term 'light-year'?
3) What is the name given to the increase in the wavelength of light from distant galaxies?
4) What is cosmic microwave background radiation?
5) What is the name of the ratio of the speed that a galaxy is receding to its distance from Earth?

Exam Questions

1   Which of the following is part of the evidence for the Big Bang Theory?

☐   **A**   Galaxies are millions of light years away from each other.

☐   **B**   There are billions of galaxies.

☐   **C**   Light from distant galaxies is redshifted.

☐   **D**   Light from distant galaxies can be seen from Earth.

[Total 1 mark]

2   The diagram below shows the life cycle of a star.

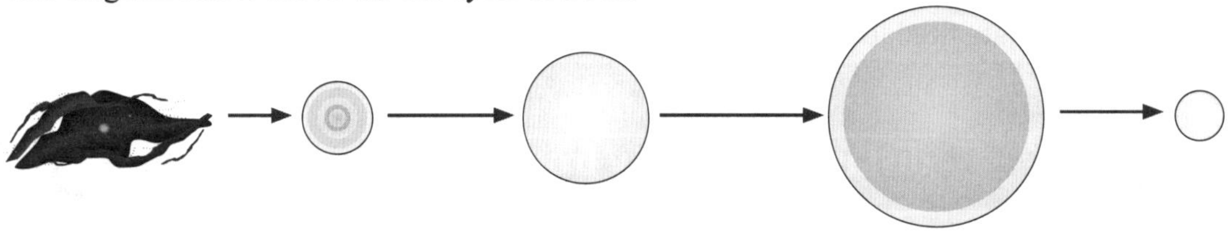

Nebula   Protostar   Stable star   X   White dwarf

(a)   What is the name of the life cycle stage marked X?

☐ **A** red supergiant   ☐ **B** red giant   ☐ **C** red dwarf   ☐ **D** neutron star

[1]

(b)   Describe how a stable star is formed from a nebula.

[3]

(c)   The stable period of a star's life cycle can last billions of years.
Explain why a star remains stable during this period.

[2]

(d)   Stars much larger than the Sun will eventually explode in a supernova.
What two objects can be left behind by a supernova?

[2]

[Total 8 marks]

Exam Questions

3 A distant star is 3.20×10^{17} m away from Earth. The speed of light in space is 3.0×10^8 m/s.

(a) Calculate the time it takes for light from the star to reach Earth in seconds.

[2]

(b) It takes light from another star, called Barnard's Star, 6 years to reach Earth.
What is the distance to Barnard's Star in light-years?

[1]

[Total 3 marks]

4 The table shows a list of galaxies and their distance from Earth in light-years.

Galaxy	Distance From Earth (light-years)
Cigar Galaxy	12 million
Sunflower Galaxy	37 million
Tadpole Galaxy	420 million

The light from the galaxies in the table shows redshift.

(a) Explain how the redshift of light from distant
galaxies provides evidence for the Big Bang model.

[3]

(b) Which of the galaxies in the table would you expect to have the largest change
in the wavelength of its light due to redshift? Explain your answer.

[3]

[Total 6 marks]

5 A scientist is observing a supernova in a distant galaxy.

(a) What property of the radiation detected from the supernova can the scientist
use to determine the distance of the galaxy from Earth?

[1]

The scientist works out some properties of the galaxy, and records them in the table below.

Distance from Earth to the galaxy	4.73×10^{24} m
Speed at which the galaxy is moving away from Earth	9.05×10^6 m/s
Diameter of the galaxy	1.42×10^{21} m

(b) What property of the radiation detected from the galaxy allowed the scientist
to determine the speed at which the galaxy is moving away from Earth?

[1]

(c) Calculate the diameter of the galaxy in light-years.

[1]

(d) Calculate a value for the Hubble constant using the relevant data in the table.

[2]

(e) State the formula that could be used to estimate the age of
the Universe using the value calculated in (d).

[1]

[Total 6 marks]

Revision Summary

Stellar job, you've finished Section 8 — now stop gazing at stars and shift your attention to some questions...
- Try these questions and tick off each one when you get it right.
- When you've done all the questions under a heading and are completely happy with it, tick it off.

The Earth and Time (p.148) ☐

1) Describe what causes 'day time' and 'night time' on Earth. ☐
2) Explain why the shape of the Moon appears to change as it orbits the Earth. ☐
3) Approximately how long does it take for the Earth to complete one full orbit around the Sun? ☐
4) What property of the Earth's axis is the cause of the seasons? ☐
5) Explain why it is summer in the southern hemisphere
   when the southern hemisphere is tilted towards the Sun. ☐

Gravity, Orbits and the Solar System (p.149-152) ☐

6) What name is given to a collection of billions of stars? ☐
7) What two elements is the Sun mostly made up of? ☐
8) True or false? The Sun mostly emits microwaves, X-rays and gamma radiation. ☐
9) Name two types of object in the solar system that orbit a planet. ☐
10) What force causes the orbits of objects in the Solar System? ☐
11) True or false? The higher the mass of a planet, the stronger its gravitational field at its surface. ☐
12) How does the strength of the Sun's gravitational field change as distance from the Sun increases? ☐
13) True or false? In our Solar System the Sun is always located
    at the centre of a planet's elliptical orbit. ☐
14) State the equation that links the average orbital speed of an object,
    its average orbital radius, and its orbital period. ☐
15) What force caused the formation of the Sun and planets from a cloud of dust and gas? ☐
16) Name the four rocky planets in the Solar System and the four gaseous planets in the Solar System. ☐

Supplement (brace around 13-14)

The Life Cycle of Stars (p.154) ☐

17) True or false? After the stable stage, a star becomes a protostar. ☐
18) When a star of a similar size to the Sun begins to run out
    of hydrogen, what type of star will it become? ☐
19) Fully describe what happens to a red giant after it becomes unstable. ☐
20) True or false? The Sun will eventually turn into a black hole. ☐

Supplement (brace around 18-19)

The Universe and its Origins (p.155-157) ☐

21) What is the approximate diameter of the Milky Way in light-years? ☐
22) What is redshift? ☐
23) True or false? Light emitted by distant galaxies is redshifted compared to light emitted on Earth. ☐
24) What is one piece of evidence that supports the Big Bang Theory? ☐
25) How does the Big Bang Theory account for cosmic microwave background radiation? ☐
26) What type of object can be studied to determine the distance of a galaxy from Earth? ☐
27) State the current estimate for the Hubble constant, H_0. ☐
28) Explain how the Hubble constant can be used to give an estimate for the age of the Universe. ☐

s (brace around 25-28)

Planning Experiments

In the Practical Test (or the alternative paper), you'll probably need to plan an experiment. This is likely to be an experiment you haven't done before, so make sure you're prepared for whatever they throw at you.

Experiments Test **Hypotheses**

1) A hypothesis is a possible explanation for something that you've observed.

2) You can use experiments to test whether a hypothesis might be right or not. This involves making a prediction of what you expect the result to be based on the hypothesis and testing it by gathering evidence (i.e. data) from investigations. If evidence from experiments backs up a prediction, you're a step closer to figuring out if the hypothesis is true.

Make an Investigation a **Fair Test** by **Controlling the Variables**

1) In a lab experiment you usually change one variable and measure how it affects another variable.

2) To make it a fair test, everything else that could affect the results should stay the same — otherwise you can't tell if the thing you're changing is causing the results or not.

3) The variable you CHANGE is called the INDEPENDENT variable.

4) The variable you MEASURE when you change the independent variable is the DEPENDENT variable.

5) The variables that you KEEP THE SAME are called CONTROL variables.

> For example, you can find how the force acting on a spring affects its extension (how much it stretches) by measuring the extension for a range of different sizes of force. The independent variable is the force. The dependent variable is the extension. Control variables include the spring being used, the initial length of the spring etc.

6) Because you can't always control all the variables, you often need to use a control experiment. This is an experiment that's kept under the same conditions as the rest of the investigation, but doesn't have anything done to it. This is so that you can see what happens when you don't change anything at all.

7) If the experiment is a fair test, and it tests what it was meant to test, then it is a VALID experiment.

You Need to Be Able to Plan a **Good Experiment**

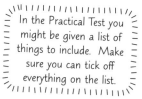

In the Practical Test you might be given a list of things to include. Make sure you can tick off everything on the list.

Here are some general tips on what to include when planning an experiment:

1) Your hypothesis, including a prediction of what your expected results would be.

2) A list of all the apparatus you will need for the experiment.

> For example, the refraction of light experiment on page 74 requires: a ray box, a transparent block of material, a piece of paper, a sharp pencil, a 30 cm ruler and a protractor.

3) Instructions for an appropriate technique for carrying out the experiment. Sometimes, drawing a diagram showing how you will set up the apparatus can be useful.

4) What the variables are:
   - What the dependent variable is (i.e. what you're measuring).
   - What the independent variable is (i.e. what you're changing). Describe how you're going to change it and which values you'll change it to. Make sure these cover as large a range as possible, they are evenly spaced and there's enough of them (usually, at least five).
   - Describe what variables you're keeping constant — and how you're going to do it.

5) How you'll increase the reliability of the results, e.g. by repeating the experiment at least three times.

6) A suitable table to record your results in. Say how you will use your results to reach a conclusion, e.g. you might draw a graph to show the relationship between variables.

7) Any safety precautions you would take (see page 166).

Making Measurements

Get your lab coat on, it's time to find out about the skills you'll need to make measurements in experiments.

Your **Equipment** has to be **Right for the Job**

1) It's important to choose the right apparatus for what you want to test. You should be able to justify your choice — e.g. a tape measure would be a better choice than a 30 cm ruler to measure a distance of a few metres because it is more likely to give accurate results.

You need to be able to identify apparatus from a diagram, and be able to draw and label diagrams of different apparatus yourself.

2) The measuring equipment you use also has to be sensitive enough to measure the changes you're looking for. For example, if you need to measure changes of 1 cm³ you need to use a measuring cylinder that can measure in 1 cm³ steps — it'd be no good trying with one that only measures 10 cm³ steps.

3) The smallest change a measuring instrument can detect is called its resolution. E.g. some mass balances have a resolution of 1 g, some have a resolution of 0.1 g, and some are even more sensitive.

4) Measuring equipment needs to be calibrated by measuring a known value. If there's a difference between the measured value and the known value you can either adjust the device so that it gives the correct value, or change it for a device that measures accurately.

Measure **Most Lengths** with a **Ruler**

1) In most cases a standard 30 centimetre ruler can be used to measure length. It depends on what you're measuring though — metre rulers are handy for large distances but a 15 cm ruler is fine for a distance of a few cm.

2) The ruler should always be parallel to what you want to measure.

3) If you're dealing with something where it's tricky to measure just one accurately (e.g. wavelengths of water ripples), you can measure the length of a number of them, and divide to find the length of one.

4) If you're taking multiple measurements of the same object (e.g. to measure changes in length) then make sure you always measure from the same point on the object. It can help to draw a mark on the object to line up your ruler against, or to attach a thin marker to it. (See p.16 for an example of this.)

5) Make sure the ruler and the object are always at eye level when you take a reading. This stops parallax affecting your results.

Parallax is where a measurement appears to change based on where you're looking from.

The blue line is the measurement taken when the spring is at eye level. It shows the correct length of the spring.

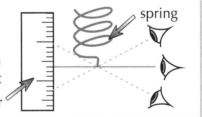

Volume measurements can be used together with mass measurements to determine density (see p.6).

You can also use length measurements to find the volume of regular 3D shapes. For example, to find the volume of a cuboid, use the formula length × width × height.

Use a **Protractor** to Find **Angles**

1) First align the vertex (point) of the angle with the mark in the centre of the protractor.

2) Line up the base line of the protractor with one line that forms the angle and then measure the angle of the other line using the scale on the protractor.

3) If the lines creating the angle are very thick, align the protractor and measure the angle from the centre of the lines. Using a sharp pencil to draw diagrams helps to reduce errors when measuring angles.

4) If the lines are too short to measure easily, you may have to extend them. Again, make sure you use a sharp pencil to do this.

Making Measurements

Did you order more measuring? Well, even if you didn't, here's some stuff about measuring volume and mass.

Measuring Cylinders Measure Liquid Volumes

1) Measuring cylinders are the most common way to measure a liquid.

2) They come in all different sizes. Make sure you choose one that's the right size for the measurement you want to make. It's no good using a huge 1000 cm³ cylinder to measure out 2 cm³ of a liquid — the graduations (markings for scale) will be too big and you'll end up with massive errors. It'd be much better to use one that measures up to 10 cm³.

3) Always read the volume from the bottom of the meniscus (the curved upper surface of the liquid) when it's at eye level.

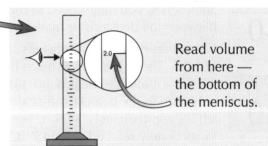

Read volume from here — the bottom of the meniscus.

Eureka Cans Measure the Volumes of Solids

1) Eureka cans are used in combination with measuring cylinders to find the volumes of irregular solids (p.6). A eureka can is essentially a beaker with a spout.

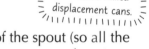
Eureka cans are sometimes called displacement cans.

2) To use a eureka can, fill it with water so the water level is above the spout.

3) Let the water drain from the spout, leaving the water level just below the start of the spout (so all the water displaced by an object goes into the measuring cylinder and gives you the correct volume).

4) Place a measuring cylinder below the end of the spout. When you place a solid in the beaker, it causes the water level to rise and water to flow out of the spout.

5) Make sure you wait until the spout has stopped dripping before you measure the volume of the water in the measuring cylinder. The object's volume is equal to the volume of the water in the measuring cylinder.

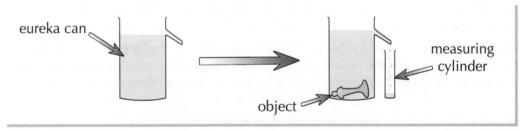

eureka can

measuring cylinder

object

Mass Should Be Measured Using a Balance

1) For a solid, set the balance to zero and then place your object onto the scale and read off the mass.

2) If you're measuring the mass of a liquid, start by putting an empty container onto the balance. Next, reset the balance to zero.

3) Then just pour your liquid into the container and record the mass displayed. Easy as that.

PRACTICAL TIP

Watch out for parallax when taking readings...

Whether you're reading off a ruler or a measuring cylinder, make sure you take all readings at eye level. And, if you're taking a reading for a volume, make sure you measure from the bottom of the meniscus (that's from the dip in the curved surface at the top of the liquid).

Making Measurements

There's lots of different equipment you need to know about. Here's some more.

Measure **Temperature** Accurately with a **Thermometer**

1) Make sure the bulb of your thermometer is completely submerged in any substance you're measuring the temperature of.

2) Wait for the temperature reading to stabilise before you take your initial reading.

3) Again, read your measurement off the scale on a thermometer at eye level.

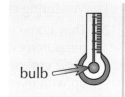

bulb

Sometimes, you might need to record a value that's between the divisions or markers on a scale.

For example, this thermometer's scale has graduations of 1 °C. The reading shown lies between 34 °C and 35 °C — it looks to be around 34.5 °C. You should only read to the nearest half-scale division — you can tell it's approximately 34.5 °C but you wouldn't be able to accurately read off e.g. 34.7 °C.

If you're using a mercury thermometer, there will be an upwards meniscus (like a little hump) at the surface of the mercury. You should take your reading from the top of the meniscus, at eye-level.

You May Have to Measure the **Time Taken** for a Change

1) You need to be able to measure an interval of time using both analogue and digital clocks.

2) Analogue and digital clocks usually have different resolutions (p.162). An analogue clock can usually measure to the nearest second, whereas a digital clock, or digital stopwatch, can measure fractions of a second.

This stopwatch can measure hundredths of a second.

3) You should use a digital stopwatch to time most experiments — because their resolution is so much greater than a regular watch, measurements made with them have greater precision.

4) Always make sure you start and stop the stopwatch at exactly the right time. Or alternatively, set an alarm on the stopwatch so you know exactly when to stop an experiment or take a reading.

5) Human reaction times are quite long compared to the resolution of a stopwatch. This can make measurements of short periods of time very inaccurate.

6) Where possible you should measure multiple time periods and then divide by the number of periods. E.g. to find the period of a pendulum (the time it takes for one complete cycle), measure the time taken to complete 10 complete cycles and then divide this by 10.

Use **Light Gates** to Measure **Acceleration**

1) A light gate sends a beam of light from one side of the gate to a detector on the other side.

2) When an object passes through the gate, the beam of light is interrupted. The light gate then measures how long the beam was undetected for.

3) You can use this to work out the speed of the object by using the length of the part that passed through the beam as the distance and dividing it by the time the beam was interrupted for.

4) You can also measure the acceleration of an object by setting up two light gates so that the object passes through one after the other.

5) Then you can use the data from the light gates to find the speed of the object at each light gate and the time at which it passed through each light gate. Then you can divide the change in speed by how long the object took to travel between the light gates to work out the acceleration.

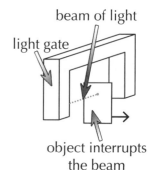

beam of light

light gate

object interrupts the beam

Making Measurements

Here's the last page on measuring equipment — we still have a few more things to cover.

Newton Meters Measure Force — in Newtons

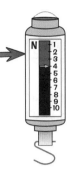

1) A newton meter contains a spring with a hook on it. When a force is applied to the hook, the spring stretches by a certain amount and you can read off the size of the force.

2) A newton meter is often used to find the weight of an object. Suspend the newton meter from the loop at the top and attach the object to the hook.

3) Make sure you are at eye level and read the value off the scale.

Measure Electrical Properties Using an Ammeter or a Voltmeter

1) If you are planning an experiment involving a circuit, you'll need to include a circuit diagram.

2) Or, if you're performing an experiment, you may be required to build a circuit from a diagram.

3) In any case, make sure you know all of the circuit symbols on page 101.

4) Don't forget, voltmeters are connected in parallel across a component, and ammeters are connected in series (p.104).

5) Make sure you use a voltmeter or ammeter with an appropriate scale for the values you are measuring. With analogue meters, you need to choose one with a suitable scale. However, with digital meters, you can usually just set them to the best scale and units.

6) Turn off your circuit in between readings to prevent wires heating up and affecting your results.

You Can Use Optical Pins to Trace the Path of Light Rays

You can use optical pins when determining the refractive index of a transparent block, or to show the path of a reflected ray to confirm the law of reflection. They can be used instead of a beam from a ray box (p.74).

If the pins shown in the diagram on the right are positioned correctly, they will appear to a viewer in the position shown to be one behind the other, in a perfectly straight line. This is because the light from the pins behind the block refracts as it enters and leaves the transparent block.

You'll be given instructions if you need to use optical pins in the Practical Test, but some basic rules are:

1) Make sure your pins are vertical.
2) When lining up the pins, get down to eye level and look at the bases of the pins.
3) Place the pins a suitable distance apart — usually greater than 5 cm.
4) When drawing a line to connect the pin positions, use a sharp pencil.

Different Substances Transmit Different Amounts of Light

1) You can use a light source (e.g. a ray box) to see how well light travels through a block of a certain material, to see if that material is transparent, translucent or opaque. Position the light source and the block so you can see the path of a light ray hitting the block.

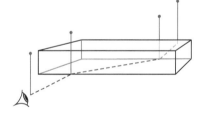

2) Transparent materials transmit almost all of the visible light that hits them — the light ray you see exiting the block would appear the same as when it was emitted by the source.

3) Translucent materials transmit some visible light, so the light ray exiting the block would be dimmer.

4) Opaque materials do not transmit any visible light — you wouldn't see a ray exiting the block.

Safety and Experiments

There's danger all around, particularly in science experiments. But don't let this put you off. Just be aware of the hazards and take sensible precautions. Read on to find out more...

Be **Careful** When You Do Experiments

There are always hazards in any experiment, so before you start an experiment you should read and follow any safety precautions to do with your method or the apparatus you're using. Hazards from science experiments might include:

- Lasers, e.g. if a laser is directed into the eye, this can cause blindness.
- Fire, e.g. an unattended Bunsen burner is a fire hazard.
- Electricity, e.g. faulty electrical equipment could give you a shock. If a large current is used, wires could get hot and cause nasty burns.

Part of planning an investigation is making sure that it's safe. You should always make sure that you identify all the hazards that you might encounter. Then you should think of safety precautions that will reduce the risks from the hazards you've identified. For example:

1) If you're working with springs, always wear safety goggles. This will reduce the risk of the spring hitting your eye if the spring snaps.

2) Stop equipment falling over by using clamp stands.

3) Make sure any masses you're using in investigations are of a sensible weight so they don't break the equipment they're used with. Also, make sure strings used in pulley systems are of a sensible length. That way, any hanging masses won't hit the floor or the table during the experiment.

4) If you're using a Bunsen burner, stand it on a heatproof mat to reduce the risk of starting a fire.

5) When heating materials, make sure you let them cool before moving them, or wear insulated gloves while handling them. After using an immersion heater to heat liquids, you should always let it dry out in air, just in case any liquid has leaked inside the heater.

6) If you're using a laser, there are a few safety rules you must follow. Always wear laser safety goggles and never look directly into the laser or shine it towards another person. Make sure you turn the laser off if it's not needed to avoid any accidents.

7) When working with electronics, make sure you use a low enough voltage and current to prevent wires overheating (and potentially melting) and also to avoid damaging components, e.g. blowing a filament bulb.

8) You also need to be aware of general safety in the lab — handle glassware carefully so it doesn't break, be careful working around open flames and avoid touching frayed wires.

BEWARE — hazardous physics experiments about...

Before you carry out an experiment, it's important to consider all of the hazards. Hazards can be anything from lasers to electrical currents, or weights to heating equipment. Whatever the hazards, make sure you know all the safety precautions you should follow to keep yourself safe.

Processing Data

Processing your data means doing some calculations with it to make it more useful.

Data Needs to be Organised

1) Results of experiments need to be recorded. Tables are really useful for recording and organising data.
2) When you draw a table use a ruler and make sure each column has a heading, including the units.
3) Each value in a column should have the same precision, and this should be appropriate for the experiment. For example, you shouldn't record one time as 3 seconds, and another as 3.568 seconds. Which degree of precision you use depends on the experiment. A datalogger might be able to measure a time accurately to a millisecond, but a human using a stopwatch certainly couldn't.
4) Some results are qualitative — they're not a number, e.g. the properties of an image formed by a lens. For qualitative results, make sure you leave plenty of space in the table, and include all the relevant details you can.

Round to the Lowest Number of Significant Figures

1) The first significant figure of a number is the first digit that's not zero. The second and third significant figures come straight after (even if they're zeros).
2) Calculated values should be rounded to the least number of significant figures (s.f.) of the raw data.

Liquid	Mass (g)	Volume (cm³)	Density of liquid (g/cm³)
1	66.1	71	66.1 ÷ 71 = 0.93098... = 0.93
2	58.4	53	58.4 ÷ 53 = 1.10188... = 1.1

Mass is measured to 3 s.f. but volume is measured to only 2 s.f., so density should be rounded to 2 s.f..

Data Should be Repeatable, Reproducible, Accurate and Precise

1) In an experiment, there will usually be differences between any sets of measurements that you take of the same thing, so you should make sure you repeat your measurements at least three times and calculate the average (the mean).
2) Your results should be precise — this is when the values you measure are all close together.
3) The mean is found by adding together all the data values and dividing by the total number of values in the sample. If you have a few results, the best way to find the mean is to use a calculator.
4) Each set of repeated measurements should be fairly similar. This means your results are repeatable. Big differences between repeated results means your results are of poor quality.

Ignore anomalous results (see next page) when calculating averages.

 **EXAMPLE:** **The results in the table show the extension of a spring when a force is applied to it. Calculate the mean of the spring's extension.**

Repeat (cm)					Mean (cm)
1	2	3	4	5	
1.8	2.0	2.0	1.9	1.8	(1.8 + 2.0 + 2.0 + 1.9 + 1.8) ÷ 5 = 1.9

5) You need to make sure your results are reproducible — meaning similar results can be obtained if someone else does the experiment, or different equipment is used. You can confirm results by taking a second set of readings with another instrument (or a different observer). If results are shown to be repeatable and reproducible, then they are reliable.
6) Your data also needs to be accurate. Really accurate results are those that are really close to the true value. The accuracy of your results usually depends on your method — you need to make sure you're measuring the right thing, you don't miss anything that should be included in the measurements and that you keep all the control variables the same. E.g. estimating the volume of an irregularly shaped solid by measuring the sides isn't very accurate because this will not take into account any gaps in the object. It's more accurate to measure the volume using a eureka can (see p.163).

Data needs to meet all these criteria to be good quality.

Anomalous Results and Uncertainty

When processing your data, you need to watch out for anomalous results — these are results that don't fit in with the rest of your data. You also need to think about how certain you are that the results are correct.

You Need to Look Out for **Errors** and **Anomalous Results**

1) The results of your experiment will always vary a bit because of random errors — unpredictable differences caused by things like human errors in measuring. For example, the errors when you take a reading from a ruler are random. You have to estimate the distance when it's between two marks — so sometimes your value will be a bit greater than the real one, and sometimes it will be a bit less than it.

2) You can reduce the effect of random errors by taking repeat readings and finding the mean. This can make your results more accurate.

3) If a measurement is wrong by the same amount every time, it's called a systematic error. For example, if you measured from the very end of your ruler instead of from the 0 cm mark every time, all your measurements would be a bit small. Repeating the experiment in the exact same way and calculating a mean won't correct a systematic error.

4) If a systematic error is caused by using equipment that isn't zeroed properly, it's called a zero error. For example, if a mass balance always reads 1 gram before you put anything on it, all your measurements will be 1 gram too heavy.

5) You can compensate for some systematic errors if you know about them, e.g. if a mass balance always reads 1 gram before you put anything on it, you can subtract 1 gram from all your results.

6) If you know the true value of the quantity you are measuring, you can work out the size of another type of error — the measurement error. This is the difference between your measured value and the true value. Results that are accurate will have a low measurement error.

7) Sometimes you get a result that doesn't fit in with the rest at all. This is called an anomalous result (or an anomaly). You should investigate it and try to work out what happened. If you can work out what happened (e.g. you measured something wrong), you can ignore it when processing your results.

Uncertainty is the Amount of **Error** in Measurements

You might be required to identify possible causes of uncertainty in your data, or in your conclusion.

1) When you repeat a measurement, you often get a slightly different figure each time you measure it due to errors (see above). This means that each result has some uncertainty in it.

2) The measurements you make will also have some uncertainty in them due to limits in the resolution of the equipment you use (see page 162).

3) The larger the range of your repeated results, the more uncertainty there will be in them — the less sure you can be that your results are accurate.

4) Measuring a greater amount of something can help to reduce uncertainty. For example, in an experiment investigating speed, measuring the distance travelled over a longer period will reduce the uncertainty in your results.

5) There can be a lot of uncertainty in a measurement of a short distance or a short time. The uncertainty can be reduced by measuring multiple distances or times, then dividing to get one (see p.162 and 164).

6) You can judge if the results of an experiment lie within the 'limits of experimental accuracy' — this is where values that should be the same as each other all lie within a margin of 10% of each other.

E.g. when investigating how the resistance of a wire varies with wire length (p.103), there will be some uncertainty in each ammeter and voltmeter reading and each wire length.

One way to judge how good the results are is by working out the ratio of resistance to wire length for each point. These ratios should have the same value, so if the ratios are all within 10% of each other, you can say the results are within the limits of experimental accuracy.

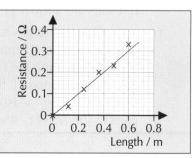

Presenting Data

Once you've processed your data, e.g. by calculating the mean, you can present your results in a nice chart or graph. This will help you to spot any patterns in your data.

If Your Data Comes in **Categories**, Present It in a **Bar Chart**

1) If the independent variable is categoric (comes in distinct categories, e.g. solid, liquid, gas) you should use a bar chart to display the data.

2) You also use them if the independent variable is discrete (the data can be counted in chunks, where there's no in-between value, e.g. number of protons is discrete because you can't have half a proton).

3) There are some golden rules you need to follow for drawing bar charts:

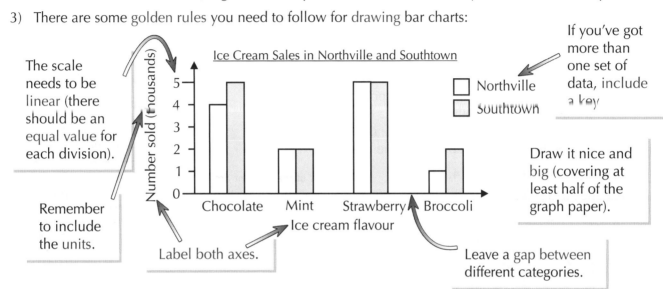

The scale needs to be linear (there should be an equal value for each division).

Remember to include the units.

Label both axes.

If you've got more than one set of data, include a key

Draw it nice and big (covering at least half of the graph paper).

Leave a gap between different categories.

If Your Data is **Continuous**, Plot a **Graph**

1) If both variables are continuous (numerical data that can have any value within a range, e.g. length, volume, temperature) you should use a graph to display the data.

2) Here are the rules for plotting points on a graph:

Use the biggest data values you've got to draw a sensible scale on your axes. Here, the longest distance is 8.8 m, so it makes sense to label the y-axis up to 10 m.

To plot points, use a sharp pencil and make neat little crosses (don't do blobs).

nice clear mark   smudged unclear marks

Your scales don't have to start at 0. E.g. if all the distance values were between 8 m and 10 m it would be better to start the scale at 8 m.

If you're asked to draw a line (or curve) of best fit, draw a line through or as near to as many points as possible, ignoring any anomalous results. Don't just join the crosses up.

The dependent variable goes on the y-axis (the vertical one).

anomalous result

The independent variable goes on the x-axis (the horizontal one).

Remember to include the units.

Draw it nice and big (covering at least half of the graph paper).

More on Graphs

You can calculate the gradient or find an intercept from a graph, which can give you some useful information.

Graphs Can Give You a Lot of Information About Your Data

1) The gradient (slope) of a graph tells you how much the dependent variable changes if you change the independent variable.

$$\text{gradient} = \frac{\text{change in } y}{\text{change in } x}$$

This graph shows the distance travelled by a vehicle against time. The graph is linear (it's a straight line graph), so you can simply calculate the gradient of the line to find out the speed of the vehicle.

- To calculate the gradient, pick two points on the line that are easy to read and a good distance apart — a line drawn between them should be at least half as long as the line of best fit.

- Draw a line down from one of the points and a line across from the other to make a triangle. The line drawn down the side of the triangle is the change in y and the line across the bottom is the change in x.

Change in y = 6.8 – 2.0 = 4.8 m

Change in x = 5.2 – 1.6 = 3.6 s

The units of the gradient are (units of y)/(units of x).

Rate = gradient = $\frac{\text{change in } y}{\text{change in } x}$ = $\frac{4.8}{3.6}$ = 1.333... = 1.3 m/s (to 2 s.f.)

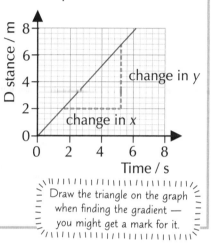

Draw the triangle on the graph when finding the gradient — you might get a mark for it.

2) Intercepts are points where lines on the graph cross either axis. In this speed-time graph, the y-intercept gives the speed at 0 s, and the x-intercept gives the time when the speed reaches 0 m/s.

3) Interpolation is estimating a value between known data points. A line of best fit helps you interpolate using your data. E.g. in the graph on the left, even though there is no data point at 3.6 s, you can interpolate using the line of best fit to get a distance of 3.2 m at this time. Interpolation can be useful when you need to pick good points to calculate a gradient (see above).

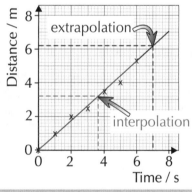

4) Extrapolation is making an estimate of a value outside the range of your data by extending the line of best fit. E.g. to find a distance for a time of 7 s in the graph above, extend the line of best fit and draw a line up from 7 s until it reaches the extended line. This gives a distance of 6.2 m.

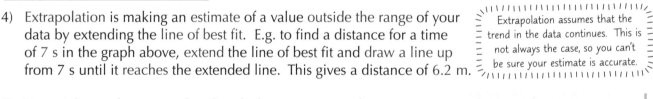

Extrapolation assumes that the trend in the data continues. This is not always the case, so you can't be sure your estimate is accurate.

5) You might need to extrapolate first, before you can work out an intercept or gradient. E.g. to find the y-intercept of a line of best fit, you would extend the line until it crosses the y-axis.

6) If you plot two or more lines on the same graph, they may intersect (cross). At this point, the x and y-values will be the same for both sets of data. E.g. the lines on this distance-time graph represent two objects travelling at different speeds and setting off at different times. At 4 s, the lines intersect — the objects have both reached a distance of 4 m at this time.

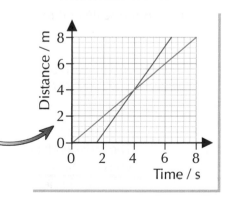

Drawing Conclusions

Once you've designed your experiment, carried it out, and processed and presented your data, it's finally time to sit down and work out exactly what your data tells you. Time for some fun with conclusions...

You Can **Only Conclude** What the Data Shows and **No More**

1) Drawing conclusions might seem pretty straightforward — you just look at your data and say what pattern or relationship you see between the dependent and independent variables.

	Current (A)	Potential difference (V)	
The table shows the potential difference across a light bulb for different currents through the bulb:	0	0	CONCLUSION: A higher current through the bulb gives a higher potential difference across the bulb, for currents up to 15 A.
	3	2	
	6	4	
	9	10	
	12	13	
	15	18	

2) But you've got to be really careful that your conclusion matches the data you've got and doesn't go any further.

- You can't conclude that the potential difference across any circuit component will be higher for a larger current — the results might be completely different.
- You can't conclude that the potential difference will keep on increasing no matter how high the current is increased.

3) You also need to be able to use your results to justify your conclusion (i.e. back up your conclusion with some specific data).

> For every increase in current, the potential difference showed an increase. For example, for a current of 3 A the p.d. was 2 V, and for a current of 6 A the p.d. was 4 V.

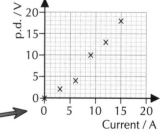

You can draw a graph to show a relationship in your data. The graph shows that potential difference increases with current. However, there aren't enough data points over a wide enough range here to know whether the relationship is linear or not.

4) When writing a conclusion you need to refer back to the original hypothesis and say whether the data supports it or not:

> The hypothesis for this experiment might have been that a higher current through the bulb would increase the potential difference across the bulb. If so, the data supports the hypothesis.

You should be able to justify your conclusion with your data...

You should always be able to explain how your data supports your conclusion. It's easy to go too far with conclusions and start making bold claims that your data simply can't back up. When you're drawing conclusions, it's also important that you refer back to the initial hypothesis (the one that was made right back at the start of the investigation) to see whether your data supports it or not.

Evaluations

Hurrah! The end of another investigation. Well, now you have to work out what you did right, and what you could have done better. That's what evaluations are all about, I'm afraid. Best get cracking with this page...

Evaluations — Describe **How** Experiments Could be **Improved**

An evaluation is a critical analysis of the whole investigation.
When evaluating an experiment, you should make comments on the procedure
as a whole and any bits in particular that could be improved.

1) You should comment on the method, including the experimental set-up — did it test what it was intended to? Were you able to control all the other variables to make it a fair test?
   - E.g. in a circuits experiment, the battery might have run down over the course of the experiment, causing the e.m.f. in the circuit to change.

   Did you encounter any difficulties?
   - E.g. did the ammeter needle stay steady to allow you to interpolate accurately between scale divisions? Were the edges of an image blurry, making it difficult to measure it accurately?

2) Comment on the quality of the results — did your data let you draw a reliable conclusion? Did it cover a wide enough range?
   - E.g. when comparing thermal insulators, measuring the temperature change over 30 seconds might not give you enough data to be certain of your conclusion.

   Were your repeated measurements fairly similar? If they were very different, there would be a lot of uncertainty in what the true value was.

   Were there any anomalous results? If there were none then say so. If there were any, try to explain them — were they caused by errors in measurement?

3) All this analysis will allow you to say how confident you are that your conclusion is right.

4) Then you can suggest changes to the method that would improve the quality of the results, e.g.
   - Using a measuring device with a higher resolution to give more precise results.
   - Taking measurements over a greater range could show a relationship more clearly.
   - Taking more measurements at narrower intervals could give you a more accurate result.

When suggesting improvements to the investigation, always make sure that you say why you think this would make the results better.

For example, springs have a limit of proportionality (a maximum force before force and extension are no longer proportional). If you are doing an experiment to find the limit of proportionality of a spring, you might apply forces of 1 N, 2 N, 3 N, 4 N and 5 N, and from the results see that it is somewhere between 4 N and 5 N. Then you could repeat the experiment with a second, identical spring, taking more measurements between 4 N and 5 N to get a more accurate value for the limit of proportionality.

5) You could also make more predictions based on your conclusion, then further experiments could be carried out to test them.

Always look for ways to improve your investigations...

You're likely to be asked for improvements to a method, or to comment on the quality of results in the Practical Test (or in the alternative paper), so make sure you know the points on this page.

Practice Papers

Once you've been through all the questions in this book, you should feel pretty confident about the exams. As final preparation, here is a set of <u>practice exam papers</u> to really get you ready for the real thing.

Cambridge International GCSE Physics

Paper 1 Multiple Choice (Core)

In addition to this paper you should have:
• A soft pencil.
• A calculator.
• An eraser.

Centre name					
Centre number					
Candidate number					

Time allowed:
• 45 minutes

Candidate name	
Candidate signature	

Instructions to candidates
• Write your name and other details in the spaces provided above.
• Use pencil to record your answers.
• For each question, clearly shade the oval next to your chosen answer. For example: ●
  If you wish to change your answer, use an eraser to remove your original answer.
• Do all rough work on the paper.
• Take the weight of a 1 kg mass to be 9.8 N, and the acceleration of free fall to be 9.8 m/s^2.

Information for candidates
• There are 40 marks available for this paper.
• Each question is worth one mark.

1   An empty plastic bottle is bobbing on water waves. The time taken for the bottle to complete
    20 oscillations is measured as 24 seconds. How long does each complete oscillation take?

    A 0.12 seconds   ⬭

    B 0.83 seconds   ⬭

    C 12 seconds   ⬭

    D 1.2 seconds   ⬭

2   The graph shows the distance-time graph for a car journey.

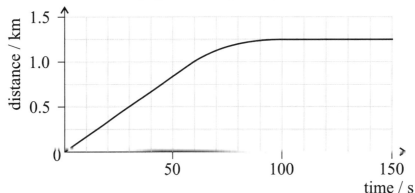

    During which time period is there a resultant force acting on the car?

    A Between 0 s and 30 s   ⬭

    B Between 30 s and 60 s   ⬭

    C Between 60 s and 100 s   ⬭

    D Between 100 s and 150 s   ⬭

3   Which quantity is represented by the area under a speed-time graph?

    A speed   ⬭

    B distance   ⬭

    C acceleration   ⬭

    D deceleration   ⬭

4   A rat has a mass of 1000 g. What is its weight?

    A 9.8 N   ⬭

    B 98 N   ⬭

    C 9800 N   ⬭

    D 0.98 N   ⬭

5   A cube is made of one of the four materials listed in the table.
    Its sides are 2 cm long and its mass is 9.6 g.

Material	Average density (g/cm^3)
Wood	0.83
Sandstone	2.4
Rubber	1.2
Gold alloy	19

    What material is the cube made from?

    A Wood ⬭   **B** Sandstone ⬭   **C** Rubber ⬭   **D** Gold alloy ⬭

6 The load-extension graph for an 18 cm long piece of elastic cord is shown on the right. What is the length of the elastic cord when a 5.6 N weight is suspended from it?

A 21.2 cm ○

B 3.2 cm ○

C 9.8 cm ○

D 27.8 cm ○

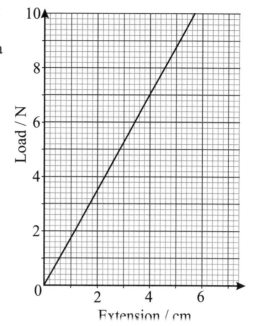

7 The diagrams show four runners who are running in windy weather. Which runner is experiencing the largest resultant force?

80 N ← → 100 N   10 N ← → 15 N   100 N ← → 130 N   190 N ← → 200 N

A ○   B ○   C ○   D ○

8 Two people reach a manual revolving door at the same time. Each person pushes one wing of the door with a different force and at a different distance from the pivot, as shown in the diagram below.

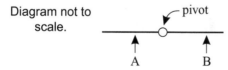

Diagram not to scale.

pivot

A   B

Person A pushes with force of 42 N, 0.5 m from the pivot.
Person B pushes with force of 30 N, 0.7 m from the pivot.
What will happen to the door?

A It will turn clockwise about the pivot. ○

B It will turn anticlockwise about the pivot. ○

C It will stay still because it is in equilibrium. ○

D It is impossible to tell from the information given. ○

9 A child releases a stretched elastic band so that it fires a ball bearing horizontally.
Which statement correctly describes the energy transfer when the elastic band is released?

A Energy is transferred mechanically from the elastic energy store
of the band to the kinetic energy store of the ball.

B Energy is transferred mechanically from the elastic energy store
of the band to the gravitational potential energy store of the ball.

C Energy is transferred mechanically from the nuclear energy store
of the band to the kinetic energy store of the ball.

D Energy is transferred mechanically from the chemical energy store
of the band to the elastic energy store of the band.

10 Which list **only** contains sources that release carbon dioxide when used to generate electricity?

A oil, nuclear fuel, coal

B nuclear fuel, gas, hydroelectricity

C wind, hydroelectricity, oil

D oil, gas, coal

11 Two cranes, X and Y, lift two identical boxes, both with the same mass.
Each box is lifted from the ground to 2 m above the ground. Both cranes have the same
efficiency and are operating at maximum power. Crane Y lifts the box faster than crane X.
Which of the following statements is correct?

A Crane X has a higher power than crane Y.

B Crane Y has a higher power than crane X.

C Crane X and crane Y have the same power.

D It is impossible to tell from the information given.

12 Two tables are shown below. The tables each have a mass of 10 kg, and each has uniform density.

X   Y

Which table exerts the lowest pressure on the ground and which is the least stable?

	Lowest pressure exerted on ground	Least stable
A	X	Y
B	Y	Y
C	X	X
D	Y	X

13 A student looks at some smoke particles suspended in air, using the equipment shown on the right.

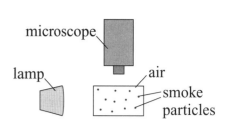

Which row of the table correctly describes the motion of the smoke particles observed by the student and the explanation for it?

	Motion of smoke particles	Explanation
A ⚬	Random	Smoke particles only change direction when they collide with other smoke particles.
B ⚬	Straight lines	Smoke particles only change direction when they collide with the container walls.
C ⚬	Random	Smoke particles change direction when air molecules collide with them.
D ⚬	Stationary	Smoke particles are bombarded equally on all sides by air molecules.

14 The diagrams below show three different containers.
They are each at the same temperature, and contain the same amount of gas.

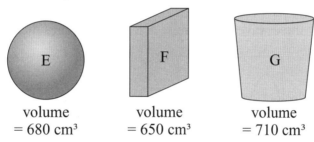

E	F	G
volume = 680 cm³	volume = 650 cm³	volume = 710 cm³

Which of the following statements is true?

A Container E contains gas at a higher pressure than container F. ⚬

B Container F contains gas at a higher pressure than container G. ⚬

C Container G contains gas at a higher pressure than container E. ⚬

D The gas in each of the containers is at the same pressure. ⚬

15 The graph on the right shows the temperature of a substance against time as it is heated.

What is the melting point of the substance?

A 7 °C ⚬

B 58 °C ⚬

C −7 °C ⚬

D −10 °C ⚬

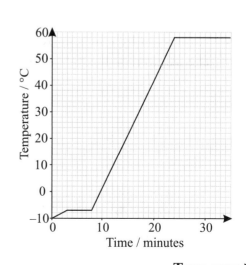

Turn over ▶

Practice Paper 1

16 An experiment is set up, as shown on the right. After some time, the temperature of the water in beaker F has risen by 8 °C. Copper is a good thermal conductor. How is energy transferred between the water in beaker E and the water in beaker F?

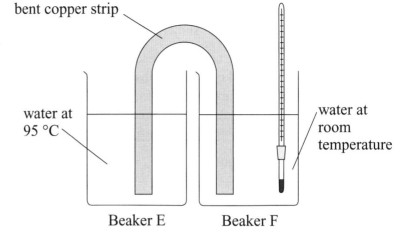

bent copper strip

water at 95 °C

water at room temperature

Beaker E   Beaker F

A convection only

B conduction only

C conduction and radiation

D radiation and evaporation

17 Which of the following is true for longitudinal waves?

A Their frequency is the distance between the same point on adjacent waves.

B They can be reflected.

C Their oscillations are at right angles to the direction that energy is transferred.

D Matter is transferred when they travel through a medium.

18 The diagrams below show three waves on strings. Each diagram has the same scale.

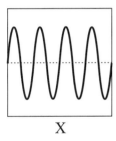
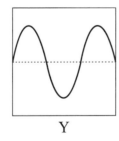
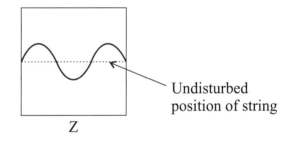

X   Y   Z

Undisturbed position of string

Which of the following statements is correct?

A X and Y have the same amplitude.

B Y and Z have the same amplitude.

C X and Z have the same amplitude.

D None of the waves have the same amplitude.

19 Two rays of light hit a mirror and are reflected.
The diagram on the right shows the paths of the two reflected rays.
Which diagram below correctly shows the paths of the incident rays?

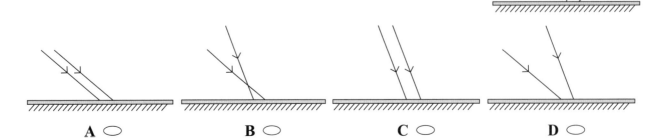

A   B   C   D

20 The diagram on the right shows a light ray reflected from
    a fish under water. Light travels faster in air than in water.
    Which ray shows how the ray refracts as it moves into the air?

    A ⬭
    B ⬭
    C ⬭
    D ⬭

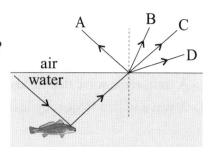

21 Which diagram correctly shows a light ray parallel to
    the principal axis refracting through a converging lens?

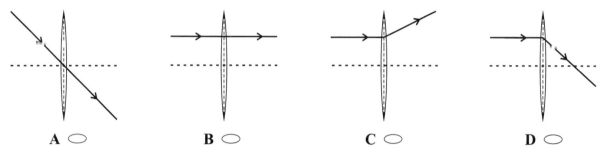

    A ⬭   B ⬭   C ⬭   D ⬭

22 A beam of light is shone through a glass prism.
    What colours appear at the sides of the emergent
    beam labelled P and Q, and why?

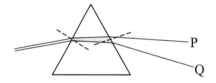

	Colour at P	Colour at Q	Reason
A ⬭	red	violet	Red light refracts more than violet light.
B ⬭	violet	red	Red light refracts more than violet light.
C ⬭	violet	red	Red light refracts less than violet light.
D ⬭	red	violet	Red light refracts less than violet light.

23 Which row gives a device which is likely to use infrared radiation
    and a device that is likely to use microwaves?

	Infrared	Microwaves
A ⬭	television remote control	satellite television
B ⬭	car radio	satellite television
C ⬭	airport baggage scanner	intruder alarm
D ⬭	satellite television	medical scanner

Turn over ▶

24 Which of the following could describe an ultrasound wave?

    A A wave that can travel through a vacuum, produced by a vibrating source. ◯

    B A longitudinal wave with a frequency greater than 20 000 Hz. ◯

    C A transverse wave that needs a medium to travel through. ◯

    D A wave with a frequency less than 20 Hz and a very low amplitude. ◯

25 Which statement about magnets is true?

    A Like poles of two magnets attract each other. ◯

    B A magnet only has a magnetic field at its north pole. ◯

    C Magnetic field lines point from the north pole to the south pole of a magnet. ◯

    D The force between a magnet and a magnetic material can be attractive or repulsive. ◯

26 An ammeter is connected to a circuit made of metal wires. It displays a reading of 0.5 A. What is the ammeter measuring?

    A The energy transferred in the circuit. ◯

    B The flow of electrons through the wires in the circuit. ◯

    C The flow of positive metal ions through the wires in the circuit. ◯

    D The overall electric charge on the wires of the circuit. ◯

27 A student measures the resistances of different pieces of wire.
The pieces are all made of the same material and all have the same length but they have different cross-sectional areas. Which graph does the student produce from his results?

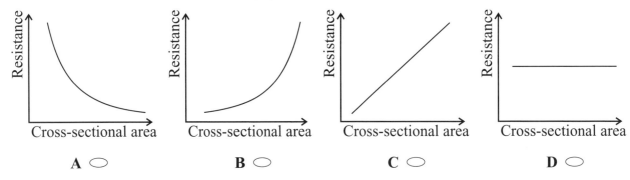

    A ◯   **B** ◯   **C** ◯   **D** ◯

28 Which of the following statements describes the circuit shown below?

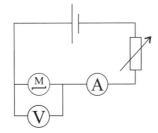

    A The circuit contains a motor and a fuse connected in parallel. ◯

    B The circuit contains a motor and a variable resistor connected in series. ◯

    C The circuit contains a variable resistor and a fuse connected in series. ◯

    D The circuit contains a motor and a variable resistor connected in parallel. ◯

29 A simple circuit is shown on the right. Each bulb has a resistance of 1 Ω. What are the currents measured by ammeters A_1 and A_2?

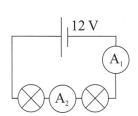

	Reading on A_1	Reading on A_2
A ○	6 A	6 A
B ○	6 A	3 A
C ○	1.5 A	1.5 A
D ○	3 A	1.5 A

30 Two resistors are connected in a circuit, as shown in the diagram on the right. Which of the following statements about the total resistance of this circuit is **true**?

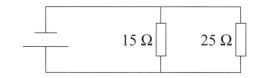

A The total resistance is equal to 40 Ω. ○

B The total resistance is equal to 15 Ω. ○

C The total resistance is less than 15 Ω. ○

D The total resistance is greater than 25 Ω. ○

31 A fault develops in the circuits below, which causes a very large current to flow through the circuits. In which circuit will both the circuit devices be cut off from the power supply when this happens?

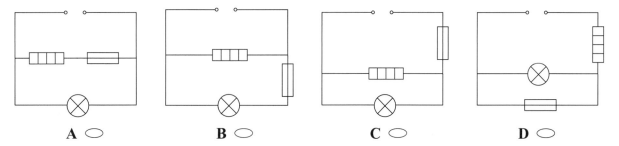

32 The diagram shows a solenoid with a current flowing through it. Five points mark where a compass has been placed.

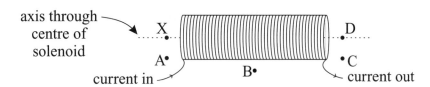

Which point (A, B, C or D) will have the compass needle pointing in the same direction as the compass needle at point X?

A ○   B ○   C ○   D ○

33 The diagram on the right shows a current-carrying wire in a
    magnetic field between the poles of two magnets. The wire
    experiences a downwards force. The direction of the current
    is reversed, and the poles of the magnets are swapped.
    Which row of the table below shows what happens to the force on the wire?

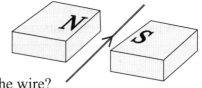

	Size of force	Direction of force
A ○	increases	no change
B ○	no change	changes
C ○	increases	changes
D ○	no change	no change

34 A student uses a transformer to reduce the voltage of an electricity supply from 12 V to 3 V.
    Which row of the table below shows the correct number of turns on the primary and secondary
    coils of the transformer?

	Number of turns on primary coil	Number of turns on secondary coil
A ○	20	40
B ○	20	5
C ○	12	12
D ○	3	12

35 The protons and neutrons in different nuclides are shown below.
    Protons are shown as black circles and neutrons are shown as grey circles.
    Which diagram shows two nuclides that are isotopes of each other?

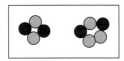   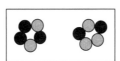   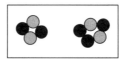   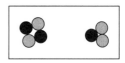

A ○   B ○   C ○   D ○

36 A nuclide contains 3 protons and 4 neutrons. What is the symbol of the nuclide?

    A $^{7}_{4}$Li ○

    B $^{4}_{3}$Li ○

    C $^{4}_{7}$Li ○

    D $^{7}_{3}$Li ○

37 A scientist carries out an experiment to investigate two different radioactive sources.
A set-up of her experiment is shown. She changes the material between the source and
the Geiger-Muller tube and measures the count rate. A table of her results is also shown.

Material	Count rate (counts per minute)	
	Source A	Source B
No material	854	1203
Paper	7	1200
Aluminium	6	8
Lead	6	7

Which of these sources is experiencing atoms decaying to form atoms of a different element?

A Both sources A and B

B Source A but not source B

C Source B but not source A

D Neither source A or source B

38 Nobelium-259 has a half-life of 58 minutes.
The count-rates of four isotopes are measured each hour and recorded in the table below.
Which row shows the count-rate for the isotope most likely to be nobelium-259?

	Initial count rate (count/second)	Count rate after 1 hour (count/second)	Count rate after 2 hours (count/second)
A	600	293	143
B	400	50	6
C	1000	685	469
D	300	252	212

39 When the northern hemisphere of the Earth is tilted towards the Sun,
it is summer in the northern hemisphere. Which statement correctly
describes the effect this will have on the southern hemisphere?

A The southern hemisphere spends more time in sunlight and
the Sun's rays are more intense, so it experiences summer.

B The southern hemisphere spends less time in sunlight and
the Sun's rays are less intense, so it experiences winter.

C The southern hemisphere spends less time in sunlight and
the Sun's rays are less intense, so it experiences summer.

D The southern hemisphere spends more time in sunlight and
the Sun's rays are more intense, so it experiences winter.

40 Some scientists are receiving a message from a probe on the surface of Mars.
The probe sends a message using radio waves. When the message is sent, the distance
between the Earth and Mars is 2.43×10^{11} m. The speed of light is 3.0×10^8 m/s.
Calculate how long it takes for the message to reach the Earth in minutes and seconds.

A 810 minutes

B 13 minutes and 50 seconds

C 13 minutes and 30 seconds

D 13 minutes and 5 seconds

END OF QUESTIONS

Practice Exam Paper
Cambridge International
GCSE Physics

Cambridge International GCSE Physics

Paper 2 Multiple Choice (Extended)

In addition to this paper you should have:
- A soft pencil.
- A calculator.
- An eraser.

Centre name					
Centre number					
Candidate number					

Time allowed:
- 45 minutes

Candidate name
Candidate signature

Instructions to candidates
- Write your name and other details in the spaces provided above.
- Use pencil to record your answers.
- For each question, clearly shade the oval next to your chosen answer. For example: ⬤
  If you wish to change your answer, use an eraser to remove your original answer.
- Do all rough work on the paper.
- Take the weight of a 1 kg mass to be 9.8 N, and the acceleration of free fall to be 9.8 m/s^2.

Information for candidates
- There are 40 marks available for this paper.
- Each question is worth one mark.

1   A student sets up two identical light gates, as shown below, so that an object
    passes through them in a straight line. He uses the light gates to record the
    time at which the object passes through them, and then calculates the difference
    to find the time taken for the object to travel between the light gates.

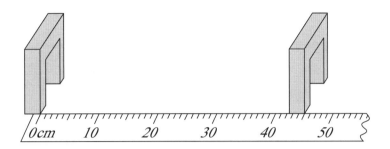

Which sentence is correct?

A   The distance travelled by the object in the time recorded is 42 cm.   ◯

B   The distance travelled by the object in the time recorded is 44 cm.   ◯

C   The distance travelled by the object in the time recorded is 45 cm.   ◯

D   The distance travelled by the object in the time recorded varies.   ◯

2   The diagram shows two forces acting on a plane — the force of lift acting
    vertically and the force of thrust provided by the engines acting horizontally.

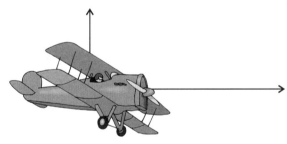

Which of the following shows the correct way to find the resultant force acting on the plane from
a scale drawing of these forces acting on it? The dashed lines represent the forces shown above,
and the solid line represents the resultant force of these forces.

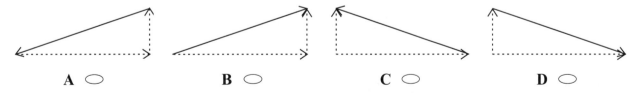

A ◯   B ◯   C ◯   D ◯

3   Which of the following describes a vector?

A   Vector quantities have magnitude but do not have direction.   ◯

B   Vector quantities show direction but do not have magnitude.   ◯

C   Vector quantities have both magnitude and direction.   ◯

D   Vector quantities do not have a magnitude or a direction.   ◯

4 A bear runs with a constant acceleration for 10 s before running at a constant speed of 8 m/s for a further 10 s. Which of the following speed-time graphs shows this?

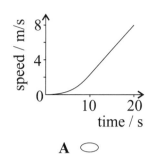
A ○

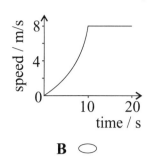
B ○

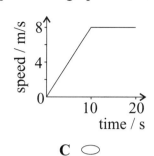
C ○

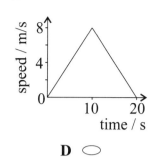
D ○

5 A rocket is moving at a constant velocity in space (a vacuum).
In order to change its velocity, it turns on its thrusters.
The mass of the rocket is 110 000 kg and it accelerates at 5.0 m/s^2.
What force is provided by the thrusters?

A 550 000 N   ○

B 55 000 N   ○

C 22 000 N   ○

D 220 000 N   ○

6 Two marbles are balanced on a plank that is pivoted at its centre of mass, as shown below.
The marbles have identical volumes. The density of marble A is 2.5 g/cm^3.

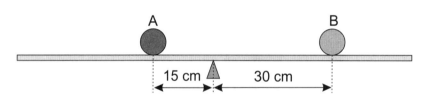

What is the density of marble B?

A 1.25 g/cm^3 ○

B 2.5 g/cm^3 ○

C 5.0 g/cm^3 ○

D It is impossible to tell from the information given.   ○

7 A full trailer is pulled by a car travelling north at 20 km/h.
The car stops and the trailer is unloaded, which halves the mass of the trailer.
The car travels back south at 40 km/h, pulling the empty trailer.
How will the trailer's momentum have changed compared to when it was travelling north?

		Momentum magnitude	Momentum sign
A	○	Doubles	Changes
B	○	No change	Changes
C	○	Doubles	No change
D	○	Halves	No change

8   Part of a tall building with an elevator (lift) is shown in the diagram.
The empty elevator has a mass of 1000 kg.
The distance between each floor is 5.00 m.

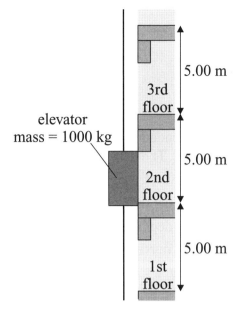

How much energy is transferred to an empty elevator's gravitational potential energy store
when it moves from the second floor to the sixth floor?

A 19.6 kJ   ⬭

B 49 kJ   ⬭

C 196 kJ   ⬭

D 1.96 kJ   ⬭

9   The flow diagram shows the energy transfers that occur when a skydiver jumps out of a plane.
One of the boxes is missing its label.

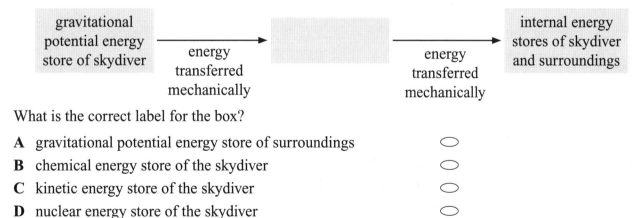

What is the correct label for the box?

A gravitational potential energy store of surroundings   ⬭

B chemical energy store of the skydiver   ⬭

C kinetic energy store of the skydiver   ⬭

D nuclear energy store of the skydiver   ⬭

10 An electric kettle has an efficiency of 75%. 2400 J of energy is transferred from the mains to the
kettle every second. When the kettle is full, it needs to transfer 540 000 J of energy to the water
to boil it. How long does a full kettle need to be switched on for in order to boil the water?

A 400 seconds   ⬭

B 169 seconds   ⬭

C 225 seconds   ⬭

D 300 seconds   ⬭

11   During a wash cycle, a washing machine operates with a power of 1000 W for 50 minutes.
     What is the work done by the washing machine during this cycle?

A   3000 kJ

B   50 kJ

C   40 kJ

D   0.2 kJ

12   An underwater camera is only recommended to be used under water if the pressure
     on it due to the water is 250 kPa or less. The density of fresh water is 1000 kg/m^3,
     and the density of seawater is 1030 kg/m^3. Which of the following statements is true?

A   The camera can be used at a greater depth in seawater than in fresh water.

B   The camera can be used at a greater depth in fresh water than in seawater.

C   The camera can be used to the same maximum depth in both fresh water and seawater.

D   The camera cannot be used in seawater.

13   Which sentence about the density of the different states of the same substance is correct?

A   The liquid state is usually less dense than the gas state.

B   The liquid state is usually more dense than the solid state.

C   The solid state is usually more dense than the gas state.

D   The solid, liquid and gas states usually have the same density.

14   What is the name and temperature of the point at which the particles of a substance
     have the minimum possible energy in their kinetic energy stores?

A   freezing point, –273 K

B   absolute zero, –273 °C

C   freezing point, 273 K

D   absolute zero, 0 °C

15   A rivet is heated and pushed through holes in two metal plates.
     A cross-section of the hot rivet and the plates is shown below.

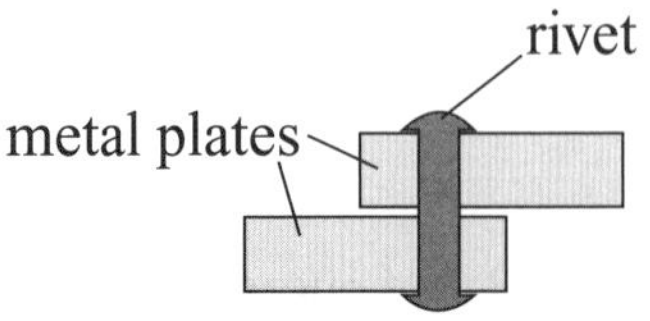

Which of the following happens as the rivet cools?

A   The particles in the rivet move closer together.

B   Energy is transferred to the kinetic energy stores of the particles in the rivet.

C   Energy is transferred to the internal energy store of the rivet.

D   The amount of infrared radiation the rivet emits each second increases.

16   The specific heat capacities of two samples of liquid, P and Q, are being investigated using the apparatus shown below. 8 kJ of energy is supplied to each sample using an immersion heater. The temperature change for each sample is shown in the table below.

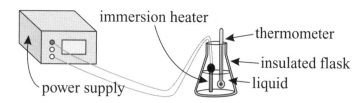

Sample	Mass (kg)	Temperature change (°C)
P	0.20	20
Q	0.10	20

Which of the following statements is true?

A   The specific heat capacities of sample P and sample Q are equal.

B   The specific heat capacity of sample P is four times larger than that of Sample Q.

C   The specific heat capacity of sample Q is twice that of sample P.

D   The specific heat capacity of sample P is twice that of sample Q.

17   A beaker contains a salt solution. A student wants the water in the solution to evaporate as quickly as possible to obtain the salt crystals. Which of the following would increase the rate of evaporation from the salt solution?

A   Pouring the solution into a narrow test tube.

B   Placing the beaker in a cooler place.

C   Fanning the surface of the solution.

D   Adding more water to the salt solution.

18   A student drops some purple potassium permanganate crystals down the side of a beaker filled with cold water. They then heat the edge of the beaker near the crystals using a Bunsen burner. The crystals slowly dissolve to form a purple solution at the bottom edge of the beaker. Which diagram shows how the purple colour will spread out in the beaker?

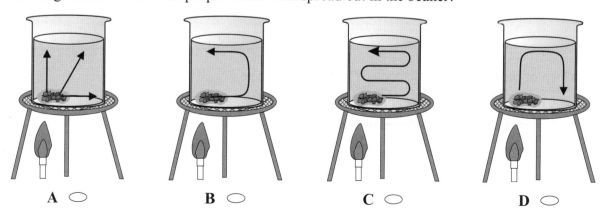

A   B   C   D

19 A ray of light meets the boundary between two media at an angle of 25° to the normal.
Light travels slower in the second medium than in the first.
Which of the following is a possible value of the angle of refraction?

A 80° ⬭

B 64° ⬭

C 25° ⬭

D 17° ⬭

20 The diagram shows light refracting at an air-glass boundary.
Which calculation gives the refractive index of the glass?

A sin(45°) ÷ sin(28°) ⬭

B sin(28°) ÷ sin(45°) ⬭

C sin(45°) × sin(28°) ⬭

D 1 ÷ sin(45°) ⬭

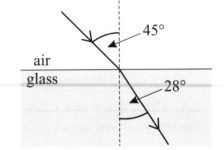

21 A ray of light is directed into a semicircular block, as shown in the diagram.
It undergoes total internal reflection. The critical angle of the boundary is *c*.

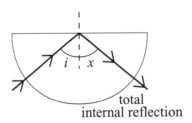

Which of the following statements is correct?

A Angle *i* is less than *c*. ⬭

B Angle *i* is greater than *c*. ⬭

C Angle i is less than angle *x*. ⬭

D *i* is equal to 1 ÷ sin *c*. ⬭

22 Which of the following statements is **false**?

A A mirror produces a virtual image. ⬭

B Real images can be produced on screens. ⬭

C Real images formed using converging lenses are always inverted. ⬭

D Real images are always formed at the principal focus of a lens. ⬭

23 Which of the following electromagnetic waves will diffract around a barrier more than microwaves?

   A radio waves   ○

   B visible light   ○

   C gamma rays   ○

   D infrared waves   ○

24 Which of the following statements about geostationary satellites is **false**?

   A Geostationary satellites orbit the Earth once every 24 hours.   ○

   B Geostationary satellites are only used for broadcasting television signals.   ○

   C Microwave signals can be sent to and from geostationary satellites.   ○

   D Satellite TV antennae can be pointed permanently at geostationary satellites.   ○

25 The diagram shows an experimental setup that a student uses to determine the speed of sound.

The student begins by positioning the speaker and the two microphones in a straight line. He then measures the distance between the microphones. The steps below outline a method he could use to determine the speed of sound, but they are not in the correct order.

	Statements
1	Work out the difference between the times to find the time it takes for a sound to travel between the microphones.
2	Use the data logger to record the time that each microphone detects a sound.
3	Use the formula speed = distance ÷ time to work out the speed of sound waves.
4	Play a sound through the speaker.

What is the correct order of the steps?

   A 1, 2, 4, 3   ○

   B 4, 2, 1, 3   ○

   C 4, 1, 3, 2   ○

   D 1, 4, 3, 2   ○

26 The diagram shows the graphs of sound waves X, Y and Z. Each graph has the same scale.

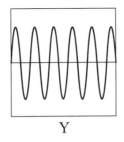
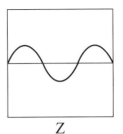

X   Y   Z

Which of the following statements is correct?

A X and Y have the same pitch and loudness. ◯

B X and Z have the same pitch but a different loudness. ◯

C X and Z have the same loudness but a different pitch. ◯

D None of the waves have the same pitch. ◯

27 Which of the following statements is **not** correct?

A All electric charges create an electric field. ◯

B An electric charge placed in an electric field will experience a force. ◯

C Electric charges only have an electric field when they're near other charges. ◯

D The forces caused by electric fields can be attractive or repulsive. ◯

28 A resistor is part of the circuit shown below.

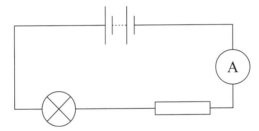

When 1 C of charge flows through the resistor, a total of 12 J of energy is transferred to the resistor. What is the potential difference across the resistor?

A 0.083 V ◯

B 1 V ◯

C 12 V ◯

D It is impossible to tell from the information given. ◯

29 Which is the correct current-voltage graph for a resistor of constant resistance?

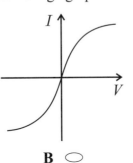
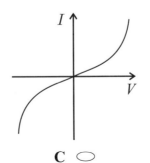
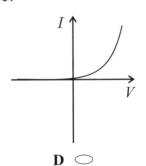

A ◯   **B** ◯   **C** ◯   **D** ◯

30 It takes 10 minutes and 72 kJ of energy for a small travel kettle to boil a certain amount of water. The kettle is connected to a 12 V electricity supply. What current flows through the circuit when the travel kettle is used?

    A 8640 A   ⬭

    B 10 A   ⬭

    C 600 A   ⬭

    D 0.1 A   ⬭

31 Which of the following is a unit of energy?

    A joules per second   ⬭

    B newtons   ⬭

    C kilowatt-hours   ⬭

    D watts   ⬭

32 A circuit is shown below. The light intensity decreases.
What happens to the resistance of the light-dependent resistor and the potential difference measured by the voltmeter?

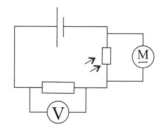

	Resistance of light-dependent resistor	Potential difference measured by voltmeter
A ⬭	decreases	decreases
B ⬭	increases	increases
C ⬭	increases	decreases
D ⬭	decreases	increases

33 A lawnmower has a power of 500 W and is run on a mains electricity supply of 120 V. Which fuse rating should the fuse fitted in the lawnmower have?

    A 2 A   ⬭

    B 3 A   ⬭

    C 5 A   ⬭

    D 7 A   ⬭

34 The diagram shows the field lines around a current-carrying wire. The current through the wire is **decreased**. Which row of the table correctly describes what happens to the field lines around the wire?

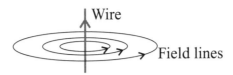

	Distance apart	Direction
A ⬭	Increases	Reverses
B ⬭	Decreases	Stays the same
C ⬭	Decreases	Reverses
D ⬭	Increases	Stays the same

35 The diagram shows a transformer. What is the current in the secondary coil? Assume the transformer is 100% efficient.

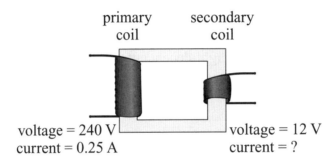

A 60 A   ⬭

B 3 A   ⬭

C 5 A   ⬭

D 0.0125 A ⬭

36 The diagram shows a shielding device used by a scientist who is doing an experiment involving a radioactive source.

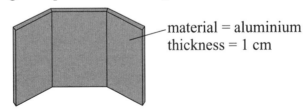

Which type of radiation is blocked by the shielding device?

A alpha radiation only   ⬭

B beta radiation only   ⬭

C alpha and beta radiation only   ⬭

D alpha, beta and gamma radiation ⬭

37 A radium nucleus $^{226}_{88}\text{Ra}$ usually decays by releasing alpha radiation.
Which of the following is a balanced equation showing this decay?

A $^{226}_{88}\text{Ra} \rightarrow {}^{222}_{86}\text{Rn} + {}^{4}_{2}\alpha$ ◯

B $^{226}_{88}\text{Ra} \rightarrow {}^{226}_{89}\text{Ac} + {}^{0}_{-1}\beta$ ◯

C $^{226}_{88}\text{Ra} \rightarrow {}^{222}_{88}\text{Ra} + {}^{4}_{2}\alpha$ ◯

D $^{226}_{88}\text{Ra} \rightarrow {}^{224}_{84}\text{Po} + {}^{2}_{4}\alpha$ ◯

38 Which of the following statements about the seasons experienced on Earth is true?

A All of Earth experiences summer at the same time. ◯

B The tilt of the Earth is what causes the different seasons. ◯

C There are two cycles through all the seasons during one orbit of the Earth around the Sun. ◯

D There is one cycle through all the seasons during one orbit of the Moon around the Earth. ◯

39 The diagram shows how the evolution of a star can continue after its stable period.

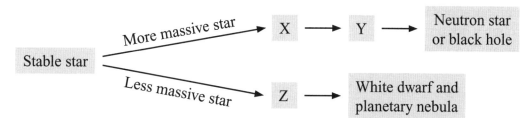

What do the labels X, Y and Z represent?

A X = red giant, Y = nebula, Z = supernova ◯

B X = red supergiant, Y = nebula, Z = red giant ◯

C X = red giant, Y = red supergiant, Z = supernova ◯

D X = red supergiant, Y = supernova, Z = red giant ◯

40 A star is moving away from Earth. Which of the following
statements about light emitted from the star is correct?

A The frequency of the light when it reaches Earth
is greater than that of the original light. ◯

B The speed of the light when it reaches Earth
is greater than that of the original light. ◯

C The wavelength of the light when it reaches Earth
is longer than that of the original light. ◯

D The light can never reach Earth. ◯

END OF QUESTIONS

Practice Exam Paper
Cambridge International
GCSE Physics

Cambridge International GCSE Physics

Paper 3 Theory (Core)

In addition to this paper you should have:
- A pen and pencil.
- A ruler.
- A calculator.

Centre name					
Centre number					
Candidate number					

Time allowed:
- 1 hour 15 minutes

Candidate name
Candidate signature

Instructions to candidates
- Write your name and other details in the spaces provided above.
- Use blue or black ink to write your answers.
- Answer all questions in the spaces provided.
- Do all rough work on the paper.
- Cross out any work you do not want to be marked.
- In calculations, show clearly how you worked out your answers.
- Take the weight of a 1 kg mass to be 9.8 N, and the acceleration of free fall to be 9.8 m/s^2.

Information for candidates
- The marks available are given in brackets at the end of each question part.
- There are 80 marks available for this paper.

1   A swimmer swims the full length of a 20 metre long swimming pool in a straight line.
    The distance-time graph in **Figure 1** shows her motion.

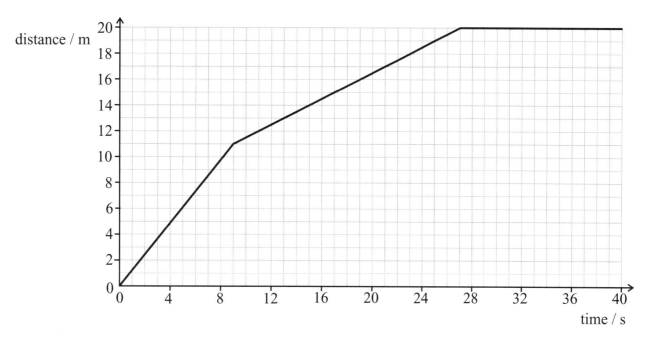

Figure 1

(a) Determine how long it takes for the swimmer to swim the length of the pool.

time = ... s

[1]

(b) Describe, without doing any calculations, how to use the graph
    to calculate the swimmer's average speed during the time she was moving.

....

....

....

....

[2]

(c) A camera travels along the length of the pool to film the swim. It sets off at the same time
    as the swimmer. It travels at a constant speed, and reaches the end of the pool in 25 s.

    (i)   Calculate the speed of the camera.

speed = ... m/s

[3]

Question 1 continues on the next page

(ii) On **Figure 1**, draw a distance-time graph to represent the motion of the camera.

[2]

(iii) The camera cannot film the swimmer if it is behind her. Using **Figure 1**, explain whether the camera will be able to film the swimmer for the whole length.

....

....

....

....

[2]

[Total 10 marks]

2 A 1.8 kg book is resting on a table.

(a) Calculate the weight of the book.

weight = ... N

[3]

(b) A 5.0 N force is applied to the book so that the book slides across the table.
A 1.4 N frictional force acts on the book in the opposite direction, as shown in **Figure 2**.

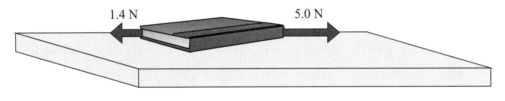

1.4 N   5.0 N

Figure 2

Calculate the size and direction of the resultant force acting on the book.

resultant force = ... N direction = ...

[2]

(c) Assuming the frictional force is always 1.4 N when the book is moving across the table, how should the 5 N force be changed so that the book moves at a constant speed?

....

[1]

(d) The applied force is removed and the book carries on moving in the same direction. Explain whether removing the force will affect the speed of the book.

....

....

[2]

[Total 8 marks]

3   Nuclear power stations and wind turbines can both be used to generate electricity.

(a) Describe the advantages and disadvantages of generating electricity using a nuclear power station compared with using wind turbines.

....

....

....

....

....

....

....

....

....

[4]

(b) Other types of power station use fossil fuels like oil or coal to generate electricity. Which energy store is energy released from when these fuels are used to generate electricity?

....

[1]

[Total 5 marks]

4 A lolly mainly consists of frozen water. The frozen lolly is removed from the freezer and is left outside on a warm day. Initially the lolly has a temperature of –3 °C. After an hour the lolly has completely melted. After four hours, the water from the melted lolly has evaporated. **Figure 3** shows the lolly starting to melt.

Figure 3

Figure 4 shows a representation of the water molecules of the lolly at one point in time.

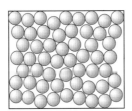

Figure 4

(a) Name the state of matter shown in **Figure 4**.

....

[1]

(b) State what happens to the amount of energy in the internal energy stores of the lolly after it is removed from the freezer.

....

[1]

(c) What happens to the temperature of the lolly as it is melting? Tick **one** box.

☐ The temperature increases.

☐ The temperature decreases.

☐ The temperature stays the same.

[1]

(d) Explain what happens to the water molecules near the surface
of the melted lolly as the water evaporates.

....

....

....

[2]

[Total 5 marks]

5 A student is investigating how good two materials are as thermal conductors.
Figure 5 shows her experimental setup. The rods are inserted into the hot water at the same time and the timer is started. She records the time taken for each bead to drop off.

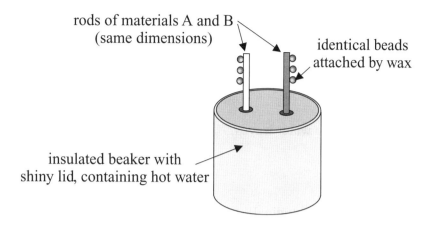

rods of materials A and B
(same dimensions)

identical beads
attached by wax

insulated beaker with
shiny lid, containing hot water

Figure 5

(a) (i) Material A is a good thermal conductor and material B is a thermal insulator.
Which rod will the beads stay on for longer? Justify your answer.

....

....

....
[2]

(ii) The shiny insulated lid is placed on the beaker to make sure that energy
is mainly transferred to the wax by conduction through the material rods.
Give two methods of thermal energy transfer that the insulating lid reduces.

....

....

....
[2]

(b) Material A is a conductive metal which is used to make kitchen pans.
A small gas flame is used to heat the bottom of a frying pan made from material A.

Explain why the food is heated evenly across the surface of the pan, even though the gas flame
only heats a small part of the bottom of the pan.

....

....

....
[2]

[Total 6 marks]

6 A stone is dropped in a pond, causing ripples to spread out across the surface.
Figure 6 shows a close-up of a cross-section of these water waves.

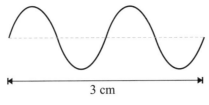

|←———— 3 cm ————→|

Figure 6

(a) What is the wavelength of the water waves?

wavelength = ... cm
[1]

(b) Waves can be transverse or longitudinal.

(i) A water wave is a transverse wave. What is meant by a transverse wave?

....

....
[1]

(ii) Give one other example of a transverse wave.

....
[1]

(c) The ripples pass from a deep part of the pond to a shallow part, causing the ripples to change
direction. **Figure 7** shows the wavefronts of the ripples changing direction.

deep water   shallow water

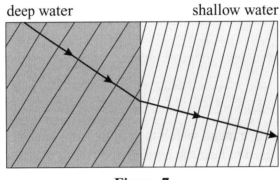

Figure 7

Tick the **two** statements below that are true.

☐ As the water waves pass into the shallower water, their wavelength increases.

☐ **Figure 7** shows the water waves undergoing refraction.

☐ As the water waves pass into the shallower water, they change speed.

☐ **Figure 7** shows the water waves undergoing diffraction.
[2]

[Total 5 marks]

7 **Figure 8** shows an incomplete ray diagram of a converging lens producing an image of an object.
The focal length and principal focus have not been labelled.

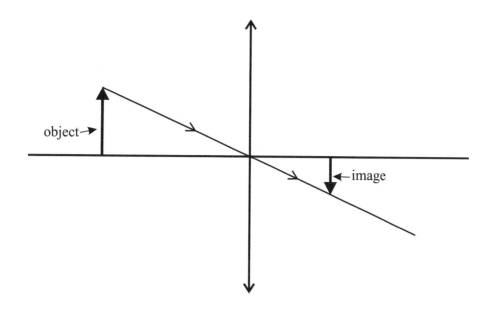

Figure 8

(a) What is meant by the focal length of a lens?

....

....

[1]

(b) Complete the ray diagram to show how the image is formed.
Mark the principal focus with a **clear cross** and label it as **F**.

[2]

(c) The image produced by the converging lens in **Figure 8** is a real image.
Describe two other characteristics of the image.

....

....

[2]

[Total 5 marks]

8   A girl combs her hair fifty times with the same comb. Afterwards, some of her hairs stand on end away from each other. The comb becomes negatively charged, as shown in **Figure 9**, and her hair becomes positively charged.

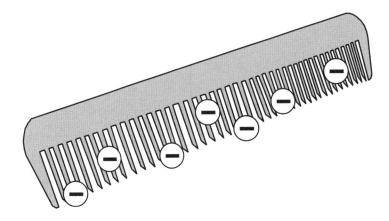

Figure 9

(a) Explain why the comb has become negatively charged.

....

....

[1]

(b) Explain why some of the girl's hairs stand on end away from each other.

....

....

....

[2]

(c) The comb is made of plastic, which is an electrical insulator. What is an electrical insulator?

....

[1]

[Total 4 marks]

9 A student is investigating the electrical circuit shown in **Figure 10**.

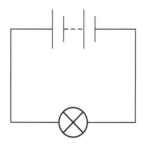

Figure 10

(a) The student wants to find the current through and potential difference across the lamp in the circuit. What **two** pieces of apparatus should she use and how should she connect each one in the circuit?

Apparatus 1 ....

Connection in circuit ....

Apparatus 2 ....

Connection in circuit ....

[4]

(b) The student finds the potential difference across the lamp is 3.0 V and the current through it is 1.2 A. Calculate the resistance of the lamp.

resistance = ... Ω

[3]

(c) Describe the energy transfer that takes place between the battery and the lamp.

....

....

[2]

(d) When a circuit used for lighting has multiple lamps, they are normally connected in parallel. State **two** advantages of connecting lamps in parallel compared to connecting them in series.

....

....

....

[2]

[Total 11 marks]

10 The generator in a power station produces a voltage of 25 000 V.
    This is changed to 400 000 V by the transformer shown in **Figure 11**.

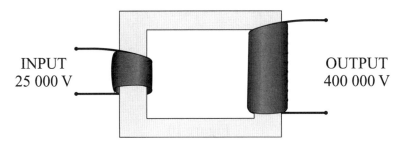

INPUT
25 000 V

OUTPUT
400 000 V

Figure 11

(a) Name the type of transformer shown in **Figure 11**.

....

[1]

(b) The primary coil has 5000 turns.
    Calculate the number of turns there must be on the secondary coil.

number of turns = ...

[3]

(c) Transformers are used to transmit electricity at a high voltage from power stations to homes.
    State one advantage of transmitting electricity at a high voltage.

....

....

[1]

(d) Transformers work because of electromagnetic induction.
    Describe how you could demonstrate electromagnetic induction.

....

....

....

....

[3]

[Total 8 marks]

11 A scientist wants to find the half-life of a source of polonium-210, which is an alpha emitter.
He sets up a Geiger-Muller tube and counter, and points it towards the source.
He records the measurement given by the Geiger-Muller tube and counter every day for 560 days.

(a) Polonium-210 has the nuclide notation $^{210}_{84}Po$.
How many neutrons are there in a polonium-210 nucleus?

....

[1]

(b) Suggest why not all of the radioactive emissions detected by the Geiger-Muller tube and
counter come from the source of polonium-210.

....

[1]

(c) **Figure 12** shows the graph of the scientist's results, corrected for the detected emissions that
were not from the source.

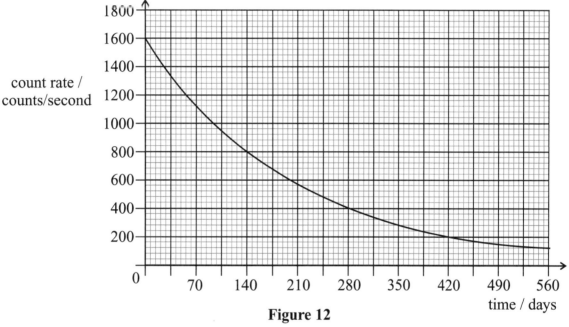

Figure 12

Using **Figure 12**, determine the half-life of polonium-210.

half-life = ... days

[3]

(d) Initially, the scientist's sample contained only polonium-210 atoms. After one half-life
has passed, what fraction of atoms in the sample will be polonium-210 atoms?
Explain your answer.

....

....

....

....

[3]

[Total 8 marks]

Turn over ▶

12 The Moon orbits the Earth due to the force of gravity between the two bodies.

(a) **Figure 13** shows how the appearance of the Moon in the night sky changes over a period of 28 days (approximately one month).

28 days

Figure 13

Explain how the motion of the Earth and Moon cause the Moon's appearance to change in this way.

....

....

....

....

[2]

(b) The gravitational field strength on the surface of the Moon is 1.6 N/kg.

(i) How does this differ from the gravitational field strength on the surface of the Earth?

....

....

[1]

(ii) State two factors that affect the gravitational field strength around a planet or moon.

1. ....

2. ....

[2]

[Total 5 marks]

END OF QUESTIONS

Cambridge International GCSE Physics

Paper 4 Theory (Extended)

In addition to this paper you should have: • A pen and pencil. • A ruler. • A calculator.	Centre name _____ Centre number ☐☐☐☐☐ Candidate number ☐☐☐☐☐

Time allowed:
• 1 hour 15 minutes

Candidate name _____

Candidate signature _____

Instructions to candidates
• Write your name and other details in the spaces provided above.
• Use blue or black ink to write your answers.
• Answer all questions in the spaces provided.
• Do all rough work on the paper.
• Cross out any work you do not want to be marked.
• In calculations, show clearly how you worked out your answers.
• Take the weight of a 1 kg mass to be 9.8 N, and the acceleration of free fall to be 9.8 m/s^2.

Information for candidates
• The marks available are given in brackets at the end of each question part.
• There are 80 marks available for this paper.

1   **Figure 1** shows a Ferris wheel at a fairground. The designers of the wheel had to consider where its centre of gravity would be, to ensure the wheel would be stable enough to be safe to ride on.

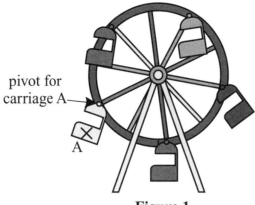

pivot for
carriage A→

A

Figure 1

(a) What is meant by the centre of gravity of an object?

....

....

[1]

(b) State the relationship between the height of the
centre of gravity of the Ferris wheel and its stability.

....

....

[1]

(c) **Figure 1** shows the point at which the Ferris wheel has just stopped moving.
Each carriage is attached to the wheel at a single point, called a pivot, that it can rotate around.
The cross on the diagram marks the position of the centre of gravity of carriage A.
Explain how carriage A will move after the wheel stops.

....

....

....

....

....

[2]

Figure 2 shows the masses, velocities and momentums of two dodgem cars just before a collision.

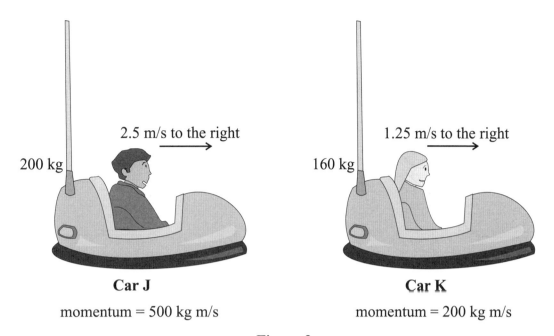

2.5 m/s to the right

200 kg

Car J

momentum = 500 kg m/s

1.25 m/s to the right

160 kg

Car K

momentum = 200 kg m/s

Figure 2

(d) The two dodgems collide when **Car J** drives into the back of **Car K**.
State the principle of conservation of momentum for this event.

....

....
[1]

(e) Immediately after the collision, **Car J** has a momentum of 250 kg m/s to the right.
Calculate the velocity of **Car K** after the collision.
Include the direction of travel in your answer.

velocity = ... to the ....
[3]

(f) Each car experiences a resultant force during the collision. The dodgem cars have rubber
bumpers added to them to increase the time they are in contact during a collision. What is the
effect of increasing the time taken for a collision on the resultant force experienced by the cars?

....
[1]

[Total 9 marks]

2 At the start of a roller coaster ride, a carriage is raised through a vertical height of 25 m from point A to point B, as shown in **Figure 3**.

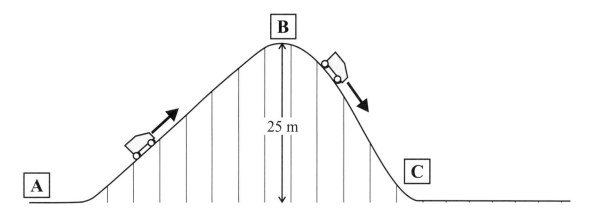

Figure 3

The mass of an empty carriage is 610 kg.

(a) Calculate the amount of energy transferred to the gravitational potential energy store of an empty carriage when it is raised from point A to point B.

energy transferred = ...

[2]

(b) During one test, the carriage is held at rest at point B and then drops from point B to point C, as shown in **Figure 3**. Point B is 25 m above point C.
Calculate the speed of an empty carriage as it reaches point C,
assuming there is no friction or air resistance acting on the carriage.

speed = ...

[3]

(c) At the end of the ride, the carriage applies its brakes to come to a stop on a flat section of track. The brakes provide a constant force of 7200 N. Assume that no friction or air resistance acts on the carriage, other than the braking force.

    (i) On one day the empty carriage travels 32 m between the brakes being applied and coming to a stop. How much energy was stored in the kinetic energy store of the empty carriage when the brakes were applied?

energy stored = ...

[2]

    (ii) On a different day the empty carriage is travelling at the same speed when the brakes are applied, but this time the brakes provide a constant force of 6500 N. State what effect this will have on the distance travelled by the empty carriage between the brakes being applied and it coming to a stop.

....

....

[1]
[Total 8 marks]

3 **Figure 4** shows a sealed gas cylinder divided into two sections. Initially, only the larger section holds helium gas. The smaller section is a vacuum. The larger section has a volume of 1.5×10^{-3} m^3 and the helium gas inside is at a pressure of 1.1×10^5 Pa and a temperature of 24 °C.

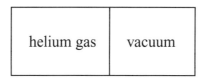

Figure 4

(a) The divider between the two sections of the cylinder is removed so that the helium gas fills the whole cylinder.

    (i)   The helium gas remains at a constant temperature of 24 °C.
         The volume of the helium gas is now 2.75×10^{-3} m^3.
         Calculate the pressure of the helium gas now.

pressure = ...

[2]

    (ii) Explain the change in the pressure of the helium that has occurred.

....

....

....

[2]

(b) The helium gas is held at a constant volume in the cylinder.
The cylinder is now heated so the temperature of the helium gas increases.
Describe and explain how this affects the pressure of the helium gas inside the cylinder.

....

....

....

....

....

[3]

[Total 7 marks]

4   A Leslie cube is shown in **Figure 5**. Each vertical side is painted with a different paint.

Figure 5

A student filled the cube with hot water and placed an infrared detector 10 cm from each face.
The student then recorded the intensity of infrared radiation measured by each detector.
The results are shown on the bar chart in **Figure 6**.

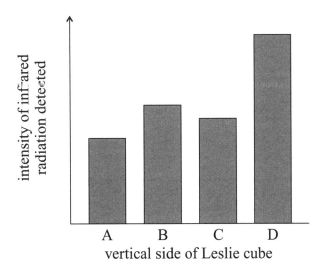

Figure 6

(a) Three of the sides are light coloured, and one side is dark coloured.
    Suggest which side, A-D, is dark coloured. Explain your answer.

    ....

    ....

    ....

    ....

    [3]

(b) State two other factors which affect the amount of radiation that would be emitted from each
    face of the cube.

    ....

    ....

    [2]

Question 4 continues on the next page

(c) The student paints four identical bricks with the same paints that were used to paint the vertical faces of the Leslie cube. He then leaves the bricks near an electric heater for the same amount of time, and at the same distance from the electric heater. When he returns, he finds that the dark coloured brick is hotter than the others. Explain this observation.

....

....

....

[1]

(d) Brick A had an initial temperature of 14 °C. After being near the electric heater, its final temperature was 15.2 °C. The specific heat capacity of the brick is 840 J/kg°C and its mass is 0.045 kg. Calculate the amount of energy that was transferred to brick A.

energy = ...

[2]

(e) The student places brick A outside in sunlight on a warm day.
He records the brick's temperature over time and finds that its
temperature increased early on but then stayed constant.
Explain the student's observations in terms of the absorption and emission of radiation.

....

....

....

....

[2]

[Total 10 marks]

5   A student is investigating light using a semicircular block of material with a refractive index of 1.5. Light is shone into the semicircular block at increasing angles to the normal. As shown in **Figure 7**, an angle, θ, is reached at which the light both refracts along the surface of the block and internally reflects.

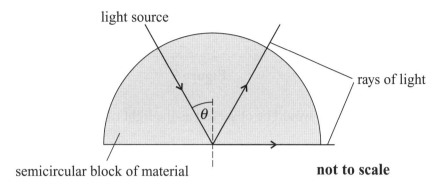

light source

rays of light

θ

semicircular block of material

not to scale

Figure 7

(a) State the name of the angle θ.

....

[1]

(b) Calculate the angle θ.

$\theta =$ ....

[2]

The material the block is made from can be used in optical fibres.
Optical fibres, such as the one shown in **Figure 8**, consist of a central core surrounded by cladding.

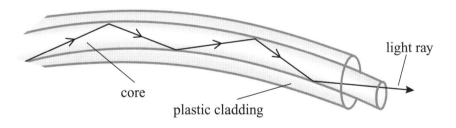

light ray

core

plastic cladding

Figure 8

(c) Explain why almost no light 'escapes' from an optical fibre when light rays travel along it.

....

....

....

[2]

[Total 5 marks]

Turn over ▶

6   A ray of white light enters a clear glass prism.
This is shown in **Figure 9**.

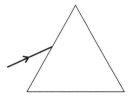

Figure 9

(a) Describe and explain what would be observed as the light ray exits the prism.

....

....

....

....

....

....

....

[4]

(b) The ray of white light is replaced by a ray of monochromatic light.
Explain any changes in observation that would result from this.

....

....

[1]

[Total 5 marks]

7   A remote control uses infrared radiation with a frequency of 2.5×10^{14} Hz
     to transmit signals to a television.

(a) State what is meant by the 'frequency' of infrared radiation.

     ....

     ....
                                                                                                                    [1]

(b) State the approximate speed of infrared radiation travelling through air.

     ....
                                                                                                                    [1]

(c) Calculate the wavelength of the infrared radiation used in the remote control.

                                                     wavelength = ...
                                                                                                                    [2]

The television is connected to a speaker, shown in **Figure 10**.
The speaker contains cones that can vibrate back and forth.

Figure 10

(d) Describe how sound waves are created by the speakers and how those sound waves then travel
    to someone's ear.

     ....

     ....

     ....

     ....

     ....
                                                                                                                    [2]
                                                                                                         [Total 6 marks]

8 Any electrically charged object creates an electric field around it.

(a) (i) What is an electric field?

    ....
    [1]

(ii) What does the direction of an electric field show?

    ....
    [1]

Figure 11 shows a negatively charged sphere supported on an insulated rod.

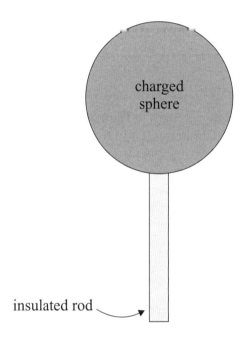

charged
sphere

insulated rod

Figure 11

(b) Sketch the pattern of the electric field around the sphere in **Figure 11**, and mark the direction of the field using arrows.

[3]

[Total 5 marks]

9   A student builds the circuit shown in **Figure 12**.

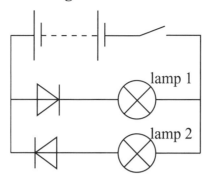

Figure 12

When the switch is closed, lamp 1 lights up, but lamp 2 does not.

(a) Explain why lamp 2 does not light up when the switch is closed.

....

....

....

....

[2]

The student connects one of the lamps into a different circuit, where she measures the current through and potential difference across the lamp for a range of values. She plots her results on a current-voltage graph and draws a line of best fit, shown in **Figure 13**.

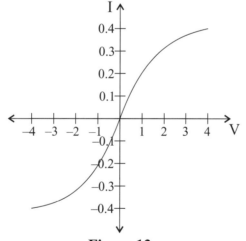

Figure 13

(b) Explain why the current-voltage graph has this shape.

....

....

....

....

....

....

[3]

Question 9 continues on the next page

Turn over ▶

The student wants to vary the brightness of the lamp. She intends to do this using a potential divider. **Figure 14** shows a potential divider.

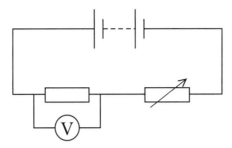

Figure 14

(c) Explain how increasing the resistance of the variable resistor changes the potential difference measured by the voltmeter.

....

....

....

....

....

....

....

....

[3]

[Total 8 marks]

10   **Figure 15** shows how a fan can be powered by an electric motor.
When current flows in the wire coil, the fan blades rotate.

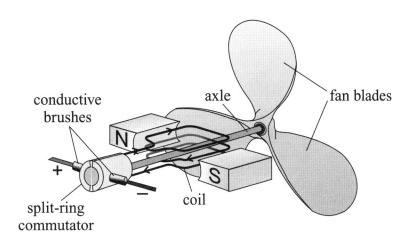

Figure 15

(a) Explain how the magnetic field causes the fan blades to rotate when current flows in the
wire coil.

....

....

....

....

....

[2]

(b) Explain the purpose of the split-ring commutator.

....

....

....

....

[2]

(c) State one way that the turning effect of the fan could be increased.

....

[1]

Question 10 continues on the next page

Figure 16 shows a set-up of a circuit within a magnetic field.
When the switch is closed, current flows through the metal bar in the direction shown by the arrows.
The metal bar is free to move along the rails and is made of a non-magnetic material.

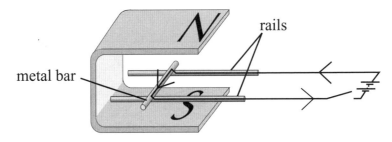

Figure 16

(d) State which way the bar will roll when the switch is closed.

....

[1]

(e) State one way that the set-up could be changed so that the bar will roll the other way.

....

[1]

[Total 7 marks]

11 A scientist is investigating a radioactive isotope called isotope X.

(a) What is meant by the term 'isotopes'?

....

....

[1]

The scientist directed radioactive emissions from isotope X between two electrically charged plates. The electric field has the same strength everywhere between the plates. The paths of the radiation through the electric field are shown in **Figure 17**.

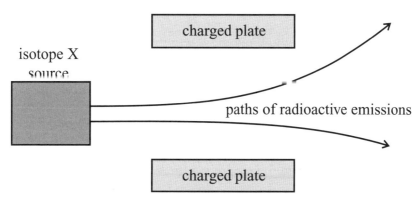

Figure 17

(b) Explain how the paths shown in **Figure 17** show that isotope X emits alpha and beta particles.
    Your answer should refer to how electric fields interact with charged particles.

....

....

....

....

....

....

....

[4]

[Total 5 marks]

12 An astronomer studies comets which orbit the Sun in an elliptical orbit.
One of these orbits is shown in **Figure 18**.

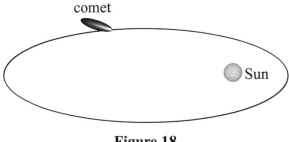

comet

Sun

Figure 18

(a) Explain, in terms of energy transfers, why the speed of a comet changes during its orbit.

....

....

....

....

....

....

[3]

(b) The astronomer determines that the average radius of another comet's
orbit is 1.13×10^{12} m and its average orbital speed is 10 900 m/s.
What is the orbital period of this comet in years? Assume that 1 year = 365 days.

orbital period = ...

[2]

[Total 5 marks]

END OF QUESTIONS

Practice Paper 5

As part of your assessment, you will take either a practical test (Paper 5) or a written alternative to the practical test (Paper 6). You should check with your teacher which one of those options you'll be taking. Both papers will test your knowledge of experimental skills and investigations. This practice paper is the equivalent of Paper 6 in the exams.

CGP Practice Exam Paper
Cambridge International
GCSE Physics

Cambridge International GCSE Physics

Paper 5 Alternative to Practical

In addition to this paper you should have:
- A pen and pencil.
- A ruler.
- A calculator.

Centre name					
Centre number					
Candidate number					

Time allowed:
- 1 hour

Candidate name	
Candidate signature	

Instructions to candidates
- Write your name and other details in the spaces provided above.
- Use blue or black ink to write your answers.
- Answer all questions in the spaces provided.
- Do all rough work on the paper.
- Cross out any work you do not want to be marked.
- In calculations, show clearly how you worked out your answers.

Information for candidates
- The marks available are given in brackets at the end of each question part.
- There are 40 marks available for this paper.

1   A student is investigating how the temperature of two different liquids, A and B, increases when energy is supplied. For each liquid, he sets up the apparatus as shown in **Figure 1**.

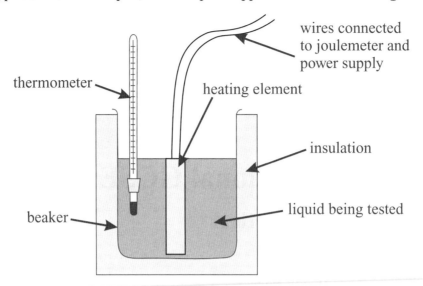

Figure 1

The student measures the initial temperature of each liquid, and then measures the temperature every minute for 4 minutes. The student uses 0.50 kg of each liquid.

(a) What other piece of apparatus does the student need to use throughout this experiment that isn't shown or mentioned in **Figure 1**?

....

[1]

The student calculates that 12 kJ of energy is supplied to the liquid each minute.
Table 1 shows the student's results for liquids A and B.

Time / min	Energy supplied / kJ	Liquid A temperature / °C	Liquid B temperature / °C
0	0	20	20
1	12	26	29
2	24	31	40
3	36	36	50
4	48	41	59

Table 1

(b) Write a conclusion stating which liquid's temperature increases more when a certain amount of energy is supplied. Justify your answer using the results of the experiment.

....

....

....

....

[2]

(c) Plot a graph of temperature / °C (*y*-axis) against energy supplied / kJ (*x*-axis) for liquid B.
Your *y*-axis does not have to start at 0 °C.

[4]

(d) Determine the gradient, *G*, of the graph. Show on the graph
how you obtained the values used in your calculation.

G = ...

[2]

(e) Determine the specific heat capacity, *c*, of liquid B.
Use the equation $c = \dfrac{1}{mG}$, where *m* is the mass in kg of the liquid.
Give your answer to 2 significant figures.

c = ... kJ/(kg°C)

[1]

(f) The student repeats the experiment for liquid B.
This time, he adds an insulated lid to the beaker before beginning the measurements.
He plots the results in a graph and calculates the gradient, *G*.
Explain why the value of *G* will be greater than that measured in the original experiment.

....

....

....

[2]

[Total 12 marks]

Turn over ▶

2 A student is investigating the period of oscillation of a spring when different masses are attached to the end of it. **Figure 2** shows the experimental set-up used.

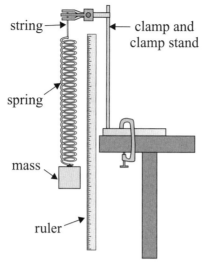

Figure 2

When the student pulls the mass down and then lets go, the mass bounces up and down on the spring. The period of the oscillation is the time taken for the mass to move from its lowest point, up to its highest point, and then back down to its lowest point.

The student measures the period of oscillation by pulling the mass down and starting a stopwatch as she releases the mass. She stops the stopwatch after the mass has completed one oscillation. She then repeats this for different masses.

(a) Give one variable the student should keep constant in this experiment.

....
[1]

The student uses a mass balance to measure the masses that will be attached to the spring. The diagram in **Figure 3** shows the reading on the balance when there is nothing on the scales. This shows the mass balance has a zero error.

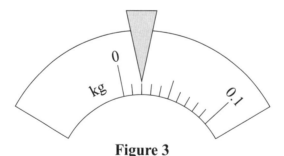

Figure 3

(b) **Table 2** shows the readings on the balance when masses A, B and C are placed on it.
Complete the table with the corrected masses.

Mass	Reading on balance / kg	Corrected mass / kg
A	0.22	
B	0.44	
C	1.02	

Table 2

[2]

The diagram in **Figure 4** shows the position of one of the masses just before the student releases it. The student always measures the starting point as the bottom of the mass.

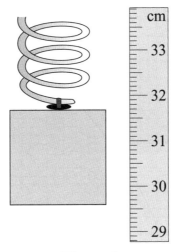

Figure 4

(c) What is the starting point for the mass shown in **Figure 4**?

....

[1]

(d) Suggest one way that the student could make it easier to accurately measure the distance that the mass has been pulled down.

....

....

....

[1]

(e) The student repeats the experiment three times and takes an average of her results for each mass. Explain why she does this.

....

....

....

[1]

Question 2 continues on the next page

The graph in **Figure 5** shows the student's results.

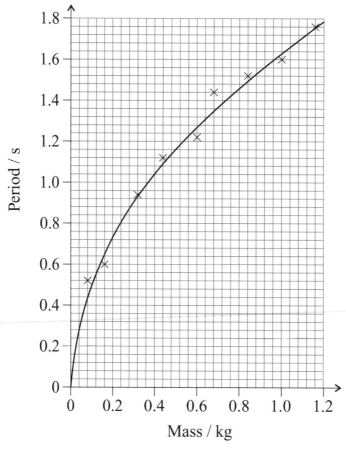

Figure 5

(f) Using the graph, how long would you expect it to take a mass of 0.4 kg to complete one oscillation?

....

[1]

(g) From her results, the student says that period is directly proportional to mass. State whether you agree with the student's conclusion or not. Use the results to justify your answer.

....

....

....

[1]

(h) Suggest one cause of uncertainty in the results due to the student's experimental procedure. Give one improvement the student could make to the experiment to reduce this uncertainty.

Cause ....

....

Improvement ....

....

[2]

[Total 10 marks]

3 A student has five 0.1 m lengths of cylindrical wire, each made of the same material, but with different known diameters. She wants to find out how the cross-sectional area of a wire affects its resistance. She uses an ohmmeter to measure the resistance of the wire directly. A circuit diagram of the student's set-up is shown in **Figure 6**.

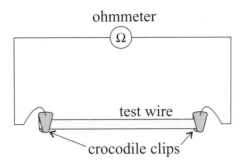

Figure 6

(a) What is the independent variable in this experiment?

....

[1]

The student records her results in a table, shown in **Table 3**.

Wire diameter / mm	Cross-sectional area, A /	Resistance, R /	R × A / Ωmm²
0.10	0.0079	7.90	
0.20	0.031	2.02	
0.30	0.071	0.88	
0.40		0.48	
0.50	0.20		

Table 3

(b) (i) Calculate the missing value of cross-sectional area for the 0.40 mm wire.
Record this in **Table 3** and complete the column heading for cross-sectional area.

[2]

(ii) **Figure 7** shows the resistance reading on the ohmmeter for the 0.50 mm wire.
Record this in **Table 3** and complete the column heading for resistance.

[2]

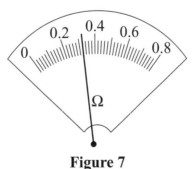

Figure 7

(c) Complete the final column of the table by calculating R × A for each wire.
Give your answers to an appropriate number of significant figures.

[1]

Question 3 continues on the next page

(d) The student says that the cross-sectional area is inversely proportional to the resistance. The student is **correct**. Explain how you can tell this from the experimental results. Use the results in **Table 3** to justify your reasoning.

....

....

....

[2]

(e) Give one precaution the student could take to ensure that her results are as accurate as possible.

....

....

[1]

(f) Give one safety precaution that should be followed when using electronics in an experiment.

....

....

[1]

(g) A second student plans an experiment to investigate the resistances of wires made of different materials. In his plan, he says that the first experiment shows that all the wires he uses should have the same diameter. Explain whether he is correct.

....

....

[1]

[Total 11 marks]

4   A student attaches a parachute to a steel ball, as shown in **Figure 8**.

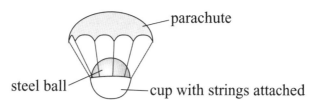

Figure 8

Design an experiment for the student to investigate how the area of the parachute affects the average speed at which the ball falls. The average speed of an object can be calculated using

$$\text{average speed} = \frac{\text{total distance}}{\text{total time}}.$$

The student has the following apparatus:

- A steel ball.

- Parachutes made of plastic in varying sizes.

- A cup (that the steel ball can sit in) with strings attached.

Your plan should include:

- Any other apparatus the student will need.

- A description of how the experiment will be carried out.

- Any variables that should be kept constant throughout the experiment.

- What values will need to be calculated.

- The headings of the table in which the results would be recorded.
  (You do not need to write any values in your table.)

- A description of any difficulties that may occur during the experiment and how to overcome these issues.

You may draw a diagram of the set-up in the space below, to help explain your plan.

....

....

....

....

Question 4 continues on the next page

236

[Total 7 marks]

END OF QUESTIONS

Answers

Section 1 — General Physics: Forces and Motion

Pages 7-8
Warm-Up Questions

1) The total distance he travels and the time taken.
2) Velocity is a measure of how fast something is going, and in what direction. Speed is just a measure of how fast something is travelling.
3) m/s^2
4) speed
5) A straight, horizontal line.
6) units of mass = kg, units of weight = N
7) density = mass ÷ volume

Exam Questions

1   C *[1 mark]*
average speed = distance ÷ time = 1500 ÷ 300 = 5 m/s

2   B *[1 mark]*
When the student gets to 100 m, she stops moving — shown by the horizontal line on the distance-time graph. She reaches 100 m after 30 s.

3 a) i)   Volume of a cube = length × length × length
             $= 5 \times 5 \times 5 = 125$ cm³ *[1 mark]*

     ii)   density = mass ÷ volume
             $= 115 \div 125 = 0.92$ g/cm³ *[1 mark]*

     iii) The density of ice is less than the density of water, so the ice cube will float *[1 mark]*.

 b)   E.g. measure and record the mass of the toy soldier using a mass balance *[1 mark]*. Fill a eureka can with water and place an empty measuring cylinder beneath the spout of the eureka can. Submerge the toy soldier in the eureka can *[1 mark]*. Measure the volume of water displaced from the eureka can using the measuring cylinder. The volume of water displaced is equal to the volume of the soldier *[1 mark]*. Use the equation 'density = mass ÷ volume / $\rho = m \div V$' to calculate the density of the toy soldier *[1 mark]*.
You could have used another method to find the volume, for example placing the toy soldier in a half-filled measuring cylinder and noting the difference in the volume reading on the measuring cylinder's scale.

4 a)   The car is moving with changing speed/accelerating *[1 mark]*.
If you are taking the extended course, a better answer would be that the car is moving with a constant acceleration.

 b)   Distance travelled = area under graph
             $= (60 - 40) \times (20 - 0) = 20 \times 20$
             $= 400$ m
[3 marks for correct answer, otherwise 1 mark for attempting to find the area under the graph between 40 and 60 seconds, 1 mark for correctly showing (60 – 40) × 20 or 20 × 20]

 c)   Between 100 s and 160 s, the graph would be a horizontal straight line at 10 m/s *[1 mark]*.

 d)   Acceleration = gradient = $\frac{20 - 0}{40 - 0} = 0.5$ m/s²
[3 marks for correct answer, otherwise 1 mark for attempting to find the gradient, 1 mark for dividing a correct change in speed by a correct change in time in the time range 0 – 40 s]

5 a) $g = \frac{W}{m} = \frac{24.5}{2.5}$
           $= 9.8$ N/kg (newtons per kilogram)
[2 marks for correct answer, otherwise 1 mark for correct rearrangement of the equation]

 b) i)   The mass of the object would not be different on the Moon *[1 mark]*.

     ii)   The weight would be smaller *[1 mark]* as the gravitational field strength, g, is lower on the Moon *[1 mark]*.

6 a) $a = \frac{\Delta v}{\Delta t} = \frac{\text{final velocity} - \text{initial velocity}}{\Delta t}$
let u = initial velocity and v = final velocity.
$\Rightarrow u = v - (a \times \Delta t) = 1 - (-2 \times 5)$
                $= 1 + 10$
                $= 11$ m/s
[2 marks for correct answer, otherwise 1 mark for correct rearrangement of the equation or substitution]

 b)

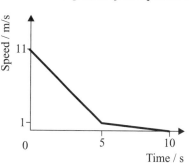

[1 mark for two lines with negative slopes, with the first steeper than the second, 1 mark for marking the necessary values on the axes]
Your sketch should look quite similar to this but it doesn't need to be accurately to scale.

Pages 13-14
Warm-Up Questions

1) Add the two forces together.
2) a) scalar   b) vector   c) vector   d) scalar
3) 0 N
4) Force = mass × acceleration or $F = ma$
5) It decreases.
6) The force between two solid objects that are moving or trying to move past each other that impedes motion and produces heating.
7) In the opposite direction to the motion.
8) The air resistance/drag on the falling object is equal to its weight/force due to gravity.

Exam Questions

1 a) i)   gravitational force / weight *[1 mark]*
     ii)   4000 – 1000 = 3000 N *[1 mark]*
     iii) 55 000 – 55 000 = 0 N *[1 mark]*

 b)   drag *[1 mark]*
Air resistance is a type of drag.

 c)   C *[1 mark]*
A constant speed means that there are no resultant forces on the object. This is either because there are no forces at all or because the forces are balanced. There must be forces acting on a moving truck (to counteract frictional force), so the driving force must equal the frictional force.

2 a)   Air resistance/drag from the air *[1 mark]*
 b) (i)   900 N *[1 mark]*, because at terminal velocity, the air resistance is equal to the parachutist's weight/the gravitational force on the parachutist *[1 mark]*.
     ii)   Upwards *[1 mark]*
 c)   Her speed will decrease / she will decelerate *[1 mark]*.
 d)   Without air resistance, the parachutist would continue accelerating to Earth *[1 mark]* at a constant rate *[1 mark]*.

3 a)

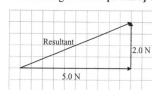

                      Resultant = 5.4 N
[2 marks for force between 5.3 N and 5.5 N, otherwise 1 mark for marking the resultant force correctly on diagram]

b)   22° *[1 mark for a value between 21° and 23°]*

You'll need to measure the angle with a protractor (or use trigonometry).

4 a)   The force is in the opposite direction to the motion, so the force is negative.

$$F = ma \Rightarrow a = \frac{F}{m} = \frac{-200}{2500} = -0.08 \text{ m/s}^2$$

[2 marks for correct answer, otherwise 1 mark for correct rearrangement of the equation or substitution]

The van is slowing down, so the acceleration is negative.

b) $F = m \times a = 10 \times 29 = 290$ N

[2 marks for correct answer, otherwise 1 mark for correct equation or substitution]

c)   The van is accelerating *[1 mark]* because in order to drive along a curved road, it must be constantly changing direction. A changing direction means a changing velocity, which is acceleration *[1 mark]*.

Pages 24-25
Warm-Up Questions

1) $k = F \div x$
2)   False
3)   If an object is balanced, the total anticlockwise moments equal the total clockwise moments.
4)   There must be no net resultant force and no resultant turning effect.
5)   Suspend the plane lamina and a plumb line from the same point, and wait until they stop moving.
Draw a line along the plumb line. Repeat this, but suspend the shape from a different pivot point.
The centre of mass is where the two lines cross.
6) $p = mv = 2.5 \times 10 = 25$ kg m/s
7) $F\Delta t = \Delta(mv)$

Exam Questions

1   D *[1 mark]*

This object has a high centre of gravity and a small base area — the worst combination for stability.

2   B *[1 mark]*

The force is acting at the furthest perpendicular distance from the pivot.

3 a)   The centre of gravity lies in the centre of the beam, at 9 m ($18 \div 2 = 9$ m) from either end.
$12 - 9 = 3$ m *[1 mark]*

b) (i)   The moment acts in the clockwise direction *[1 mark]*.
(ii)   The beam has a moment about the pivot, which is 3 m away from where the force acts.
The moment is found by: $M = Fd = 300 \times 3 = 900$ Nm
[2 marks for correct answer, otherwise 1 mark for correct equation or substitution]

4 a)   Reading from the graph gives an extension of 8 mm for a load of 3 N.
Natural length = new length – extension
          = $51.4 - 0.8 = 50.6$ cm
[2 marks for correct answer, otherwise 1 mark for reading the correct value from the graph]

The extension scale is in mm, but you're given the spring's length in cm. Make sure the values are in the same units before you subtract.

b)   Draw a triangle on graph from (0,0) to (15, 0) to (15, 5.5).
Gradient = $\frac{\text{change in } y}{\text{change in } x} = \frac{5.5 - 0}{15 - 0} = \frac{5.5}{15} = 0.366...$
          = 0.37 (to 2 s.f.)
Spring constant = 0.37 N/mm
[1 mark for a value between 0.36 and 0.38]

5 a) $p = mv = 65 \times 14 = 910$ kg m/s
[2 marks for correct answer, otherwise 1 mark for correct equation or substitution]

b) $F\Delta t = \Delta(mv)$ so $F = \Delta(mv) \div \Delta t$
          = $910 \div 1.3 = 700$ N
[2 marks for correct answer, otherwise 1 mark for correct rearrangement of the equation or substitution]

You'll get full marks if an incorrect answer from part a) is used and the calculations are done correctly.

6 a)   20 cm = 0.2 m
moment = force × perpendicular distance from the pivot = $2 \times 0.2 = 0.4$ Nm
[2 marks if answer correct, otherwise 1 mark for correct equation or substitution]

b)   clockwise moments = anticlockwise moments
$\text{force}_C \times \text{perpendicular distance}_C = 0.4 + 0.8$

$\text{perpendicular distance}_C = \frac{0.4 + 0.8}{8} = 0.15$ m

[3 marks for correct answer, otherwise 1 mark for attempting to use the principle of moments, and 1 mark for correct rearrangement of the equation or substitution]

Again, you'll get full marks if an incorrect answer from part a) is used and the calculations are done correctly.

Section 2 — General Physics: Energy and Pressure

Page 30
Warm-Up Questions

1)   Kinetic energy store.
2)   Any two from: e.g. mechanically (work is done by a force moving or deforming an object) / electrically (work is done by an electrical current) / by heating / by waves.
3)   The principle of conservation of energy states that energy can be stored, transferred from one type to another, or dissipated — but it can never be created or destroyed.
4)   kinetic energy = ½ × mass × (speed)^2 / $E_k = \frac{1}{2}mv^2$

Exam Questions

1   C *[1 mark]*
2   Energy is transferred mechanically from the kinetic energy store of the golf club to the ball's kinetic energy store, because the ball's speed increases *[1 mark]*.
Energy is transferred by sound waves to the internal energy store of the surroundings, because a sound is made when the club hits the ball *[1 mark]*.

3 a) $E_k = \frac{1}{2}mv^2$
$E_k = \frac{1}{2} \times 105 \times 2.39^2$
    = 299.8852... J
    = 300 J (to 3 s.f.)
[2 marks for correct answer, otherwise 1 mark for correct equation or substitution]

b) i)   energy lost from gravitational potential energy store
$= \Delta E_p = mg\Delta h = 105 \times 9.8 \times 20.2$
    = 20 785.8 J
    = 20 800 J (to 3 s.f.)
[2 marks for correct answer, otherwise 1 mark for correct equation or substitution]

ii)   20 800 J (or 20 785.8 J) *[1 mark]*. All the energy transferred away from the gravitational potential energy store of the cart must be transferred to the cart's kinetic energy store, because energy must be conserved (and no energy is wasted due to resistive forces) *[1 mark]*.

Pages 36-37
Warm-Up Questions

1)   160 J
2)   W (watts) or J/s (joules per second)
3)   Efficiency is a measure of the proportion of the input energy a device or process will transfer usefully.
4)   Pressure is the force per unit area.
5)   The depth beneath the surface of the liquid and the density of the liquid.

If you're taking the extended course, you could also have said the gravitational field strength.

Exam Questions

1   B *[1 mark]*

2 a)   Student C *[1 mark]*, e.g. because work done depends on the force and distance moved in the direction of the force ($W = Fd$). Each student pushed the box the same distance, so the amount of work done just depends on the force. Student C did the did the most work, so they must have applied the largest force *[1 mark]*.

  b)   Device X would waste more energy. This is because it has the lower efficiency, so it transfers less of the input energy usefully and therefore wastes more energy *[1 mark]*.

3 a) $p = F \div A$
$p = 175 \div 0.25$
$= 700$ Pa
[2 marks for correct answer, otherwise 1 mark for correct equation or substitution]

  b)   Since the pressure is the same at all points in the liquid, the pressure on piston 2 is equal to the pressure applied by piston 1.
$p = F \div A$
So, $F = p \times A$
$= 700 \times 1.3 = 910$ N
[2 marks for correct answer, otherwise 1 mark for correct equation or substitution]

4 a)   Input energy = 200 J
The input energy arrow is 20 squares wide, so the value of each square is 200 J ÷ 20 = 10 J *[1 mark]*

  b)   The useful energy arrow is 5 squares wide, and each square represents 10 J. So the amount of energy usefully transferred = 5 × 10 J = 50 J *[1 mark]*

5 a)   efficiency = (useful energy output ÷ total energy input) × 100%
$= (480 \div 1200) \times 100\%$
$= 40\%$
[2 marks for correct answer, otherwise 1 mark for correct equation or substitution]

  b) $P = \Delta E \div t$
1 minute = 60 seconds
So, output power = 540 ÷ 60
$= 9$ W
[2 marks for correct answer, otherwise 1 mark for correct equation or substitution]

  c)   efficiency = (useful power output ÷ total power input) × 100%
So, total power input = (useful power output ÷ efficiency) × 100
input power = (9 ÷ 55) × 100
$= 16.3636...$
$= 16$ W (to 2 s.f.)
[2 marks for correct answer, otherwise 1 mark for correct rearrangement of equation or substitution]

  d)   Disagree. Torch B transfers less energy per minute than torch A (as 16 × 60 = 960, and 960 < 1200) *[1 mark]*.

Even if you got the answer to 5 c) wrong, if your conclusion is correct for your answer to 5 d), you'd get the mark for this question. You could also answer this question by comparing the input powers of the torches.

6   depth of water = 50 cm = 0.50 m
diameter of ball = 8 cm = 0.08 m
$\Delta p = \rho g \Delta h$
$\Delta h = 0.50 - 0.08 = 0.42$ m
$\Delta p = 1000 \times 9.8 \times 0.42$
$= 4116 = 4100$ Pa (to 2 s.f.)
[3 marks for correct answer, otherwise 1 mark for correct conversion of units for depth and diameter and 1 mark for correct rearrangement of equation or substitution]

Pages 45-46
Warm-Up Questions

1)   Any three from: coal, oil, (natural) gas, nuclear fuel (plutonium or uranium).

2)   A renewable energy resource is an energy resource that is being, or can be, made at the same rate (or faster) than it's being used, so it will never run out.

3)   Any two from: e.g. burning coal releases CO_2/greenhouse gases, which contributes to the greenhouse effect and global warming. / Burning coal releases sulfur dioxide, which causes acid rain. / Coal mining damages the landscape/animal habitats.

4)   Energy in the thermal energy stores of hot rocks underground is used to heat water and produce steam. The steam then turns a turbine, which turns a generator and generates electricity.

Exam Questions

1   C *[1 mark]*

2   D *[1 mark]*

3 a)   Fission *[1 mark]*

  b) i)   Nuclear fuels don't release any greenhouse gases (e.g. carbon dioxide) that contribute to global warming *[1 mark]*.

    ii)   Any two from: e.g. processing the nuclear fuel before it is used causes pollution. / Nuclear power stations carry the risk of major catastrophes. / Nuclear waste is dangerous and difficult to dispose of safely.
[2 marks — 1 mark for each correct answer]

4 a)   The energy in the water's gravitational potential energy store is transferred to its kinetic energy store as it flows down from the reservoir *[1 mark]*. The energy in the water's kinetic energy store is then transferred mechanically to the kinetic energy stores of a turbine and a generator *[1 mark]*. The energy is transferred away electrically from the generator *[1 mark]*.

  b)   Any two from: e.g. they can cause the loss of wildlife habitats. / They can cause people to lose their homes. / Rotting vegetation in flooded areas releases methane/CO_2/greenhouse gases.
[2 marks — 1 mark for each correct answer]

  c)   Any two from: e.g. they cause no atmospheric pollution. / They use a renewable energy source. / Tides are regular and predictable, so this is a fairly reliable energy source. *[2 marks — 1 mark for each correct answer]*

5 a)   nuclear fusion *[1 mark]*

  b)   When the biofuels are burnt, energy in their chemical energy stores is transferred by heating to the internal energy store of water/steam in the boiler *[1 mark]*. This causes the steam to drive a turbine and generator, transferring energy mechanically from the internal energy store of the steam to the kinetic energy stores of the turbine and the generator *[1 mark]*. The energy is then transferred away electrically from the generator *[1 mark]*.

  c)   E.g. both biofuels and fossil fuels release carbon dioxide (CO_2) when they are burned in vehicles *[1 mark]*. However, plants are grown to make biofuels, and take in CO_2 from the atmosphere as they grow *[1 mark]*. If plants are grown at the same rate that they're burned, the overall CO_2 emitted by using biofuels is zero, so using biofuels overall contributes less CO_2 to the environment *[1 mark]*.

6 a)   Seconds in 5 hours = 5 × 60 × 60 = 18 000 s
Energy provided by a single 1 m² solar panel in 5 hours = 200 × 18 000 = 3 600 000 J
Number of panels needed = energy needed ÷ energy provided
$= 34\,000\,000 \div 3\,600\,000$
$= 9.444...$
= 10 panels (to next whole number)
[4 marks for correct answer, otherwise 1 mark for correct number of seconds in 5 hours, 1 mark for energy provided by one panel in 5 hours, and 1 mark for attempting to divide energy needed by energy per panel]

Remember, because you have to have a set number of whole panels, if you get a decimal answer, you need to round up to the next whole number to be able to provide the right amount of energy.

  b)   They will need 10 m² of space, but only have 8 m² of space on their roof, so the family cannot install a sufficient number of solar panels *[1 mark]*.

c) E.g. solar panels are less reliable than coal-fired power stations *[1 mark]*. The energy output of the solar panels will vary based on the number of hours of good sunlight, and may not be able to provide enough energy on a given day *[1 mark]*. The energy output of coal-fired power stations is not influenced by environmental factors like weather as coal can be stored so it is readily available to burn *[1 mark]*.

Section 3 — Thermal Physics

Page 53
Warm-Up Questions
1) In a liquid, the particles are held close together, but can move past each other. They form irregular arrangements. The particles move in random directions at low speeds.
2) Brownian motion is the zigzag movement of microscopic particles suspended in a fluid due to collisions of fluid particles with them.
Remember that a fluid can be a liquid or a gas.
3) True
4) 12 + 273 = 285 K
5) E.g. for particles in a liquid to escape by evaporation, the particles must be moving in the right direction to escape the liquid (i.e. towards the surface), and have enough energy in their kinetic energy stores (to overcome the attractive forces of the other liquid particles).

Exam Questions
1 a) Absolute zero is at –273°C *[1 mark]*.
  b) At absolute zero particles have the least possible energy in their kinetic energy stores *[1 mark]*.
2 a) i) melting *[1 mark]*
    ii) The temperature stays the same *[1 mark]*.
  b) i) boiling *[1 mark]*.
    ii) E.g. increasing the area of the surface of the liquid / increasing the air movement over the liquid / increasing the temperature of the liquid *[1 mark]*.
    iii) When a liquid evaporates, the fastest particles are most likely to escape the liquid *[1 mark]*. When they do, the average speed, and so the average energy in the kinetic energy stores, of the remaining particles in the liquid decreases *[1 mark]*. Temperature is a measure of the average energy in the kinetic energy stores of the particles in a substance, so the decrease in average energy in these stores causes a decrease in temperature *[1 mark]*.
3 a) The gas particles collide with the canister walls *[1 mark]*. This causes them to exert a force on the walls *[1 mark]*. Pressure is the force per unit area *[1 mark]*.
  b) The pressure of the gas within the container would increase as the container is heated *[1 mark]*. This is because the speed / energy in the kinetic energy stores of the particles would increase *[1 mark]*, meaning they would exert larger forces on the canister walls when they collide with them *[1 mark]*. The increased speed / energy in the kinetic energy stores of the particles would also mean more collisions with the canister walls, which would also increase the total force *[1 mark]*.
  c) pV = constant, so $p_1V_1 = p_2V_2$
    V_1 = 0.034 m³, p_1 = 98 kPa, V_2 = 0.031 m³
    So $p_2 = (p_1V_1) \div V_2$
      = (98 × 0.034) ÷ 0.031
      = 107.483... = 110 kPa (to 2 s.f.)
    [2 marks for correct answer, otherwise 1 mark for correct equation or substitution]
Make sure the units for both pressures and volumes are the same before you plug your numbers into the equation.

Page 57
Warm-Up Questions
1) The specific heat capacity of a material is the amount of energy needed to raise the temperature of 1 kg of the material by 1 °C.
2) False
3) False
4) There are almost no forces between gas particles so they can move furthest when heated. There are stronger forces between liquid and solid particles so they can't move as far apart.

Exam Questions
1 Heating the outer ring will cause it to expand due to thermal expansion *[1 mark]*. This will increase the size of the gap in the ring, and allow it to fit easily around the train wheel *[1 mark]*. When the outer ring is allowed to cool, it will contract/get smaller again, allowing it to fit tightly around the train wheel *[1 mark]*.
2 a) $c = \Delta E \div m\Delta\theta$
    $\Delta\theta$ = 100 – 20 = 80 °C
    c = 36 000 ÷ (0.5 × 80) = 900 J/kg°C
    [2 marks for correct answer, otherwise 1 mark for correct substitution]
  b) Rearrange the equation for specific heat capacity to get
    $\Delta\theta = \Delta E \div mc$
      = 71 600 ÷ (0.2 × 1790) = 200 °C *[1 mark]*
    initial temperature = final temperature + ΔT
      = 20 + 200 = 220 °C *[1 mark]*
3 a) Use a mass balance to measure the mass of the insulated flask. Fill the flask with the liquid sample and measure the mass again. The difference in mass is the mass of the liquid in the flask *[1 mark]*.
  b) The energy transferred to the liquid and the temperature rise of the liquid *[1 mark]*.
  c) To minimise the energy transferred from the liquid to the surroundings *[1 mark]* and to stop evaporation from the liquid *[1 mark]*.

Pages 65-66
Warm-Up Questions
1) False
2) The higher the surface temperature, the greater the rate at which it emits infrared radiation.
3) Because less radiation is being absorbed by the Earth than emitted.
4) Conduction in a solid is when vibrating particles collide with other nearby particles, transferring energy to their kinetic energy stores, and transferring energy through the solid.
5) E.g. immersion heater / kettle / radiator/convector heater

Exam Questions
1 a) By conduction *[1 mark]*.
  b) By radiation *[1 mark]*.
2 a) E.g.

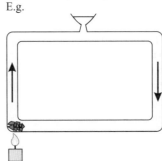

[1 mark for 2 arrows drawn anywhere inside the glass tube showing the correct flow of water]

b) The water particles near the heater gain energy (and get further apart) *[1 mark]*. This causes the water near the heater to expand and become less dense, so it rises up the pipe *[1 mark]*. Colder, denser water elsewhere in the pipe sinks down, causing water to flow around the tube *[1 mark]*.

3 a) Any one from: e.g. place the thermometers at equal distances away from the cube / place the thermometers at the same height as each other / make sure no thermometers are in direct sunlight/a draught *[1 mark]*.

b) C *[1 mark]*

Thermometer Y will heat up fastest, since it is the one in front of the face which is dull and black and so is the best infrared emitter.

c) The times recorded would be longer *[1 mark]*. Cooler objects emit infrared radiation at a lower rate *[1 mark]*.

4 a) Conduction *[1 mark]*. The fabric of the oven gloves is a thermal insulator/poor thermal conductor, so energy is transferred more slowly by conduction through the gloves to the chef's hands than it would be without them *[1 mark]*.

b) The free electrons in the metal that are closest to the source of the heat move faster, as they have more energy in their kinetic energy stores *[1 mark]*. These electrons move through the metal, colliding with other particles in the metal, and transferring energy to their kinetic energy stores (leading to an increase in temperature) *[1 mark]*.

c) Baking tray A will cool down faster than tray B because it has a larger surface area *[1 mark]*. The larger the surface area, the more infrared radiation it will emit, and so the faster it will cool down *[1 mark]*.

You could also have said that the larger surface area means A will conduct heat away to a larger area of air.

Section 4 — Properties of Waves

Page 70
Warm-Up Questions

1) Waves only transfer energy. They do not transfer matter (in this case, the leaf and the water particles around the leaf).
2) hertz (Hz)
3) E.g. sound waves / seismic P-waves
4) wave speed = frequency × wavelength / $v = f \times \lambda$

Exam Questions

1 a) transverse *[1 mark]*
b) 5 cm *[1 mark]*
c) 2 m *[1 mark]*
2 a) There are 9 wavelengths in the distance of 18 cm. Therefore, wavelength = 18 cm ÷ 9 = 2 cm *[1 mark]*
b) 2 cm = 2 ÷ 100 = 0.02 m
$v = f\lambda = 12 \times 0.02$
$= 0.24$ m/s
[2 marks if answer correct, otherwise 1 mark for correct equation or substitution]

Pages 79-80
Warm-Up Questions

1) angle of incidence = angle of reflection
2) Its speed changes.
3) True
4) $n = \dfrac{\sin i}{\sin r}$ (where n = the refractive index of the material, i = the angle of incidence and r = the angle of refraction)
5) Total internal reflection is when light attempts to pass from a material where it travels at a lower speed into a material where it travels at a higher speed at such an angle that it is all reflected back into the first material instead.
6) E.g. diamonds sparkling
7) The water waves spread out as they bend around the edge of the obstacle.

Exam Questions

1 D *[1 mark]*
2 a) 20° *[1 mark]*
b) The image produced by the mirror will be the same size as the pencil *[1 mark]*, and located on the opposite side of the mirror to the pencil at the same distance from the mirror as the object *[1 mark]*.
c) E.g.

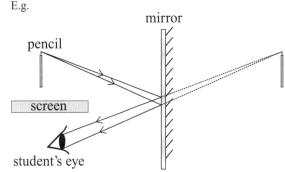

[1 mark for correctly drawn reflected rays, 1 mark for correctly draw second incident ray, 1 mark for image drawn at point of intersection of extended reflected rays]

3 a) E.g. the angle of incidence for which the angle of refraction is 90° *[1 mark]*.
b) It will be reflected back into the acrylic / it will be totally internally reflected *[1 mark]*.
c) $n = \dfrac{1}{\sin c}$
$= \dfrac{1}{\sin 41.8°}$
$= 1.5003... = 1.50$ (to 3 s.f.)
[3 marks if answer correct, otherwise 1 mark for correct equation and 1 mark for substitution]

4 a) Angle of incidence *[1 mark]*
b) Light refracts as it enters and leaves the block *[1 mark]*. As it enters the block it refracts towards the normal *[1 mark]*. As it leaves the block it refracts away from the normal *[1 mark]*.
c) $n = \dfrac{\sin i}{\sin r} = \dfrac{\sin 30°}{\sin 11°}$
$= 2.6204... = 2.6$ (to 2 s.f.)
[2 marks if answer correct, otherwise 1 mark for correct equation or substitution]

Page 86
Warm-Up Questions

1) The principal focus of a converging lens is where rays hitting the lens parallel to the principal axis all meet.
2) It passes through the lens without being refracted.
3) They are spread out / diverged by the lens, appearing to have come from the principal focus.
4) False

A virtual image can't be projected onto a screen because the rays never actually come together at a point.

5) Between the principal focus and the lens.
6) Red, orange, yellow, green, blue, indigo and violet.

Exam Questions

1 a) C *[1 mark]*
b) White light is made up of a mixture of all other colours *[1 mark]*. Each colour of light refracts by a different amount as it passes into and out of the prism *[1 mark]*. This causes the colours of light to spread out, splitting the white beam into a spectrum of colours *[1 mark]*.

2

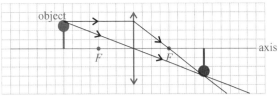

[1 mark for ray through middle of the lens carried on in a straight line, 1 mark for ray parallel to the axis bending at the lens and passing through principal focus, 1 mark for image drawn at the point where the rays meet]

3 a)   The lens in the person's eye is too powerful/converges the rays too much, so it focuses rays in front of the retina *[1 mark]*. This means the person's eye can't focus on objects in the distance / distant objects will appear blurry to the person *[1 mark]*.

   b)   The person's vision could be corrected by placing a diverging lens in front of their eye *[1 mark]*.

Page 95
Warm-Up Questions

1)   radio waves
2)   False

All EM waves travel at the same speed through a vacuum.

3)   infrared radiation
4)   E.g. revealing security markings on property / sterilising water
5)   Analogue signals can take any value within a range. Digital signals can only take certain values.
6)   amplitude

Exam Questions

1   C *[1 mark]*

Remember, the fewer waveforms there are in the same time, the lower the frequency and the lower the pitch.

2 a)   A detector is placed behind the truck *[1 mark]*. The X-rays are absorbed by some objects but are transmitted by others *[1 mark]*. Objects that absorb the X-rays form a shadow on the detector *[1 mark]*.

   b)   X-rays can damage cells / cause mutations so they could harm the driver and passengers *[1 mark]*

   c)   E.g. producing images of broken bones *[1 mark]*.

3   The infrared signal will reach the television before her voice *[1 mark]*. This is because infrared radiation is a form of electromagnetic radiation, so it travels faster than sound through air *[1 mark]*.

Electromagnetic radiation travels through air at approximately 3.00 × 10⁸ m/s, while sound waves travel through air at around 330 – 350 m/s.

Section 5 — Electricity
Page 100
Warm-Up Questions

1)   attract
2)   E.g. suspend a rod with a known charge from a piece of string. Bring the object being investigated near the suspended charged rod. If the object has the same charge as the suspended rod it will repel the rod, and if it has the opposite charge it will attract the rod.
3)   E.g. copper

You could name any metal here.

4)   An area where a force acts on an electric charge.
5)   electrically charged objects

6)

Your field lines should be equally spaced and parallel/straight as the field is uniform.

Exam Questions

1 a)   Positive *[1 mark]*.
   b)   Electrons were transferred from the cloth and onto the sphere *[1 mark]*.
   c)   *[1 mark]*

2 a)   The bulb will light up when the aluminium foil is attached to both clips *[1 mark]*. It will switch off again when the foil is removed and it will stay unlit when the rubber band is attached to the clips *[1 mark]*.
   b)   The aluminium foil is made up of a lattice of positive ions surrounded by free electrons, which are able to move through the metal as an electric current flows, which lights the bulb *[1 mark]*. The rubber band doesn't have any free electrons in its structure, so a current can't flow through it to complete the circuit and light the bulb *[1 mark]*.

Pages 108-109
Warm-Up Questions

1)   False. It's the flow of negative electrons.
2)   Conventional current flows from positive to negative.
3)   True
4)   A voltmeter should be connected in parallel with the component.
5) $P = IV$ (electrical power = current × potential difference)

Exam Questions

1   B *[1 mark]*
2 a) $R = V \div I = 1.5 \div 0.30 = 5\ \Omega$
          [2 marks if answer correct, otherwise 1 mark for correct equation or substitution]
   b) (i) $E = IVt = 0.30 × 1.5 × 35 = 15.75\ J = 16\ J$ (to 2 s.f.)
          [2 marks if answer correct, otherwise 1 mark for correct equation or substitution]
      (ii) $I = \dfrac{Q}{t} \Rightarrow Q = It = 0.30 × 35 = 10.5\ C = 11\ C$ (to 2 s.f.)
          [2 marks if answer correct, otherwise 1 mark for correct equation or substitution]
   c)

[1 mark]

Your graph must go through the origin and start to level off at the top and bottom.

   d)   It increases *[1 mark]*.
3 a)   Time in hours = 90 ÷ 60 = 1.5 hours
          Energy transferred = power × time = 3.0 × 1.5 = 4.5 kWh
          [2 marks if answer correct, otherwise 1 mark for correct time conversion]
   b)   Cost = energy transferred × price per kWh
             = 4.5 × 15.9 = 71.55p = 72p to the nearest penny.
          [2 marks if answer correct, otherwise 1 mark for correct substitution]
4 a)   Diodes only allow current to flow in one direction *[1 mark]*.
   b)   At point A, $V = 6$ V, $I = 3$ A
          $R = V \div I = 6 \div 3 = 2\ \Omega$
          [2 marks if answer correct, otherwise 1 mark for correct equation or substitution]
5 a) $P = IV \Rightarrow I = P \div V = 10 \div 120 = 0.0833...$ A
             $= 0.083$ A (to 2 s.f.)
          [2 marks if answer correct, otherwise 1 mark for correct equation or substitution]

b) time = 3 × 60 × 60 = 10 800 seconds
$E = IVt = 0.0833... \times 120 \times 10\,800 = 108\,000$ J
[3 marks if answer correct, otherwise 1 mark for converting time to seconds and 1 mark for correct equation or substitution]

c) $V = W \div Q \Rightarrow Q = W \div V = 108\,000 \div 120 = 900$ C
[2 marks if answer correct, otherwise 1 mark for a correct equation or substitution]

You can use this equation because energy transferred = work done. Alternatively, you could have used Q = It (with the time in seconds).

d) Energy is transferred electrically from the mains supply to the internal energy store of the light bulb *[1 mark]*. This energy is then transferred to the internal energy store of the surroundings by heating and by light *[1 mark]*.

Pages 114-115
Warm-Up Questions
1) True
2) To calculate the combined e.m.f. you add the separate e.m.f.s together.
3) The resistors in series have the higher total resistance.
4) False. The current from the source is greater than the current in any branch.
5) True
6) The 10 Ω resistor will have the greater potential difference across it.

Exam Questions
1 a) total resistance = $R_1 + R_2 = 2 + 3 = 5$ Ω *[1 mark]*
   b) The reading on A_2 will be 0.8 A *[1 mark]* because in a series circuit, the same current flows through all parts of the circuit *[1 mark]*.
   c) $V_1 = 4 - 2.4 = 1.6$ V *[1 mark]*

2 C *[1 mark]*
The current in a branch is lower than the source current, and the combined resistance of two resistors in parallel is lower than the resistance of either resistor.

3 a) A large current flows through the earth wire *[1 mark]*. This melts the fuse, cutting the kettle off from the live supply (and preventing people who touch it from getting an electric shock) *[1 mark]*.
   b) The appliance must be double-insulated / must have a plastic casing *[1 mark]*.
   c) Impure water can conduct electricity *[1 mark]*, so damp conditions could cause current to flow outside of the circuitry of the kettle, and give the user an electric shock *[1 mark]*.

4 a) As $P = IV$, the current through the dishwasher,
   $I = P \div V$ *[1 mark]*
      $= 1800 \div 230 = 7.8$ A *[1 mark]*.
   The 8 A fuse is the best choice as its rating is slightly higher than the current *[1 mark]*.
   b) a trip switch *[1 mark]*

5 $\dfrac{R_1}{R_2} = \dfrac{V_1}{V_2} \Rightarrow V_1 = V_2 \times \dfrac{R_1}{R_2} = 6 \times \dfrac{100}{200} = 3$ V
   [2 marks if answer correct, otherwise 1 mark for correct equation or substitution]

6 $\dfrac{1}{R_{total}} = \dfrac{1}{4} + \dfrac{1}{1} = \dfrac{1}{4} + \dfrac{4}{4}$
   $\dfrac{1}{R_{total}} = \dfrac{5}{4} \Rightarrow R_{total} = \dfrac{4}{5} = 0.8$ Ω
   $R = V \div I$ rearranges to $I = V \div R = 12 \div 0.8 = 15$ A
   [3 marks if answer correct, otherwise 1 mark for correct total resistance equation or substitution, and 1 mark for correct R = V ÷ I equation or substitution]

Section 6 — Magnetism and Electromagnetism
Page 122
Warm-Up Questions
1) A magnetic field is a region where a magnetic pole experiences a force acting on it.
2) E.g.

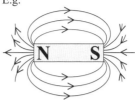

3) It's made up of concentric circles with the wire at the centre.
4) True
5) When the electromagnet is switched on, it attracts an iron contact attached to a rocker. The rocker pivots, pushing contacts together, which completes a second circuit and switches it on.

Exam Questions
1 a) Attraction *[1 mark]* because unlike (opposite) poles attract *[1 mark]*.
   b) The force is in the opposite direction to the direction of the field lines *[1 mark]*.
   c) E.g. to draw each field line, place a compass next to the pole of one of the magnets and mark the direction of the compass needle by drawing two dots — one at each end of the needle *[1 mark]*. Then move the compass so that the tail end of the needle is where the tip of the needle was in the previous position and put a dot by the tip of the needle *[1 mark]*. Repeat this until you reach another pole and then join up the marks you've made. *[1 mark]*. The compass needle shows the direction of each magnetic field line *[1 mark]*.

2 a) A current-carrying coil of wire *[1 mark]*.
   b) Straight parallel field lines *[1 mark]* which all go in the same direction *[1 mark]*.
   c) When current flows through the electromagnet a magnetic field is produced *[1 mark]*. Iron is a magnetic material so it is attracted to the electromagnet *[1 mark]*. When the current stops, there is no longer a magnetic field around the electromagnet so the bar is no longer attracted to it *[1 mark]*.
   d) E.g. when steel is magnetised it can become a permanent magnet *[1 mark]*, so when the electromagnet is turned off the core will stay magnetic, meaning the crane won't drop the iron and steel *[1 mark]*.
You could also say that steel isn't easily magnetised, so the electromagnet might not lift the iron and steel.

Pages 130-131
Warm-Up Questions
1) First finger — magnetic field
   Second finger — current
   Thumb — force (motion)
2) E.g. put a set of electrically conducting rails into a horseshoe magnet with a freely moving metal bar across them. Connect a power supply so that a current flows through the rails and metal bar. The bar will roll along the rails, showing that a force is acting.
3) Electromagnetic induction is the creation of an e.m.f. (and a current if there's a complete circuit) in a conductor which is experiencing a change in a magnetic field or which is moving relative to a magnetic field.
4) False
5) the secondary coil

Exam Questions

1 a) X = north pole, Y = south pole *[1 mark]*

You need to use Fleming's left hand rule for this. Point your thumb in the direction of the force (movement) and your second finger towards you, as the current is coming out of the page. Your first finger shows that the direction of the field is from left to right, so X must be a north pole and Y must be a south pole.

b) The direction of the force would be reversed *[1 mark]*.

c) Any two from: e.g. increase the current in the coil / increase the number of turns on the coil / increase the strength of the magnetic field. *[2 marks — 1 mark for each correct answer]*

2 Downwards *[1 mark]*.

Use Fleming's left-hand rule to work this out — your first finger points in the direction of the magnetic field (out the page) and your second finger points in the direction of conventional current (which is in the same direction as the motion of the positively charged particles, which is to the right). The direction in which your thumb points shows the direction of the force acting on the beam of particles (downwards).

3 a) The coil and the magnetic field are moving relative to each other, so an e.m.f./potential difference is induced across the coil *[1 mark]*.

b) Any one from: e.g. move the magnet out of the coil / move the coil away from the magnet / insert the south pole of the magnet into the same end of the coil / insert the north pole of the magnet into the other end of the coil *[1 mark]*.

c) Any one from: e.g. push the magnet into the coil more quickly / use a stronger magnet / add more turns per unit length of wire *[1 mark]*.

d) Zero / no reading *[1 mark]*.

4 a) A step-up transformer is used to increase the voltage of electricity supplied by the power stations for transmission through cables *[1 mark]*. Step-down transformers are then used to bring the voltage of the supply back down to a safe level to be supplied to the consumer *[1 mark]*.

b) For a set value of power, transmitting electricity at a high voltage means transmitting it at a low current, because $P = IV$ *[1 mark]*. The power loss in a wire due to heating is given by $P = I^2R$ *[1 mark]*. This equation shows that the power loss is lower when current is lower. So transmission is more efficient when the wire has a lower current, and therefore a higher voltage *[1 mark]*.

c) $V_s \div V_p = N_s \div N_p$
So, $N_s = (V_s \div V_p) \times N_p$
$N_s = (4.0 \div 12) \times 15 = 5$ turns
[2 marks for correct answer, otherwise 1 mark for correct equation or substitution]

d) $I_p \times V_p = I_s \times V_s$

$I_s = \dfrac{I_p \times V_p}{V_s} = \dfrac{2.5 \times 12}{4.0}$

$I_s = 7.5$ A
[2 marks for correct answer, otherwise 1 mark for correct equation or substitution]

5 a) i) slip rings *[1 mark]*

ii) To allow current to flow continuously between the coil and the brushes/rest of the circuit *[1 mark]*.

b) It is perpendicular to the magnetic field/vertical *[1 mark]*. At 10 ms the voltage output is zero *[1 mark]* so the coil is not cutting through any magnetic field lines *[1 mark]*.

Section 7 — Atomic Physics

Page 139
Warm-Up Questions

1) In the nuclear model of the atom, there is a central, tiny positively charged nucleus which contains protons and neutrons and most of the atom's mass. The rest of the atom is mostly empty space, with negatively charged electrons that orbit the nucleus at set distances.

2) That it is mostly made up of empty space.

3) 22

In nuclide notation, the bottom number is the proton number.

4) beta particles

5) Alpha particles have a much greater mass, giving them more energy in their kinetic energy stores, and have more charge than beta particles. This means they are more likely to remove electrons from atoms when they collide with them.

6) a) alpha emissions

b) alpha and beta emissions

c) alpha, beta and gamma emissions

7) alpha and beta decay

8) Alpha and beta emissions are both deflected, but gamma rays aren't. Alpha emissions are deflected to the negative end of the electric field and beta emissions towards the positive end. The beta emissions are deflected more than the alpha emissions.

9) Nuclear fission is when a large, unstable nucleus splits into smaller nuclei and releases energy. Nuclear fusion is when nuclei join together to produce a different element (and release energy).

10) The total mass before fission or fusion is higher than the total mass after. The extra mass is converted to energy and released.

Exam Questions

1 a) Protons, which have a relative charge of +1 and neutrons, which have a relative charge of 0 *[2 marks available — 1 mark for each particle with its relative charge]*.

b) The total number of protons and neutrons in the nucleus of that nuclide *[1 mark]*.

c) Nuclides A and B *[1 mark]* because isotopes of the same element have the same proton number, but different nucleon numbers *[1 mark]*.

2 a) E.g. the process in which unstable nuclei change to become more stable by emitting ionising radiation *[1 mark]*.

b) beta decay *[1 mark]*

c) $^{32}_{15}P \rightarrow\ ^{32}_{16}S\ +\ ^{0}_{-1}e$

[1 mark for both the proton number and nucleon number of S, 1 mark for both the proton and nucleon number of e]

Pages 145-146
Warm-Up Questions

1) false

Radioactive decay is entirely spontaneous and can't be predicted.

2) The half-life is the time taken for the number of nuclei of the radioactive isotope in a sample to halve.

3) 1000 counts/hour

The half-life is also the time taken for the count rate to halve.

4) Any three from: e.g. radon gas / food and drink / rocks / building materials / cosmic rays.

5) E.g. it can be used to test the thickness of sheets of paper. Beta decay is suitable for this because beta particles are not immediately absorbed by paper sheets (like alpha particles would be) and don't all pass straight through them (like gamma rays would), so any slight variations in thickness can be detected as the number of particles passing through the sheets would change.

6) A low dose can cause e.g. minor cell damage / cell mutation / cancer.

7) Any two from: e.g. sources should be handled with tongs or tweezers / gloves or protective clothing should be worn when handling the source / the source shouldn't be out of its lead-lined box for longer than necessary / distance from the source should be maintained / time with the source should be minimised.

Exam Questions

1 a) They will be destroyed/damaged/mutated *[1 mark]*
   b) E.g. it could cause cancer/radiation sickness/death *[1 mark]*
   c) Ionising radiation can be directed at cancer cells to kill them *[1 mark]*.

2 a) The count rate is due to the detection of background radiation *[1 mark]*.
   b) E.g. radioactive decay is a random process, so the amount of background radiation varies *[1 mark]*.
   c) Average = (22 + 23 + 18 + 19 + 23) ÷ 5
               = 21 counts/minute
   [2 marks for correct answer, otherwise 1 mark for attempting to add the values and divide by the number of them that there are]
   d) The student should subtract this value from the count rates recorded *[1 mark]*. This is because the radiation detected will be from both the sample and background radiation *[1 mark]*.
   e) E.g. tongs (or tweezers) *[1 mark]* and gloves (or any type of protective clothing) *[1 mark]*
   f) The number of half-lives in 4 weeks = 4 ÷ 2 = 2.
   After 1 half-life: 860 ÷ 2 = 430 mg,
   After 2 half-lives: 430 ÷ 2 = 215 mg.
   [2 marks for correct answer, otherwise 1 mark for correctly finding the number of half-lives in 4 weeks]

3 a) i) A medical tracer should have a much shorter half-life than 80 days *[1 mark]*, so that the radioactivity inside the patient disappears quickly after use *[1 mark]*.
     ii) A thickness gauge should use a beta source rather than a gamma source *[1 mark]*, so that the change in thickness of the paper causes a change in the number of emissions absorbed *[1 mark]*.
   b) E.g. sterilising food/medical equipment/ treating cancer *[1 mark]*.

4 After 1 half-life, count rate = $8.8 \times 10^{14} \div 2 = 4.4 \times 10^{14}$.
  After 2 half-lives, count rate = $4.4 \times 10^{14} \div 2 = 2.2 \times 10^{14}$.
  After 3 half-lives, count rate = $2.2 \times 10^{14} \div 2 = 1.1 \times 10^{14}$.
  So 6 hours is the same as 3 half-lives which means that 1 half-life is 6 hours ÷ 3 = 2 hours
  [3 marks for correct answer, otherwise 1 mark for attempting to halve count rate values, 1 mark for finding number of half-lives]

5 a)

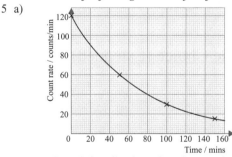

   [1 mark for all points plotted correctly, 1 mark for smooth curve joining the points]

   Start the graph at 120 counts/min. After 50 mins, this will have halved to 60 counts/min. After another 50 mins (i.e. 100 mins altogether), it will have halved again, to 30 counts/min. After yet another 50 mins (i.e. 150 mins altogether), it will have halved again, to 15 counts/min. Plot these points, then join them up with a nice smooth curve.

   b) E.g. after 1 half-life, 50% of the mass will remain. After 2 half-lives 25% will remain.
   1 half-life = 50 mins, so 2 half-lives = 2 × 50 = 100 mins
   [2 marks for correct answer, otherwise 1 mark for recognising that 25% of the initial mass will remain after 2 half-lives]

6 Corrected initial count rate = 180 counts/min
  Half of initial count rate = 180 ÷ 2 = 90 counts/min
  When the corrected count rate is 90 counts/min, the uncorrected count rate will be 90 + 30 = 120 counts/min.
  This happens at 3 minutes,
  so the half-life of the gas is 3 minutes.
  [3 marks for correct answer, otherwise 1 mark for calculating a corrected initial count rate of 180 counts/min, and 1 mark for attempting to halve a corrected count rate]

Section 8 — Space Physics

Page 153
Warm-Up Questions
1) 24 hours
2) Mercury, Venus, Earth, Mars, Jupiter, Saturn, Uranus, Neptune
3) Any three from: e.g. moons/natural satellites, artificial satellites, comets, dwarf planets, asteroids
4) gravity
5) The orbital speeds of the planets increase as you get closer to the Sun.

Exam Questions
1 A *[1 mark]*
2 a) An accretion disc is a disc made of dust and gas *[1 mark]*.
  b) The temperature was higher closer to the Sun than further from it *[1 mark]*. This meant that lighter elements were vaporised closer to the Sun, so closer to the Sun the accretion disc was made up of heavier elements, and further away it was made from lighter elements *[1 mark]*. The heavier elements formed the inner rocky planets and the lighter elements formed the outer gas giants *[1 mark]*.
3 a) Convert orbital period to seconds,
   $T = 687 \times 24 \times 60 \times 60 = 59\,356\,800$ s
   $v = \dfrac{2\pi r}{T} = \dfrac{2 \times \pi \times 2.28 \times 10^{11}}{59\,356\,800} = 24\,134.829...$ m/s
   $= 2.41 \times 10^4$ m/s (to 3 s.f.)
   [3 marks for correct answer, otherwise 1 mark for correct conversion of the orbital period to seconds, and 1 mark for correct substitution]
  b) Object A is the gaseous planet *[1 mark]*.
   Any from e.g. Object A must be the furthest from the Sun because it has the longest orbital period / the lowest surface temperature / the lowest density *[1 mark]*.

Pages 158-159
Warm-Up Questions
1) False.
   The stages they go through depends on their size.
2) A unit of distance equal to the distance travelled by light moving through space in 1 year.
3) redshift
4) Low level microwave radiation that can be detected coming from every part of the Universe.
5) the Hubble constant

Exam Questions
1 C *[1 mark]*
2 a) B *[1 mark]*
  b) A star forms from a nebula/a cloud of dust and gas which is pulled together by gravitational attraction *[1 mark]*. As the density increases, the temperature rises *[1 mark]*. When the temperature gets high enough, hydrogen nuclei undergo nuclear fusion to form helium nuclei and a huge amount of energy is released, which keeps the core hot *[1 mark]*.

c) The forces acting on a main sequence star are balanced, so it doesn't collapse or explode *[1 mark]*. The outward pressure from thermal expansion provides an outward force to balance the force of gravity pulling everything inwards *[1 mark]*.

d) neutron star, black hole *[2 marks]*

3 a) $v = \dfrac{s}{t}$,

so $t = \dfrac{s}{v} = \dfrac{3.20 \times 10^{17}}{3.0 \times 10^{8}} = 1.066... \times 10^{9}$ s
$= 1.1 \times 10^{9}$ s (to 2 s.f.)

[2 marks for correct answer, otherwise 1 mark for correct rearrangement and substitution]

b) 6 light-years *[1 mark]*

4 a) The redshift of light from distant galaxies shows that all the distant galaxies (whichever direction you look in) are moving away from us more quickly than closer galaxies are *[1 mark]*. This suggests that the universe is expanding from a single point *[1 mark]*, which is consistent with the Big Bang idea that the matter in the Universe once occupied a single point *[1 mark]*.

b) Tadpole Galaxy *[1 mark]*. It is the furthest away *[1 mark]*, so it is likely to be travelling away fastest and so will have the greatest redshift *[1 mark]*.

5 a) the brightness of the radiation that reaches Earth *[1 mark]*

b) the redshift of light from the galaxy *[1 mark]*

c) diameter $= (1.42 \times 10^{21}) \div (9.5 \times 10^{15})$
$= 1.494... \times 10^{5}$
$= 1.5 \times 10^{5}$ light-years (to 2 s.f.) *[1 mark]*

d) $H_0 = \dfrac{v}{d} = \dfrac{9.05 \times 10^{6}}{4.73 \times 10^{24}} = 1.9133... \times 10^{-18}$
$= 1.91 \times 10^{-18}$ per second (to 3 s.f.)

[2 marks for correct answer, otherwise 1 mark for correct substitution]

e) age $= \dfrac{1}{H_0}$ *[1 mark]*

Paper 1 Multiple Choice (Core)

Pages 173-183

1 D *[1 mark]*

2 C *[1 mark]*

The car is changing speed between these times, so a resultant force must be acting.

3 B *[1 mark]*

4 A *[1 mark]*

1000 g = 1 kg, and weight = mass × gravitational field strength
= 1 × 9.8 = 9.8 N.

5 C *[1 mark]*

Volume of the cube = 2 × 2 × 2 = 8 cm³.
Density = mass ÷ volume = 9.6 ÷ 8 = 1.2 g/cm³,
so the cube is made from rubber.

6 A *[1 mark]*

Reading from the graph, when the load is 5.6 N, the extension is 3.2 cm. The question has asked you for the total length of the cord, so you need to add this to the original length: 18 + 3.2 = 21.2 cm.

7 C *[1 mark]*

8 C *[1 mark]*

The moment from A is 42 × 0.5 = 21 Nm clockwise. The moment from B is 30 × 0.7 = 21 Nm anticlockwise. The clockwise and anticlockwise moments are equal, so the door is in equilibrium and will stay still.

9 A *[1 mark]*

10 D *[1 mark]*

11 B *[1 mark]*

The same amount of energy is transferred to each box (as they're lifted to the same height), but crane Y transfers this energy faster, so it has a higher power.

12 D *[1 mark]*

13 C *[1 mark]*

14 B *[1 mark]*

15 C *[1 mark]*

16 C *[1 mark]*

17 B *[1 mark]*

18 A *[1 mark]*

19 B *[1 mark]*

20 D *[1 mark]*

21 D *[1 mark]*

22 D *[1 mark]*

23 A *[1 mark]*

24 B *[1 mark]*

25 C *[1 mark]*

26 B *[1 mark]*

27 A *[1 mark]*

The resistance of a wire decreases as its cross-sectional area increases. Graph A is the only graph that shows this type of relationship.

28 B *[1 mark]*

29 A *[1 mark]*

The total resistance of the circuit is the sum of the resistances of the bulbs: 1 + 1 = 2 Ω. The current is constant throughout the circuit, and is equal to the source p.d. divided by the total resistance: current = 12 ÷ 2 = 6 A.

30 C *[1 mark]*

31 C *[1 mark]*

32 D *[1 mark]*

33 D *[1 mark]*

Reversing the direction of the current swaps the direction of the force, but swapping the poles of the magnets swaps the direction of the force again. So overall, the force remains the same.

34 B *[1 mark]*

The voltage decreases to a quarter of its original value, so the number of turns on the secondary coil must be a quarter of the number of turns on the primary coil.

35 A *[1 mark]*

36 D *[1 mark]*

37 A *[1 mark]*

The emissions from source A are stopped by paper, so it must undergo alpha decay. The emissions from source B are stopped by aluminium but not paper, so it must undergo beta decay. Both alpha and beta decay cause the decaying nucleus to change element.

38 A *[1 mark]*

58 minutes is almost an hour (60 minutes), so after each hour, the count rate should have dropped by just over half.

39 B *[1 mark]*

40 C *[1 mark]*

Time = distance ÷ speed = 2.43 × 10¹¹ m ÷ 3.0 × 10⁸ m/s = 810 s.
810 seconds ÷ 60 = 13.5 minutes. Half of a minute is 30 seconds so the answer is 13 minutes and 30 seconds.

Paper 2 Multiple Choice (Extended)

Pages 184-195

1 C *[1 mark]*

2 B *[1 mark]*

3 C *[1 mark]*

4 C *[1 mark]*

5 A *[1 mark]*

F = ma = 110 000 × 5.0 = 550 000 N

6 A *[1 mark]*

Moment = force × perpendicular distance. Since marble B is twice the distance from the pivot, it must be providing half the force (weight) of marble A. So marble B must have half the mass of A. Since they have the same volume and $\rho = \dfrac{m}{V}$, B must have half the density of A: 2.5 ÷ 2 = 1.25 g/cm³.

7 B *[1 mark]*

Momentum is given by p = mv. After the trailer has been unloaded, its mass has halved, but its velocity has doubled in magnitude but changed to the opposite direction. The halved mass and doubled speed cancel each other out (0.5 × 2 = 1), so only the sign of the momentum changes.

8 C *[1 mark]*

There are 4 floors between the 2nd and 6th floor, so the total change in height = 4 × 5.00 = 20 m.
Change in g.p.e. = mass × gravitational field strength × change in height
= 1000 × 9.8 × 20 = 196 000 J = 196 kJ.

9 C *[1 mark]*

10   D *[1 mark]*

The total energy transferred usefully by the kettle each second is 75% of 2400 J = 2400 × 0.75 = 1800 J. To find the time taken to transfer 540 000 J, divide it by the useful energy transfer per second: 540 000 ÷ 1800 = 300 s.

11   A *[1 mark]*

50 minutes = 50 × 60 = 3000 s.
P = W ÷ t, so W = P × t = 1000 × 3000 = 3 000 000 J
= 3000 kJ

12   B *[1 mark]*

The change in pressure between different depths in a liquid is given by Δp = ρgΔh, so the lower the density of the liquid, the greater the depth below the surface at which the pressure due to the water is 250 kPa.

13   C *[1 mark]*
14   B *[1 mark]*
15   A *[1 mark]*
16   C *[1 mark]*

c = ΔE ÷ (mΔθ). Since the changes in energy and temperature are the same for both, but Q has half the mass of P, it must have double the specific heat capacity of P.

17   C *[1 mark]*
18   D *[1 mark]*
19   D *[1 mark]*
20   A *[1 mark]*
21   B *[1 mark]*
22   D *[1 mark]*
23   A *[1 mark]*
24   B *[1 mark]*
25   B *[1 mark]*
26   B *[1 mark]*
27   C *[1 mark]*
28   C *[1 mark]*

V = W ÷ Q = 12 ÷ 1 = 12 V.

29   A *[1 mark]*
30   B *[1 mark]*

10 minutes = 10 × 60 = 600 s. 72 kJ = 72 000 J.
E = IVt, so I = E ÷ (Vt) = 72 000 ÷ (12 × 600) = 10 A.

31   C *[1 mark]*
32   C *[1 mark]*

The resistance of the light-dependent resistor increases as the light intensity decreases. This means that the total resistance of the circuit also increases and so the current through the fixed resistor decreases. Since the potential difference across the fixed resistor = IR and I decreases, then the potential difference across the fixed resistor must decrease.

33   C *[1 mark]*

P = IV, so I = P ÷ V = 500 ÷ 120 = 4.16... A. The fuse rating must be just above the operating current of the device, so 5 A is the best choice.

34   D *[1 mark]*
35   C *[1 mark]*

$I_pV_p = I_sV_s$ so $I_s = (I_pV_p) ÷ V_s = (240 × 0.25) ÷ 12 = 5$ A.

36   C *[1 mark]*
37   A *[1 mark]*
38   B *[1 mark]*
39   D *[1 mark]*
40   C *[1 mark]*

Paper 3 Theory (Core)

Pages 196-208

1 a)   27 s *[1 mark]*
  b)   Take the total distance travelled (20 m) *[1 mark]*, and divide by the total time she takes to swim the distance (27 s, calculated in part a) *[1 mark]*.
  c) i)   Speed = total distance ÷ time taken = 20 ÷ 25 = 0.8 m/s
        [3 marks for correct answer, otherwise 1 mark for correct equation and 1 mark for correct substitution]

ii)
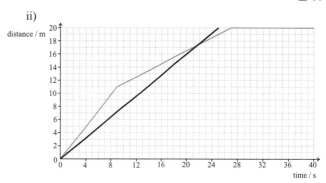
[1 mark for straight line, 1 mark for correct start and end point]

iii)   No, the camera will not be able to film the swimmer for the whole length because the camera's distance-time graph isn't always above the swimmer's *[1 mark]*, and so the camera isn't always ahead of the swimmer *[1 mark]*.

2 a)   gravitational field strength = weight ÷ mass, so weight = mass × gravitational field strength
        = 1.8 × 9.8 = 17.64 N
        = 18 N (to 2 s.f.)
        [3 marks for correct answer, otherwise 1 mark for using the correct equation and 1 mark for correct rearrangement and substitution]
  b)   Let right be the positive direction, so
        5.0 – 1.4 = 3.6 N *[1 mark]* to the right *[1 mark]*
  c)   It should be decreased to 1.4 N *[1 mark]*.

The forces act in opposite directions, so if they're both 1.4 N, then there is no resultant force on the book. If there is no resultant force on an object, it will move at a constant speed.

  d)   The book's speed will change (it slows down) *[1 mark]* as a resultant force (the frictional force) acts on it *[1 mark]*.

3 a)   E.g. nuclear power stations provide a more reliable supply of electricity than wind turbines (as they don't depend on the weather) *[1 mark]*. Nuclear power stations can in general produce a larger power output than wind turbines *[1 mark]*. However, nuclear fuels are non-renewable, unlike the wind (so the fuel will run out one day) *[1 mark]*. Nuclear power stations also produce dangerous nuclear waste, while wind turbines do not *[1 mark]*.
  b)   chemical energy store *[1 mark]*

4 a)   liquid *[1 mark]*
  b)   it increases *[1 mark]*

The ice lolly's temperature will increase, therefore it will have more energy in its internal energy stores.

  c)   The temperature stays the same *[1 mark]*.
  d)   Particles travelling in the right direction/towards the surface with enough energy in their kinetic energy stores/with a high enough speed *[1 mark]* will escape and become gas molecules *[1 mark]*.

5 a) i)   Material B *[1 mark]* because it is a thermal insulator, so it will take a longer time than material A for energy to be transferred from the end of the rod in the hot water to the end of the rod with the beads attached, causing the wax to melt *[1 mark]*.
     ii)   Convection (via the air above the surface of the hot water) *[1 mark]* and radiation from the top of the apparatus *[1 mark]*.

You could also have said conduction through the air above the water as one of the methods, but not just 'conduction'.

  b)   Because the pan is made from a conductive metal, the energy is transferred by conduction throughout the pan *[1 mark]*. The pan transfers energy by conduction to the food evenly across the surface of the pan *[1 mark]*.

6 a)   Figure 6 contains two full wavelengths. So the wavelength = 3 ÷ 2 = 1.5 cm *[1 mark]*.
  b) i)   A wave where the vibrations are perpendicular to the direction of propagation *[1 mark]*.

ii) Any one from: e.g. electromagnetic radiation, seismic S-waves (secondary waves) *[1 mark]*

c) Figure 7 shows the water waves undergoing refraction. *[1 mark]* As the water waves pass into the shallower water, they change speed. *[1 mark]*

Whenever a wave refracts, it changes speed.

7 a) The distance from the centre of the lens to the principal focus *[1 mark]*.

b)

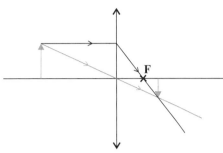

[1 mark for the second ray drawn correctly with arrows and 1 mark for labelling the principal focus correctly]

c) Diminished *[1 mark]* and inverted *[1 mark]*.

8 a) Because electrons have been transferred from the girl's hair to the comb *[1 mark]*.

b) The hairs all have a positive charge *[1 mark]*. Like charges repel, so the hairs repel each other and stand on end *[1 mark]*.

c) A material that doesn't conduct charge very well / a material that current can't flow through *[1 mark]*.

9 a) Apparatus: Ammeter *[1 mark]* Connection in circuit: in series *[1 mark]*. Apparatus: Voltmeter *[1 mark]* Connection in circuit: in parallel (with the lamp) *[1 mark]*.

b) Resistance = potential difference ÷ current $= 3.0 ÷ 1.2 = 2.5 \ \Omega$

[3 marks for correct answer, otherwise 1 mark for using the correct equation and 1 mark for correct substitution]

c) Energy is transferred electrically from the chemical energy store of the battery *[1 mark]* to the lamp's internal energy store *[1 mark]*.

d) E.g. if one lamp fails, the rest of the circuit will still work *[1 mark]*. The lamps can be switched on and off individually *[1 mark]*.

10 a) step-up transformer *[1 mark]*

Step-up transformers increase the voltage.

b) $V_p ÷ V_s = N_p ÷ N_s$ So, $N_s = N_p ÷ (V_p ÷ V_s)$ $N_s = 5000 ÷ (25\ 000 ÷ 400\ 000)$ $= 80\ 000$

[3 marks for correct answer, otherwise 1 mark for correct equation and 1 mark for correct substitution]

c) E.g. it means electricity can be transmitted at a high power without massive power losses *[1 mark]*.

d) E.g. connect a voltmeter to a conductor *[1 mark]*. Move the conductor through a magnetic field (or move a magnet relative to the conductor placed nearby) *[1 mark]*. The voltmeter will show an induced e.m.f. *[1 mark]*.

Electromagnetic induction is when an e.m.f. is induced in a conductor by a magnetic field that's either changing, or is moving relative to the conductor.

11 a) 126 *[1 mark]*

Polonium-210 has a nucleon number of 210. As polonium-210 has 84 protons in its nucleus, it must have 210 − 84 = 126 neutrons in its nucleus.

b) Some emissions come from background radiation *[1 mark]*.

c) Half-life is the time taken for the count rate to halve. The initial count rate is 1600 counts/second. $1600 ÷ 2 = 800$ counts/second. Using Figure 14, when count rate = 800 counts/second, time = 140 days. Therefore, half-life = 140 days *[3 marks for correct answer, otherwise 1 mark for choosing an initial count rate from the graph and 1 mark for halving the count rate value]*

d) Half of the atoms in the sample will be polonium-210 atoms *[1 mark]*. During alpha decay the nucleus changes to that of a different element *[1 mark]*. After one half-life, half of the polonium-210 atoms in the sample will have decayed *[1 mark]*.

12 a) The Moon orbits the Earth every 28 days *[1 mark]*. Only the half of the Moon that faces the Sun reflects sunlight, so as the Moon orbits the Earth, the amount of the lit up half of the Moon that can be seen from Earth changes (between us seeing the entire lit up side and none of it) causing the Moon's appearance from Earth to change *[1 mark]*.

b) i) It is lower than Earth's gravitational field strength (9.8 N/kg) *[1 mark]*.

ii) mass of the planet or moon *[1 mark]* distance from the planet or moon *[1 mark]*

Paper 4 Theory (Extended)

Pages 209-226

1 a) The point through which all of the weight of the object acts *[1 mark]*.

b) E.g. the lower the centre of gravity of the wheel, the more stable it will be *[1 mark]*.

c) The weight of the carriage acts from the centre of gravity which is at a distance from the pivot, creating a moment *[1 mark]*. So the carriage will swing until its centre of gravity is vertically below the point where it is attached to the wheel, at which point there will be no moment acting *[1 mark]*.

d) The total momentum before the collision is equal to the total momentum after the collision, as long as no external forces act *[1 mark]*.

e) Let momentum of car K after the collision be $p_k = m_k v_k$, where m_k = mass of car K, and v_k = velocity of car K after collision. Total momentum before = total momentum after $500 + 200 = 250 + p_k$ so, $p_k = 700 − 250 = 450$ kg m/s $p_k = m_k v_k$ so, $v_k = \dfrac{p_k}{m_k} = \dfrac{450}{160} = 2.8125 = 3$ m/s (to 1 s.f.) So the velocity of car K is 3 m/s to the right.

[3 marks for correct answer, otherwise 1 mark for use of conservation of momentum and correct equation for momentum, 1 mark for correct numerical answer and 1 mark for correct direction]

f) Increasing the collision time causes the resultant forces acting on the cars to decrease *[1 mark]*.

Since FΔt = Δ(mv), for a given change in momentum of an object (or change in velocity), increasing Δt reduces F, the force acting on the object.

2 a) $ΔE_p = mgΔh$ $= 610 × 9.8 × 25 = 149\ 450$ J $= 150\ 000$ J (to 2 s.f.)

[2 marks for correct answer, otherwise 1 mark for using the correct equation]

b) $E_k = ½mv^2$ Conservation of energy: total energy before = total energy after There is no friction or air resistance, so by conservation of energy, all energy lost from the gravitational potential energy store is transferred to the kinetic energy store. So, $ΔE_p = E_k = 149\ 450$ J So, $v = \sqrt{\dfrac{2 × E_k}{m}} = \sqrt{\dfrac{2 × 149\ 450}{610}} = 22.13...$ m/s $= 22$ m/s (to 2 s.f.)

[3 marks for correct answer, otherwise 1 mark for correct value for E_k and 1 mark for using the correct equation for E_k]

c) i) $E_k = W = Fd = 7200 \times 32 = 230\ 400$ J $= 230\ 000$ J (to 2 s.f.)
[2 marks for correct answer, otherwise
1 mark for using the correct equation]

As the carriage slows down to a stop, all of the energy stored in its kinetic energy store is transferred out of that store as work is done by the brakes. So the initial amount of energy in the kinetic energy store is equal to the work done by the braking force.

ii) The distance travelled will increase *[1 mark]*.

The initial amount of energy in the carriage's kinetic energy store will be the same as before, as the carriage is going at the same speed. So the energy transferred/work done will be the same, so as the force is decreased, the distance travelled will increase, because W = Fd.

3 a) i) Let p_1V_1 be before the divider was removed and p_2V_2 be after the divider was removed.
$p_1V_1 = 1.1 \times 10^5 \times 1.5 \times 10^{-3} = 165$
$pV =$ constant so $p_2V_2 = p_1V_1 = 165$
So $p_2 = 165 \div V_2 = 165 \div (2.75 \times 10^{-3}) = 6 \times 10^4$ Pa
[2 marks for correct answer, otherwise
1 mark for using the correct equation]

ii) The pressure decreases because the volume increases *[1 mark]*, so the helium particles have more room to move and so collide with the cylinder walls less often *[1 mark]*.

b) The pressure of the helium gas will increase *[1 mark]*. This is because increasing the temperature will increase the speed of the helium particles *[1 mark]*, meaning they will collide with the walls of the cylinder more often and with a larger force *[1 mark]*.

4 a) Side D *[1 mark]*. The highest infrared intensity is recorded from this side, so that face emits the most infrared radiation *[1 mark]*. Dark surfaces are better emitters of infrared radiation than light ones, so side D is most likely to be dark coloured *[1 mark]*.

b) Any two from: texture of paint, area of face, temperature of water/surface
[2 marks total — 1 mark for each correct answer]

c) The dark coloured coating is the best absorber of infrared radiation, so it absorbs more infrared radiation than the other bricks and so its temperature increases more *[1 mark]*.

d) $c = \dfrac{\Delta E}{m\Delta\theta}$, so $\Delta E = mc\Delta\theta = 0.045 \times 840 \times (15.2 - 14)$
$= 45.36$ J $= 45$ J (to 2 s.f.)
[2 marks for correct answer, otherwise
1 mark for using the correct equation]

e) To begin with, the brick is absorbing more radiation than it is emitting, so its temperature increases *[1 mark]*. As it heats up, the amount of radiation it emits increases, until it is emitting as much as it is absorbing, at which point its temperature stops changing/remains the same *[1 mark]*.

5 a) critical angle *[1 mark]*

b) $\theta =$ critical angle (c)
$n = \dfrac{1}{\sin c}$, so $\sin c = \dfrac{1}{n}$ which means $\sin\theta = \dfrac{1}{n}$
$\theta = \sin^{-1}\left(\dfrac{1}{n}\right) = \sin^{-1}\left(\dfrac{1}{1.5}\right) = 41.81...° = 42°$ (to 2 s.f.)
[2 marks for correct answer, otherwise
1 mark for using the correct equation]

c) Light rays travel through the core and always hit the core-cladding boundary at angles greater than the critical angle *[1 mark]*, meaning they are always totally internally reflected *[1 mark]*.

6 a) A rainbow/spectrum of colours will be observed as the light leaves the prism *[1 mark]*. This is because white light is made up of all the different colours of light, which all have different frequencies *[1 mark]*. When these different frequencies enter and leave the prism they refract by different amounts *[1 mark]*. This causes the colours in the white light to separate slightly (disperse) *[1 mark]*.

b) No rainbow/spectrum would be observed. Monochromatic light only consists of a single frequency of light, so it would emerge from the prism as a single ray *[1 mark]*.

7 a) The number of complete infrared waves passing a certain point per second *[1 mark]*.

b) 3.0×10^8 m/s *[1 mark]*

c) $v = f\lambda$
So, $\lambda = v \div f$
$\lambda = 3.0 \times 10^8 \div 2.5 \times 10^{14}$
$= 1.2 \times 10^{-6}$ m
[2 marks for correct answer, otherwise
1 mark for using the correct equation]

d) The cone vibrating back and forth causes the surrounding air to vibrate back and forth, creating areas of compressions and rarefactions (sound waves) *[1 mark]*. The sound waves then travel through the air as a series of compressions and rarefactions until they hit someone's ear *[1 mark]*.

8 a) i) An area where a force acts on an electric charge *[1 mark]*.
ii) The direction of the force on a positive charge at that point *[1 mark]*.

b)

[1 mark for the lines being perpendicular to the surface of the sphere, 1 mark for them being equally spaced, 1 mark for the lines having arrows pointing towards the centre of the sphere.]

9 a) Diodes only let current through in one direction *[1 mark]*. Current can pass through the diode in series with lamp 1, since it lights up. So it can't pass through the diode in series with lamp 2, since that diode is connected in the opposite direction *[1 mark]*.

b) When current increases the graph curves off, meaning the resistance of the lamp increases *[1 mark]*. This is because increasing the current increases the temperature of the lamp, making the ions in it vibrate more vigorously *[1 mark]*. The electrons are more likely to collide with vigorously vibrating ions and so are slowed down, increasing the resistance *[1 mark]*.

c) Increasing the resistance of the variable resistor will also increase the potential difference (p.d.) across it *[1 mark]*. As the two resistors are connected in series, the p.d. across the energy source is shared between them *[1 mark]*. This means that when the p.d. across the variable resistor is increased, the p.d. across the fixed resistor measured by the voltmeter decreases *[1 mark]*.

10 a) A current-carrying wire perpendicular to a magnetic field it is in feels a force, so when current flows in the coil, the wire on each side feels a force *[1 mark]*. The force on one side of the coil acts upwards, and the force on the other side acts downwards, so the coil rotates, and turns the attached fan blades *[1 mark]*.

b) It swaps which sides of the coil are in contact with which brushes every half turn, which swaps the direction of the current down each side of the coil every half turn *[1 mark]*. This changes the direction of the force on each side of the coil and so keeps the motor rotating in the same direction *[1 mark]*.

So whichever side of the coil happens to be closest to, say, the north pole at any moment always has the current going in the same direction through it, and so the force on it is always acting in the same direction.

c) Any one from: e.g. increase the current / increase the number of turns on the coil / increase the strength of the magnetic field e.g. by using stronger magnets *[1 mark]*.

d) The metal bar will roll along the rails to the right *[1 mark]*.
Using Fleming's left-hand rule, first finger (field) points vertically down and second finger (current) points towards your body, leaving your thumb (force) pointing right.

e) Reverse the direction of the current / reverse the direction of the magnetic field *[1 mark]*.

11 a) Atoms of the same element with the same number of protons but a different number of neutrons *[1 mark]*.

b) When charged particles pass through an electric field, they experience a force, causing them to deflect from their initial path *[1 mark]*. The force from the field on positive charges is in the opposite direction to the force from the field on negative charges *[1 mark]*. Since the paths of radioactive emissions from isotope X curve in opposite directions, the particles in each path must have opposite charges *[1 mark]*. Alpha particles and beta particles are oppositely charged, so the two paths show that isotope X must emit alpha and beta particles *[1 mark]*.

12 a) As a comet gets closer to the Sun, the energy stored in its gravitational potential energy store decreases *[1 mark]*. This energy is transferred to the comet's kinetic energy store, so it speeds up *[1 mark]*. As the comet moves further away from the Sun, energy is transferred away from its kinetic energy store to its gravitational potential energy store, so it slows down again *[1 mark]*.

b) $v = \frac{2\pi r}{T}$ so $T = \frac{2\pi r}{v} = \frac{2\pi \times 1.13 \times 10^{12}}{10\,900} = 6.513... \times 10^8$ s
$6.513... \times 10^8 \div (365 \times 24 \times 60 \times 60) = 20.65...$ years
$= 20.7$ years (to 3 s.f.)
[2 marks for correct answer, otherwise 1 mark for correct equation or substitution]

Paper 5 Alternative to Practical

Pages 227-236

1 a) A stopwatch (or other timer) *[1 mark]*.

b) Liquid B's temperature increases more than liquid A's when a certain amount of energy is supplied *[1 mark]*. E.g. 48 kJ of energy is supplied to both liquids over 4 minutes. The liquids both started at the same temperature, but liquid B's temperature increased to 59 °C, whereas liquid A's only increased to 41 °C *[1 mark]*.

c) E.g.

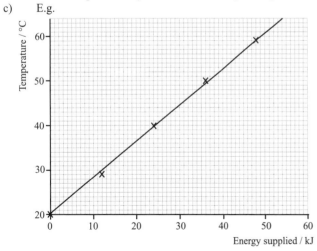

[1 mark for correctly labelled axes, 1 mark for suitable scales on both axes that each take up more than half the grid, 1 mark for all points plotted correctly and 1 mark for a sensible line of best fit]

d) E.g.

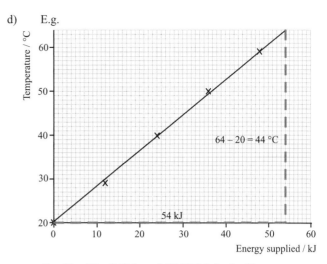

$G = 44 \div 54 = 0.814... = 0.81$ °C/kJ (to 2 s.f.)
[1 mark for triangle marked on graph and finding vertical change and horizontal change, 1 mark for correctly calculating the gradient from these values for the vertical change and the horizontal change]

e) $c = 1 \div (0.50 \times 0.814...) = 2.454... = 2.5$ kJ/(kg°C) (to 2 s.f.)
[1 mark for substituting mass and gradient from part d into equation and calculating value to 2 significant figures]
You might get a slightly different answer here, depending on your answer to part d). As long as your answer is correct for your value of the gradient in part d), you'll get the mark.

f) Less energy will be transferred by heating to the surroundings *[1 mark]* so a greater rise in temperature of liquid B will be measured for a given amount of energy supplied *[1 mark]*.

2 a) E.g. the spring used in the experiment / the distance the mass is pulled down *[1 mark]*.

b)

Mass	Reading on balance / kg	Corrected mass / kg
A	0.22	0.22 – 0.02 = 0.20
B	0.44	0.44 – 0.02 = 0.42
C	1.02	1.02 – 0.02 = 1.00

[2 marks for corrected masses, otherwise 1 mark for attempting to subtract 0.02 kg from each reading]

c) 29.6 cm *[1 mark]*

d) E.g. attach a thin strip of card to the ruler at the correct point / attach a thin strip of card to the bottom of the mass to line up with the marking on the ruler / move the ruler closer to the mass / use a set square to line up the bottom of the mass with the ruler *[1 mark]*.

e) E.g. single measurements are likely to be affected by random errors. Repeating the experiment and calculating the average will reduce the effect of random errors *[1 mark]*.

f) 1.04 s *[1 mark]*

g) No, period is not directly proportional to mass.
E.g. the graph doesn't show a straight line through the origin / doubling the mass doesn't double the period / the ratio of period to mass varies a lot between points *[1 mark]*.

h) E.g. Cause: The time measurements are very short, so there's a large uncertainty in the results due to the student's reaction time *[1 mark]*.
Improvement: Measure the time taken for 10 oscillations, and divide the measurement by 10 to find the period *[1 mark]*.

3 a) The wire's cross-sectional area *[1 mark]*.
b) i) $A = \pi \times \text{radius}^2 = \pi \times (0.40 \div 2)^2 = 0.12566...$
   $= 0.13 \text{ mm}^2$ (to 2 s.f.)

Wire diameter / mm	Cross-sectional area, A / mm²	Resistance, R /	$R \times A$ / Ωmm²
0.10	0.0079	7.90	
0.20	0.031	2.02	
0.30	0.071	0.88	
0.40	**0.13**	0.48	
0.50	0.20		

[1 mark for correct value of A, 1 mark for correct column heading]

ii)

Wire diameter / mm	Cross-sectional area, A / mm²	Resistance, R / Ω	$R \times A$ / Ωmm²
0.10	0.0079	7.90	
0.20	0.031	2.02	
0.30	0.071	0.88	
0.40	0.13	0.48	
0.50	0.20	**0.32**	

[1 mark for correct value of R, 1 mark for correct column heading]

c)

Wire diameter / mm	Cross-sectional area, A / mm²	Resistance, R / Ω	$R \times A$ / Ωmm²
0.10	0.0079	7.90	0.062
0.20	0.031	2.02	0.063
0.30	0.071	0.88	0.062
0.40	0.13	0.48	0.062
0.50	0.20	0.32	0.064

[1 mark for calculating the values of R × A correctly and giving them to 2 significant figures]

Always round calculated values so they have the same number of significant figures as the raw data value with the least significant figures.

d) $R \times A$ is roughly constant *[1 mark]*,

so R is proportional to $\frac{1}{A}$ *[1 mark]*.

e) E.g. attach the crocodile clips at the very ends of the lengths of wire *[1 mark]*.

f) E.g. ensure equipment is not faulty / ensure a low voltage and current is being used to reduce the risk of wires overheating / unplug equipment when not using it *[1 mark]*.

g) He is correct — it is important that the wires being tested have the same diameters because the first experiment shows that the diameter affects the resistance *[1 mark]*.

4   E.g. Additional apparatus needed:
a long tape measure/ruler and a stopwatch *[1 mark]*
How the experiment will be carried out:
Set up the tape measure/ruler so that it is vertical, and attach one of the parachutes to the steel ball. Drop the ball from a certain height next to the tape measure/ruler. Time how long it takes for the steel ball to hit the floor *[1 mark]*. Repeat the experiment with a different sized parachute attached to the steel ball *[1 mark]*.
Variables that should be kept constant:
Keep the height from which the steel ball is dropped constant for each experiment *[1 mark]*.
Values that need to be calculated:
For each size of parachute, the average speed of the steel ball should be calculated using the equation 'average speed = total distance ÷ total time', where total distance is the distance the ball falls, and total time is the time it takes for the ball to fall *[1 mark]*.
Table headings:
Area of parachute / cm², Time taken to fall / s, Average speed of ball / m/s *[1 mark]*
Difficulties that may occur and how to overcome them:
It may be difficult to make sure that the parachute is fully open at the same point in the descent each time. The errors due to this could be reduced by dropping the ball from a greater height, and starting the stopwatch once the ball has passed a certain point (i.e. where the parachute is definitely open) *[1 mark]*.

You're told what your plan should include, so make sure you include all these things clearly. You might have come up with a different plan to the one here. As long as it will still investigate how the area of the parachute affects the average speed at which the ball falls, you'll still get the marks.

Glossary

absolute zero	The lowest possible temperature, equal to 0 K (–273 °C). It is the point where the particles of a substance have the minimum possible energy in their kinetic energy stores.
acceleration	The change in velocity per unit time.
alpha particle (α)	A type of radioactive emission consisting of two neutrons and two protons (the same as a helium nucleus).
alternating current (a.c.)	A current that constantly changes direction.
amplitude (of a wave)	The maximum displacement of a point on the wave from its undisturbed position.
analogue signal	Electronic signal that can have any value within a range (it shows continuous variation).
artificial satellite	A man-made object that orbits a much larger object, usually the Earth.
background radiation	The low-level radiation that is around us all the time.
beta particle (β)	A type of radioactive emission that is a fast-moving electron emitted from a decaying nucleus.
Big Bang theory	The idea that the Universe began from a very hot and dense single point, which exploded and has been expanding ever since.
black hole	A super dense region of space that light can't escape from.
boiling	When a substance changes state from liquid to gas. This happens at the boiling point of the substance.
Brownian motion	The random motion of microscopic particles of a solid suspended in a fluid, that is due to bombardment by the fluid molecules.
centre of gravity	The point through which the weight of an object can be thought to act.
chemical energy store	Energy store in which an object has energy that can be released by a chemical reaction.
comet	A lump of ice and dust that orbits a star, usually in a highly elliptical orbit.
condensation	When a substance changes state from gas to liquid.
conduction	A type of thermal energy transfer where energy is transferred through a material. Vibrating particles transfer energy from their kinetic energy stores to those of neighbouring particles.
conductor (electrical)	Material that conducts charge easily, so a current can flow through it. Examples include copper and silver.
conductor (thermal)	Material that transfers energy by conduction quickly. Most metals are good thermal conductors.
convection	A type of thermal energy transfer where more energetic particles of a substance move from a hotter region to a cooler region.
conventional current	The way current is defined, with charge flowing from the positive terminal to the negative terminal. This is in the opposite direction to the actual flow of electrons in a metal.
converging lens	A lens that bulges outwards. It causes rays of light parallel to the principal axis to be brought together (converge).

Glossary

cosmic microwave background radiation (CMBR)	Microwave radiation of a specific, low frequency coming from all directions. It is leftover radiation from the Big Bang.
critical angle	The angle of incidence on a boundary that will cause the angle of refraction to be 90°. An angle of incidence greater than the critical angle will cause total internal reflection.
current	The electric charge flowing around a circuit. It is measured in amperes, A.
deceleration	The change in velocity per unit time for something slowing down. It is a negative acceleration.
density	A measure of the 'compactness' of a substance. It is a substance's mass per unit volume.
diffraction	When waves spread out as they 'bend round' obstacles.
digital signal	Electronic signal that can only take certain values.
direct current (d.c.)	A current that always flows in the same direction.
dispersion	The separation of light into different frequencies, caused by each frequency being refracted by a different amount.
diverging lens	A lens that caves inwards. It causes rays of light parallel to the principal axis to spread out (diverge).
double-insulated	This describes an appliance that has a plastic casing (rather than metal) which can't become live. Double-insulated appliances don't need an earth wire.
drag	Frictional force acting on an object as it moves through a gas or liquid.
efficiency	A measure of the proportion of input energy that is transferred usefully by a device or process.
elastic (strain) energy store	Energy store in which an object has energy when it is stretched.
electric field	An area where a force acts on an electric charge.
electromagnet	A solenoid with a soft iron core. It becomes magnetic when a current flows through the solenoid.
electromagnetic induction	The creation of an e.m.f. (and a current if there's a complete circuit) in a conductor which is experiencing a change in a magnetic field or which is moving relative to a magnetic field.
electromotive force (e.m.f.)	The electrical work done moving each unit of charge around a circuit. It's measured in volts, V.
electrostatic energy store	Energy store in which two charged objects that attract or repel each other have energy.
equilibrium	A system is in equilibrium if there is no resultant force on it and no resultant moment on it.
evaporation	When particles escape from the surface of a liquid and become gas particles. It happens at temperatures below the boiling point of the liquid.
fission	A type of nuclear reaction where a heavy unstable nucleus splits into two smaller nuclei and releases energy.

Glossary

focal length	The distance from the centre of a lens to the principal focus.
frequency (of a wave)	The number of complete waves passing a certain point per second. It is measured in hertz, Hz.
friction (solid)	A force between two objects that are in contact, and are moving or trying to move relative to each other. Solid friction impedes motion and can result in heating.
fuse	A circuit component that contains a thin piece of wire that melts if the current through it becomes too high. This breaks the circuit. It can be replaced with a trip switch.
fusion	A reaction in which light nuclei join together (fuse) to create a larger, heavier nucleus. This releases a lot of energy.
gamma ray (γ)	A type of radioactive emission that is an electromagnetic wave.
gravitational field strength	The force exerted by gravity per unit mass, at a particular point in the Universe.
gravitational potential energy store	Energy store in which an object has energy if it will fall (or would fall if it wasn't supported).
half-life	The time taken for the number of nuclei of a radioactive isotope in a sample (or the count rate) to halve.
Hubble constant	The ratio of the speed that a galaxy is receding (moving away) from Earth to its distance from Earth.
impulse	The size of a force acting on an object multiplied by the length of time it acts for. It is equal to the object's change in momentum.
induced magnet	A magnet which is only producing a magnetic field because it is in another magnetic field. Magnetic materials become induced magnets when placed in magnetic fields.
insulator (electrical)	Material that doesn't conduct charge very well, so a current can't flow. Examples include plastic and rubber.
insulator (thermal)	Material that transfers energy by conduction slowly. Examples include plastics, most fabrics and wool.
internal (thermal) energy store	Energy store in which all objects have energy. The hotter the object, the more energy it has in its internal energy store.
ionising power	How likely a radioactive emission is to remove electrons from atoms it collides with.
ion	An atom or molecule that has lost or gained electrons, giving it an overall charge. Positive ions have lost electrons and negative ions have gained electrons.
isotope	An atom is an isotope of another atom if it has the same number of protons (same proton number) but a different number of neutrons (different nucleon number) as it.
kilowatt-hour	The amount of energy that is transferred by a 1 kW device running for 1 hour.
kinetic energy store	Energy store in which an object has energy when it is moving.
kinetic particle model	A model that describes all matter as being made up of particles.
law of reflection	The law that states that the angle of incidence always equals the angle of reflection.
light-year	The distance travelled by light moving through space in one year.

Glossary

limit of proportionality	The point beyond which an object's extension is no longer proportional to the load producing it.
longitudinal wave	Wave in which the vibrations are parallel to the direction in which the wave is propagated.
magnetic field	A region where a magnetic pole experiences a force acting on it.
magnetic material	A material (e.g. iron, steel, nickel or cobalt) which experiences a force in a magnetic field. Magnetic materials are always attracted to magnets.
mass	The amount of matter in an object that is at rest relative to the observer. It is measured in kilograms, kg.
melting	When a substance changes state from solid to liquid. This happens at the melting point of the substance.
Milky Way	The galaxy that our solar system is in.
moment	A measure of the turning effect of a force acting around a pivot. The units of moment are Nm.
momentum	The product of the mass and velocity of an object.
monochromatic light	Light made up of waves that all have the same frequency.
moon	A natural satellite that orbits a planet.
nebula	A cloud of dust and gas in space.
neutron star	The very dense core of a star that can be left behind when a red supergiant explodes in a supernova.
non-renewable energy resource	An energy resource that cannot be made at the same rate as it is being used, so it will one day run out, e.g. coal, oil.
nuclear energy store	Energy store in which an object has energy that can be released by atomic nuclei in nuclear reactions.
nucleon number	The total number of protons and neutrons in an atom's nucleus.
nucleus	The positively-charged centre of an atom, consisting of protons and neutrons.
nuclide	An atom with a particular number of protons and neutrons.
parallel circuit	An electrical circuit that has branches which are separately connected to the positive and negative ends of the power supply.
penetrating power	How far into a material a radioactive emission can travel before being absorbed.
permanent magnet	A magnet which produces its own magnetic field all the time.
potential difference (p.d.)	The amount of work done by each unit of charge as it passes through a component. It is measured in volts, V.
potential divider	A circuit used to split the source voltage, e.g. using multiple resistors in series with components connected across them.
power	The energy transferred or work done per unit time. It is measured in watts, W.
pressure	The force being applied to a surface per unit area.
principal focus	Where rays hitting the lens parallel to the axis all meet (for a converging lens) or appear to have come from (for a diverging lens).

Glossary

principle of conservation of energy	Energy can be stored, transferred from one store to another, or dissipated — but it can never be created or destroyed.
principle of conservation of momentum	The total momentum before an event is equal to the total momentum after the event, as long as no external forces act.
principle of moments	An object is balanced if the total anticlockwise moments equal the total clockwise moments.
proton number	The number of protons in an atom's nucleus.
protostar	An interstellar cloud of dust and gas pulled together by internal gravitational attraction.
radiation (thermal energy transfer)	A type of thermal energy transfer where energy is transferred by infrared electromagnetic waves.
radioactive decay	The process in which unstable nuclei become more stable by emitting ionising radiation.
real image	An image formed where the light from an object comes together.
red giant (or supergiant)	A type of star that forms when a star starts to run out of hydrogen in its core.
redshift	An increase in the observed wavelength of the electromagnetic radiation emitted from stars and galaxies that are receding (moving away) from an observer on Earth.
reflection	When a wave bounces back off a surface.
refraction	When a wave changes direction as it crosses a boundary between two materials at an angle to the normal. It is caused by a change in wave speed.
refractive index	The refractive index of a material is the ratio of the speed of light in a vacuum to the speed of light in the material.
relay	A switch that turns a circuit on or off using an electromagnet.
renewable energy resource	A renewable energy resource is an energy resource that is being, or can be, made at the same rate (or faster) than it's being used, so it will never run out, e.g. wind, solar.
resistance	Anything in a circuit which slows down the flow of charge. It is measured in ohms, Ω.
resultant force	A single force that has the same effect as all the forces acting on an object. The resultant force is equal to the rate of change of momentum.
Sankey diagram	A diagram showing how much input energy is transferred usefully and wasted by a process or device.
scalar quantity	A quantity which has only magnitude (size) and no direction.
series circuit	An electrical circuit in which all the components are connected in a line, end to end, between the positive and negative ends of the power supply.
solenoid	A current-carrying coil of wire. It produces a magnetic field when the current flows.
solidification	When a substance changes state from liquid to solid. Also known as freezing.
specific heat capacity	The amount of energy needed to raise the temperature of 1 kg of a substance by 1 °C.

Glossary

speed	The distance an object travels per unit time.
split-ring commutator	A part of a d.c. electric motor which swaps the direction of the current through the coil every half-turn, keeping the motor rotating in the same direction.
spring constant	The force per unit extension when a spring is stretched by a force.
static electricity	A build-up of charge that occurs when electrons are transferred from one material to another by friction.
supernova	The explosion of a red supergiant.
temperature	A measure of the average energy in the kinetic energy stores of the particles of a substance.
terminal velocity	The maximum speed that a freely falling object reaches.
thermal energy store	Another term for internal energy store.
thermal expansion	When a substance gets bigger as its temperature increases.
total internal reflection	When a ray of light is completely reflected back into a material at a boundary, rather than exiting into another material.
transformer	A device consisting of two coils wrapped around a soft iron core used to change the size of the voltage of an alternating electricity supply.
transverse wave	Wave in which the vibrations are perpendicular (at 90°) to the direction in which the wave is propagated.
ultrasound wave	Sound waves with a frequency greater than 20 kHz (20 000 Hz).
vector quantity	A quantity which has magnitude (size) and a direction.
velocity	The speed an object is travelling at in a specified direction.
virtual image	An image formed by diverging (spreading out) rays of light, meaning the light from the object appears to be coming from a completely different place, found by extrapolating the rays backwards.
wave speed	The speed at which energy is being transferred by a wave (or the speed the wave is moving at).
wavefront	An imaginary plane that cuts across multiple waves that are moving together in the same direction. It connects points which are oscillating together.
wavelength (of a wave)	The distance between the same point on two adjacent waves (e.g. between the trough of one wave and the trough of the next wave).
weight	The gravitational force (in newtons) that acts on an object that has mass.
white dwarf	The hot, dense core left behind when a red giant becomes unstable and ejects its outer layer of dust and gas.
work done (electrical)	The energy transferred by a charge moving through a potential difference.
work done (mechanical)	The energy transferred by a force moving an object through a distance.

Index

Index

Index